Stanley Gibbons
Commonwealth Star

CW00661267

Ireland

6th edition 2015

STANLEY GIBBONS
CATALOGUES
—— 1865 - 2015 ——

Stanley Gibbons Ltd • London and Ringwood

By Appointment to
Her Majesty The Queen
Philatelists
Stanley Gibbons Ltd
London

Published by Stanley Gibbons Ltd
Editorial, Publications Sales Offices
and Distribution Centre:
7 Parkside, Christchurch Road, Ringwood,
Hants BH24 3SH

1st Edition – 2000
2nd Edition – 2004
3rd Edition – 2006
4th Edition – 2008
5th Edition – 2011
6th Edition – 2015

© Stanley Gibbons Ltd 2015

British Library Cataloguing in
Publication Data.
A catalogue record for this book is available
from the British Library.

Errors and omissions excepted
the colour reproduction of stamps is only as
accurate as the printing process will allow.

ISBN-10: 0-85259-924-2
ISBN-13: 978-0-85259-924-2

Item No. R2975-15

Printed by
Latimer Trend

Contents

Stanley Gibbons Holdings Plc

Stanley Gibbons Limited, Stanley Gibbons Auctions
399 Strand, London WC2R 0LX
Tel: +44 (0)207 836 8444
Fax: +44 (0)207 836 7342
E-mail: help@stanleygibbons.com
Website: www.stanleygibbons.com
for all departments, Auction and Specialist Stamp Departments.

Open Monday–Friday 9.30 a.m. to 5 p.m.
Shop. Open Monday–Friday 9 a.m. to 5.30 p.m. and Saturday 9.30 a.m. to 5.30 p.m.

Stanley Gibbons Publications Gibbons Stamp Monthly and Philatelic Exporter
7 Parkside, Christchurch Road, Ringwood, Hampshire BH24 3SH.
Tel: +44 (0)1425 472363
Fax: +44 (0)1425 470247
E-mail: help@stanleygibbons.com
Publications Mail Order.
FREEPHONE 0800 611622

Monday–Friday 8.30 a.m. to 5 p.m.

Stanley Gibbons (Guernsey) Limited
18–20 Le Bordage, St Peter Port, Guernsey GY1 1DE.
Tel: +44 (0)1481 708270
Fax: +44 (0)1481 708279
E-mail: investment@stanleygibbons.com

Stanley Gibbons (Jersey) Limited
18 Hill Street, St Helier, Jersey, Channel Islands JE2 4UA.
Tel: +44 (0)1534 766711
Fax: +44 (0)1534 766177
E-mail: investment@stanleygibbons.com

Stanley Gibbons (Asia) Limited
Room 618, 6/F,
100 Queen's Road Central
Central,
Hong Kong
Tel: +852 3180 9370
E-mail: elee@stanleygibbons.com

Benham Collectibles Limited
Unit K, Concept Court,
Shearway Business Park
Folkestone Kent CT19 4RG
E-mail: benham@benham.com

Stanley Gibbons Publications Overseas Representation
Stanley Gibbons Publications are represented overseas by the following

Australia *Renniks Publications PTY LTD*
Unit 3 37-39 Green Street, Banksmeadow, NSW 2019, Australia
Tel: +612 9695 7055
Website: www.renniks.com

Canada *Unitrade Associates*
99 Floral Parkway, Toronto, Ontario M6L 2C4, Canada
Tel: +1 416 242 5900
Website: www.unitradeassoc.com

Germany *Schaubek Verlag Leipzig*
Am Glaeschen 23, D-04420 Markranstaedt, Germany
Tel: +49 34 205 67823
Website: www.schaubek.de

Italy *Ernesto Marini S.R.L.*
V. Struppa, 300, Genova, 16165, Italy
Tel: +3901 0247-3530
Website: www.ernestomarini.it

Japan *Japan Philatelic*
PO Box 2, Suginami-Minami, Tokyo 168-8081, Japan
Tel: +81 3330 41641
Website: www.yushu.co.jp

Netherlands (also covers Belgium Denmark, Finland & France)
Uitgeverij Davo BV
PO Box 411, Ak Deventer, 7400 Netherlands
Tel: +315 7050 2700
Website: www.davo.nl

New Zealand *House of Stamps*
PO Box 12, Paraparaumu, New Zealand
Tel: +61 6364 8270
Website: www.houseofstamps.co.nz

New Zealand *Philatelic Distributors*
PO Box 863
15 Mount Edgecumbe Street
New Plymouth 4615, New Zealand
Tel: +6 46 758 65 68
Website: www.stampcollecta.com

Norway *SKANFIL A/S*
SPANAV. 52 / BOKS 2030
N-5504 HAUGESUND, Norway
Tel: +47-52703940
E-mail: magne@skanfil.no

Singapore *C S Philatelic Agency*
Peninsula Shopping Centre #04-29
3 Coleman Street, 179804, Singapore
Tel: +65 6337-1859
Website: www.cs.com.sg

South Africa *Mr. Thematic*
737 Redwood Street
Randparkridge Ext 14
Gauteng, South Africa
Tel: +1606 553107
E-mail: ianfrith146@gmail.com, chrisb@asapcc.co.za

Sweden *Chr Winther Sorensen AB*
Box 43, S-310 20 Knaered, Sweden
Tel: +46 43050743
Website: www.collectia.se

USA *Regency Superior Ltd*
229 North Euclid Avenue
Saint Louis, Missouri 63108, USA

PO Box 8277, St Louis,
MO 63156-8277, USA
Toll Free Tel: (800) 782-0066
Tel: (314) 361-5699
Website: www.RegencySuperior.com
Email: info@regencysuperior.com

General Philatelic Information and Guidelines to the Scope of Stanley Gibbons Commonwealth Catalogues

These notes reflect current practice in compiling the Stanley Gibbons Commonwealth Catalogues.

The Stanley Gibbons Stamp Catalogue has a very long history and the vast quantity of information it contains has been carefully built up by successive generations through the work of countless individuals. Philately is never static and the Catalogue has evolved and developed over the years. These notes relate to the current criteria upon which a stamp may be listed or priced. These criteria have developed over time and may have differed somewhat in the early years of this catalogue. These notes are not intended to suggest that we plan to make wholesale changes to the listing of classic issues in order to bring them into line with today's listing policy, they are designed to inform catalogue users as to the policies currently in operation.

PRICES

The prices quoted in this Catalogue are the estimated selling prices of Stanley Gibbons Ltd at the time of publication. They are, unless it is specifically stated otherwise, for examples in fine condition for the issue concerned. Superb examples are worth more; those of a lower quality considerably less.

All prices are subject to change without prior notice and Stanley Gibbons Ltd may from time to time offer stamps below catalogue price. Individual low value stamps sold at 399 Strand are liable to an additional handling charge. Purchasers of new issues should note the prices charged for them contain an element for the service rendered and so may exceed the prices shown when the stamps are subsequently catalogued. Postage and handling charges are extra.

No guarantee is given to supply all stamps priced, since it is not possible to keep every catalogued item in stock. Commemorative issues may, at times, only be available in complete sets and not as individual values.

Quotation of prices. The prices in the left-hand column are for unused stamps and those in the right-hand column are for used.

A dagger (†) denotes that the item listed does not exist in that condition and a blank, or dash, that it exists, or may exist, but we are unable to quote a price.

Prices are expressed in pounds and pence sterling. One pound comprises 100 pence (£1 = 100p).

The method of notation is as follows: pence in numerals (e.g. 10 denotes ten pence); pounds and pence, up to £100, in numerals (e.g. 4.25 denotes four pounds and twenty-five pence); prices above £100 are expressed in whole pounds with the '£' sign shown.

Unused stamps. Great Britain and Commonwealth: the prices for unused stamps of Queen Victoria to King George V are for lightly hinged examples. Unused prices for King Edward VIII, King George VI and Queen Elizabeth issues are for unmounted mint.

Some stamps from the King George VI period are often difficult to find in unmounted mint condition. In such instances we would expect that collectors would need to pay a high proportion of the price quoted to obtain mounted mint examples. Generally speaking lightly mounted mint stamps from this reign, issued before 1945, are in considerable demand.

Used stamps. The used prices are normally for fine postally used stamps, but may be for stamps cancelled-to-order where this practice exists.

A pen-cancellation on early issues can sometimes correctly denote postal use. Instances are individually noted in the Catalogue in explanation of the used price given.

Prices quoted for bisects on cover or large piece are for those dated during the period officially authorised.

Stamps not sold unused to the public (e.g. some official stamps) are priced used only.

The use of 'unified' designs, that is stamps inscribed for both postal and fiscal purposes, results in a number of stamps of very high face value. In some instances these may not have been primarily intended for postal purposes, but if they are so inscribed we include them. We only price such items used, however, where there is evidence of normal postal usage.

Cover prices. To assist collectors, cover prices are quoted for issues up to 1945 at the beginning of each country.

The system gives a general guide in the form of a factor by which the corresponding used price of the basic loose stamp should be multiplied when found in fine average condition on cover.

Care is needed in applying the factors and they relate to a cover which bears a single of the denomination listed; if more than one denomination is present the most highly priced attracts the multiplier and the remainder are priced at the simple figure for used singles in arriving at a total.

The cover should be of non-philatelic origin; bearing the correct postal rate for the period and distance involved and cancelled with the markings normal to the offices concerned. Purely philatelic items have a cover value only slightly greater than the catalogue value for the corresponding used stamps. This applies generally to those high-value stamps used philatelically rather than in the normal course of commerce. Low-value stamps, e.g. ¼d. and ½d., are desirable when used as a single rate on cover and merit an increase in 'multiplier' value.

First day covers in the period up to 1945 are not within the scope of the system and the multiplier should not be used. As a special category of philatelic usage, with wide variations in valuation according to scarcity, they require separate treatment.

Oversized covers, difficult to accommodate on an album page, should be reckoned as worth little more than the corresponding value of the used stamps. The condition of a cover also affects its value. Except for 'wreck covers', serious damage or soiling reduce the value where the postal markings and stamps are ordinary ones. Conversely, visual appeal adds to the value and this can include freshness of appearance, important addresses, old-fashioned but legible hand-writing, historic town-names, etc.

The multipliers are a base on which further value would be added to take account of the cover's postal historical importance in demonstrating such things as unusual, scarce or emergency cancels, interesting routes, significant postal markings, combination usage, the development of postal rates, and so on.

Minimum price. The minimum catalogue price quoted is 10p. For individual stamps prices between 10p. and 95p. are provided as a guide for catalogue users. The lowest price charged for individual stamps or sets purchased from Stanley Gibbons Ltd is £1

Set prices. Set prices are generally for one of each value, excluding shades and varieties, but including major colour changes. Where there are alternative shades, etc., the cheapest is usually included. The number of stamps in the set is always stated for clarity. The prices for sets containing *se-tenant* pieces are based on the prices quoted for such combinations, and not on those for the individual stamps.

Varieties. Where plate or cylinder varieties are priced in used condition the price quoted is for a fine used example with the cancellation well clear of the listed flaw.

Specimen stamps. The pricing of these items is explained under that heading.

Stamp booklets. Prices are for complete assembled booklets in fine condition with those issued before 1945 showing normal wear and tear. Incomplete booklets and those which have been 'exploded' will, in general, be worth less than the figure quoted.

Repricing. Collectors will be aware that the market factors of supply and demand directly influence the prices quoted in this Catalogue. Whatever the scarcity of a particular stamp, if there is no one in the market who wishes to buy it cannot be expected to achieve a high price. Conversely, the same item actively sought by numerous potential buyers may cause the price to rise.

All the prices in this Catalogue are examined during the preparation of each new edition by the expert staff of Stanley Gibbons and repriced as necessary. They take many factors into account, including supply and demand, and are in close touch with the international stamp market and the auction world.

Commonwealth cover prices and advice on postal history material originally provided by Edward B Proud.

GUARANTEE

All stamps are guaranteed originals in the following terms:

If not as described, and returned by the purchaser, we undertake to refund the price paid to us in the original transaction. If any stamp is certified as genuine by the Expert Committee of the Royal Philatelic Society, London, or by BPA Expertising Ltd, the purchaser shall not be entitled to make any claim against us for any error, omission or mistake in such certificate.

Consumers' statutory rights are not affected by the above guarantee.

The recognised Expert Committees in this country are those of the Royal Philatelic Society, 41 Devonshire Place, London W1G, 6JY, and BPA Expertising Ltd, PO Box 1141, Guildford, Surrey GU5 0WR. They do not undertake valuations under any circumstances and fees are payable for their services.

MARGINS ON IMPERFORATE STAMPS

| Superb | Very fine | Fine | Average | Poor |

GUM

| Unmounted | Very lightly mounted | Lightly mounted | Mounted/ large part original gum (o.g.). | Heavily mounted small part o.g. |

CENTRING

| Superb | Very fine | Fine | Average | Poor |

CANCELLATIONS

| Superb | Very fine | Fine | Average | Poor |

| Superb | Very fine |

| Fine | Average | Poor |

CONDITION GUIDE

To assist collectors in assessing the true value of items they are considering buying or in reviewing stamps already in their collections, we now offer a more detailed guide to the condition of stamps on which this catalogue's prices are based.

For a stamp to be described as 'Fine', it should be sound in all respects, without creases, bends, wrinkles, pin holes, thins or tears. If perforated, all perforation 'teeth' should be intact, it should not suffer from fading, rubbing or toning and it should be of clean, fresh appearance.

Margins on imperforate stamps: These should be even on all sides and should be at least as wide as half the distance between that stamp and the next. To have one or more margins of less than this width, would normally preclude a stamp from being described as 'Fine'. Some early stamps were positioned very close together on the printing plate and in such cases 'Fine' margins would necessarily be narrow. On the other hand, some plates were laid down to give a substantial gap between individual stamps and in such cases margins would be expected to be much wider.

An 'average' four-margin example would have a narrower margin on one or more sides and should be priced accordingly, while a stamp with wider, yet even, margins than 'Fine' would merit the description 'Very Fine' or 'Superb' and, if available, would command a price in excess of that quoted in the catalogue.

Gum: Since the prices for stamps of King Edward VIII, King George VI and Queen Elizabeth are for 'unmounted' or 'never hinged' mint, even stamps from these reigns which have been very lightly mounted should be available at a discount from catalogue price, the more obvious the hinge marks, the greater the discount.

Catalogue prices for stamps issued prior to King Edward VIII's reign are for mounted mint, so unmounted examples would be worth a premium. Hinge marks on 20th century stamps should not be too obtrusive, and should be at least in the lightly mounted category. For 19th century stamps more obvious hinging would be acceptable, but stamps should still carry a large part of their original gum—'Large part o.g.'—in order to be described as 'Fine'.

Centring: Ideally, the stamp's image should appear in the exact centre of the perforated area, giving equal margins on all sides. 'Fine' centring would be close to this ideal with any deviation having an effect on the value of the stamp. As in the case of the margins on imperforate stamps, it should be borne in mind that the space between some early stamps was very narrow, so it was very difficult to achieve accurate perforation, especially when the technology was in its infancy. Thus, poor centring would have a less damaging effect on the value of a 19th century stamp than on a 20th century example, but the premium put on a perfectly centred specimen would be greater.

Cancellations: Early cancellation devices were designed to 'obliterate' the stamp in order to prevent it being reused and this is still an important objective for today's postal administrations. Stamp collectors, on the other hand, prefer postmarks to be lightly applied, clear, and to leave as much as possible of the design visible. Dated, circular cancellations have long been 'the postmark of choice', but the definition of a 'Fine' cancellation will depend upon the types of cancellation in use at the time a stamp was current—it is clearly illogical to seek a circular datestamp on a Penny Black.

'Fine', by definition, will be superior to 'Average', so, in terms of cancellation quality, if one begins by identifying what 'Average' looks like, then one will be half way to identifying 'Fine'. The illustrations will give some guidance on mid-19th century and mid-20th century cancellations of Great Britain, but types of cancellation in general use in each country and in each period will determine the appearance of 'Fine'.

As for the factors discussed above, anything less than 'Fine' will result in a downgrading of the stamp concerned, while a very fine or superb cancellation will be worth a premium.

Combining the factors: To merit the description 'Fine', a stamp should be fine in every respect, but a small deficiency in one area might be made up for in another by a factor meriting an 'Extremely Fine' description.

Some early issues are so seldom found in what would normally be considered to be 'Fine' condition, the catalogue prices are for a slightly lower grade, with 'Fine' examples being worth a premium. In such cases a note to this effect is given in the catalogue, while elsewhere premiums are given for well-centred, lightly cancelled examples.

Stamps graded at less than fine remain collectable and, in the case of more highly priced stamps, will continue to hold a value. Nevertheless, buyers should always bear condition in mind.

The Catalogue in General

Contents. The Catalogue is confined to adhesive postage stamps, including miniature sheets. For particular categories the rules are:

(a) Revenue (fiscal) stamps are listed only where they have been expressly authorised for postal duty.

(b) Stamps issued only precancelled are included, but normally issued stamps available additionally with precancel have no separate precancel listing unless the face value is changed.

(c) Stamps prepared for use but not issued, hitherto accorded full listing, are nowadays foot-noted with a price (where possible).

(d) Bisects (trisects, etc.) are only listed where such usage was officially authorised.

(e) Stamps issued only on first day covers or in presentation packs and not available separately are not listed but may be priced in a footnote.

(f) New printings are only included in this Catalogue where they show a major philatelic variety, such as a change in shade, watermark or paper. Stamps which exist with or without imprint dates are listed separately; changes in imprint dates are mentioned in footnotes.

(g) Official and unofficial reprints are dealt with by footnote.

(h) Stamps from imperforate printings of modern issues which occur perforated are covered by footnotes, but are listed where widely available for postal use.

Exclusions. The following are excluded:

(a) non-postal revenue or fiscal stamps;

(b) postage stamps used fiscally (although prices are now given for some fiscally used high values);

(c) local carriage labels and private local issues;

(d) bogus or phantom stamps;

(e) railway or airline letter fee stamps, bus or road transport company labels or the stamps of private postal companies operating under licence from the national authority;

(f) cut-outs;

(g) all types of non-postal labels and souvenirs;

(h) documentary labels for the postal service, e.g. registration, recorded delivery, air-mail etiquettes, etc.;

(i) privately applied embellishments to official issues and privately commissioned items generally;

(j) stamps for training postal officers.

Full listing. 'Full listing' confers our recognition and implies allotting a catalogue number and (wherever possible) a price quotation.

In judging status for inclusion in the catalogue broad considerations are applied to stamps. They must be issued by a legitimate postal authority, recognised by the government concerned, and must be adhesives valid for proper postal use in the class of service for which they are inscribed. Stamps, with the exception of such categories as postage dues and officials, must be available to the general public, at face value, in reasonable quantities without any artificial restrictions being imposed on their distribution.

For errors and varieties the criterion is legitimate (albeit inadvertent) sale through a postal administration in the normal course of business. Details of provenance are always important; printers' waste and deliberately manufactured material are excluded.

Certificates. In assessing unlisted items due weight is given to Certificates from recognised Expert Committees and, where appropriate, we will usually ask to see them.

Date of issue. Where local issue dates differ from dates of release by agencies, 'date of issue' is the local date. Fortuitous stray usage before the officially intended date is disregarded in listing.

Catalogue numbers. Stamps of each country are catalogued chronologically by date of issue. Subsidiary classes are placed at the end of the country, as separate lists, with a distinguishing letter prefix to the catalogue number, e.g. D for postage due, O for official and E for express delivery stamps.

The catalogue number appears in the extreme left-column. The boldface Type numbers in the next column are merely cross-references to illustrations.

Once published in the Catalogue, numbers are changed as little as possible; really serious renumbering is reserved for the occasions when a complete country or an entire issue is being rewritten. The edition first affected includes cross-reference tables of old and new numbers.

Our catalogue numbers are universally recognised in specifying stamps and as a hallmark of status.

Illustrations. Stamps are illustrated at three-quarters linear size. Stamps not illustrated are the same size and format as the value shown, unless otherwise indicated. Stamps issued only as miniature sheets have the stamp alone illustrated but sheet size is also quoted. Overprints, surcharges, watermarks and postmarks are normally actual size. Illustrations of varieties are often enlarged to show the detail. Stamp booklet covers are illustrated half-size, unless otherwise indicated.

Designers. Designers' names are quoted where known, though space precludes naming every individual concerned in the production of a set. In particular, photographers supplying material are usually named only where they also make an active contribution in the design stage; posed photographs of reigning monarchs are, however, an exception to this rule.

CONTACTING THE CATALOGUE EDITOR

The editor is always interested in hearing from people who have new information which will improve or correct the Catalogue. As a general rule he must see and examine the actual stamps before they can be considered for listing; photographs or photocopies are insufficient evidence.

Submissions should be made in writing to the Catalogue Editor, Stanley Gibbons Publications at the Ringwood office. The cost of return postage for items submitted is appreciated, and this should include the registration fee if required.

Where information is solicited purely for the benefit of the enquirer, the editor cannot undertake to reply if the answer is already contained in these published notes or if return postage is omitted. Written communications are greatly preferred to enquiries by telephone or e-mail and the editor regrets that he or his staff cannot see personal callers without a prior appointment being made. Correspondence may be subject to delay during the production period of each new edition.

The editor welcomes close contact with study circles and is interested, too, in finding reliable local correspondents who will verify and supplement official information in countries where this is deficient.

We regret we do not give opinions as to the genuineness of stamps, nor do we identify stamps or number them by our Catalogue.

TECHNICAL MATTERS

The meanings of the technical terms used in the catalogue will be found in our *Philatelic Terms Illustrated*.

References below to (more specialised) listings are to be taken to indicate, as appropriate, the Stanley Gibbons *Great Britain Specialised Catalogue* in five volumes or the *Great Britain Concise Catalogue*.

1. Printing

Printing errors. Errors in printing are of major interest to the Catalogue. Authenticated items meriting consideration would include: background, centre or frame inverted or omitted; centre or subject transposed; error of colour; error or omission of value; double prints and impressions; printed both sides; and so on. Designs *tête-bêche*, whether intentionally or by accident, are listable. *Se-tenant* arrangements of stamps are recognised in the listings or footnotes. Gutter pairs (a pair of stamps separated by blank margin) are not included in this volume. Colours only partially omitted are not listed. Stamps with embossing omitted are reserved for our more specialised listings.

Printing varieties. Listing is accorded to major changes in the printing base which lead to completely new types. In recess-printing this could be a design re-engraved; in photogravure or photolithography a screen altered in whole or in part. It can also encompass flat-bed and rotary printing if the results are readily distinguishable.

To be considered at all, varieties must be constant.

Early stamps, produced by primitive methods, were prone to numerous imperfections; the lists reflect this, recognising re-entries, retouches, broken frames, misshapen letters, and so on. Printing technology has, however, radically improved over the years, during which time photogravure and lithography have become predominant. Varieties nowadays are more in the nature of flaws and these, being too specialised for this general catalogue, are almost always outside the scope.

In no catalogue, however, do we list such items as: dry prints, kiss prints, doctor-blade flaws, colour shifts or registration flaws (unless they lead to the complete omission of a colour from an individual stamp), lithographic ring flaws, and so on. Neither do we recognise fortuitous happenings like paper creases or confetti flaws.

Overprints (and surcharges). Overprints of different types qualify for separate listing. These include overprints in different colours; overprints from different printing processes such as litho and typo; overprints in totally different typefaces, etc. Major errors in machine-printed overprints are important and listable. They include: overprint inverted or omitted; overprint double (treble, etc.); overprint diagonal; overprint double, one inverted; pairs with one overprint omitted, e.g. from a radical shift to an adjoining stamp; error of colour; error of type fount; letters inverted or omitted, etc. If the overprint is handstamped, few of these would qualify and a distinction is drawn. We continue, however, to list pairs of stamps where one has a handstamped overprint and the other has not.

Albino prints or double prints, one of them being albino (i.e. showing an uninked impression of the printing plate) are listable unless they are particularly common in this form (see the note below Travancore No. 32fa, for example). We do not, however, normally list reversed albino overprints, caused by the accidental or deliberate folding of sheets prior to overprinting (British Levant Nos. 51/8).

Varieties occurring in overprints will often take the form of broken letters, slight differences in spacing, rising spaces, etc. Only the most important would be considered for listing or footnote mention.

Sheet positions. If space permits we quote sheet positions of listed varieties and authenticated data is solicited for this purpose.

De La Rue plates. The Catalogue classifies the general plates used by De La Rue for printing British Colonial stamps as follows:

VICTORIAN KEY TYPE

Die I

1. The ball of decoration on the second point of the crown appears as a dark mass of lines.
2. Dark vertical shading separates the front hair from the bun.
3. The vertical line of colour outlining the front of the throat stops at the sixth line of shading on the neck.
4. The white space in the coil of the hair above the curl is roughly the shape of a pin's head.

Die II

1. There are very few lines of colour in the ball and it appears almost white.

2. A white vertical strand of hair appears in place of the dark shading.

3. The line stops at the eighth line of shading.

4. The white space is oblong, with a line of colour partially dividing it at the left end.

Plates numbered 1 and 2 are both Die I. Plates 3 and 4 are Die II.

GEORGIAN KEY TYPE

Die I

A. The second (thick) line below the name of the country is cut slanting, conforming roughly to the shape of the crown on each side.

B. The labels of solid colour bearing the words "POSTAGE" and "& REVENUE" are square at the inner top corners.

C. There is a projecting "bud" on the outer spiral of the ornament in each of the lower corners.

Die II

A. The second line is cut vertically on each side of the crown.

B. The labels curve inwards at the top.

C. There is no "bud" in this position.

Unless otherwise stated in the lists, all stamps with watermark Multiple Crown CA (w **8**) are Die I while those with watermark Multiple Crown Script CA (w **9**) are Die II. The Georgian Die II was introduced in April 1921 and was used for Plates 10 to 22 and 26 to 28. Plates 23 to 25 were made from Die I by mistake.

2. Paper

All stamps listed are deemed to be on (ordinary) paper of the wove type and white in colour; only departures from this are normally mentioned.

Types. Where classification so requires we distinguish such other types of paper as, for example, vertically and horizontally laid; wove and laid bâtonné; card(board); carton; cartridge; glazed; granite; native; pelure; porous; quadrillé; ribbed; rice; and silk thread.

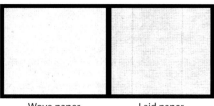

Wove paper   Laid paper

Granite paper   Quadrillé paper

Burelé band

The various makeshifts for normal paper are listed as appropriate. The varieties of double paper and joined paper are recognised. The security device of a printed burelé band on the back of a stamp, as in early Queensland, qualifies for listing.

Descriptive terms. The fact that a paper is handmade (and thus probably of uneven thickness) is mentioned where necessary. Such descriptive terms as "hard" and "soft"; "smooth" and "rough"; "thick", "medium" and "thin" are applied where there is philatelic merit in classifying papers.

Coloured, very white and toned papers. A coloured paper is one that is coloured right through (front and back of the stamp). In the Catalogue the colour of the paper is given in italics, thus:

black/*rose* = black design on rose paper.

Papers have been made specially white in recent years by, for example, a very heavy coating of chalk. We do not classify shades of whiteness of paper as distinct varieties. There does exist, however, a type of paper from early days called toned. This is off-white, often brownish or buffish, but it cannot be assigned any definite colour. A toning effect brought on by climate, incorrect storage or gum staining is disregarded here, as this was not the state of the paper when issued.

"Ordinary" and "Chalk-surfaced" papers. The availability of many postage stamps for revenue purposes made necessary some safeguard against the illegitimate re-use of stamps with removable cancellations. This was at first secured by using fugitive inks and later by printing on paper surfaced by coatings containing either chalk or china clay, both of which made it difficult to remove any form of obliteration without damaging the stamp design.

This catalogue lists these chalk-surfaced paper varieties from their introduction in 1905. Where no indication is given, the paper is "ordinary".

The "traditional" method of indentifying chalk-surfaced papers has been that, when touched with a silver wire, a black mark is left on the paper, and the listings in this catalogue are based on that test. However, the test itself is now largely discredited, for, although the mark can be removed by a soft rubber, some damage to the stamp will result from its use.

The difference between chalk-surfaced and pre-war ordinary papers is fairly clear: chalk-surfaced papers being smoother to the touch and showing a characteristic sheen when light is reflected off their surface. Under good magnification tiny bubbles or pock marks can be seen on the surface of the stamp and at the tips of the perforations the surfacing appears "broken". Traces of paper fibres are evident on the surface of ordinary paper and the ink shows a degree of absorption into it.

Initial chalk-surfaced paper printings by De La Rue had a thinner coating than subsequently became the norm. The characteristics described above are less pronounced in these printings.

During and after the Second World War, substitute papers replaced the chalk-surfaced papers, these do not react to the silver test and are therefore classed as "ordinary", although differentiating them without recourse to it is more difficult, for, although the characteristics of the chalk-surfaced paper remained the same, some of the ordinary papers appear much smoother than earlier papers and many do not show the watermark clearly. Experience is the only solution to identifying these, and comparison with stamps whose paper type is without question will be of great help.

Another type of paper, known as "thin striated" was used only for the Bahamas 1s. and 5s. (Nos. 155a, 156a, 171 and 174) and for several stamps of the Malayan states. Hitherto these have been described as "chalk-surfaced" since they gave some reaction to the silver test, but they are much thinner than usual chalk-surfaced papers, with the watermark showing clearly. Stamps on this paper show a slightly 'ribbed' effect when the stamp is held up to the light. Again, comparison with a known striated paper stamp, such as the 1941 Straits Settlements Die II 2c. orange (No. 294) will prove invaluable in separating these papers.

Glazed paper. In 1969 the Crown Agents introduced a new general-purpose paper for use in conjunction with all current printing processes. It generally has a marked glossy surface but the degree varies according to the process used, being more marked in recess-printing stamps. As it does not respond to the silver test this presents a further test where previous printings were on chalky paper. A change of paper to the glazed variety merits separate listing.

Green and yellow papers. Issues of the First World War and immediate postwar period occur on green and yellow papers and these are given separate Catalogue listing. The original coloured papers (coloured throughout) gave way to surface-coloured papers, the stamps having "white backs"; other stamps show one colour on the front and a different one at the back. Because of the numerous variations a grouping of colours is adopted as follows:

Yellow papers

(1) The original *yellow* paper (throughout), usually bright in colour. The gum is often sparse, of harsh consistency and dull-looking. Used 1912–1920.

(2) The *white-backs*. Used 1913–1914.

(3) A bright lemon paper. The colour must have a pronounced greenish tinge, different from the "yellow" in (1). As a rule, the gum on stamps using this lemon paper is plentiful, smooth and shiny, and the watermark shows distinctly. Care is needed with stamps printed in green on yellow paper (1) as it may appear that the paper is this lemon. Used 1914–1916.

(4) An experimental *orange-buff* paper. The colour must have a distinct brownish tinge. It is not to be confused with a muddy yellow (1) nor the misleading appearance (on the surface) of stamps printed in red on yellow paper where an engraved plate has been insufficiently wiped. Used 1918–1921.

(5) An experimental *buff* paper. This lacks the brownish tinge of (4) and the brightness of the yellow shades. The gum is shiny when compared with the matt type used on (4). Used 1919–1920.

(6) A *pale yellow* paper that has a creamy tone to the yellow. Used from 1920 onwards.

Green papers

(7) The original "green" paper, varying considerably through shades of blue-green and yellow-green, the front and back sometimes differing. Used 1912–1916.

(8) The *white backs*. Used 1913–1914.

(9) A paper blue-green on the surface with *pale olive* back. The back must be markedly paler than the front and this and the pronounced olive tinge to the back distinguish it from (7). Used 1916–1920.

(10) Paper with a vivid green surface, commonly called *emerald-green*; it has the olive back of (9). Used 1920.

(11) Paper with *emerald-green* both back and front. Used from 1920 onwards.

3. Perforation and Rouletting

Perforation gauge. The gauge of a perforation is the number of holes in a length of 2 cm. For correct classification the size of the holes (large or small) may need to be distinguished; in a few cases the actual number of holes on each edge of the stamp needs to be quoted.

Measurement. The Gibbons *Instanta* gauge is the standard for measuring perforations. The stamp is viewed against a dark background with the transparent gauge put on top of it. Though the gauge measures to decimal accuracy, perforations read from it are generally quoted in the Catalogue to the nearest half. For example:

Just over perf 12¾ to just under 13¼ = perf 13
Perf 13¼ exactly, rounded up   = perf 13½
Just over perf 13¼ to just under 13¾ = perf 13½
Perf 13¾ exactly, rounded up   = perf 14

However, where classification depends on it, actual quarter-perforations are quoted.

Notation. Where no perforation is quoted for an issue it is imperforate. Perforations are usually abbreviated (and spoken) as follows, though sometimes they may be spelled out for clarity. This notation for rectangular stamps (the majority) applies to diamond shapes if "top" is read as the edge to the top right.

P 14: perforated alike on all sides (read: "perf 14").

P 14×15: the first figure refers to top and bottom, the second to left and right sides (read: "perf 14 by 15"). This is a compound perforation. For an upright triangular stamp the first figure refers to the two sloping sides and second to the base. In inverted triangulars the base is first and the second figure to the sloping sides.

P 14–15: perforation measuring anything between 14 and 15: the holes are irregularly spaced, thus the gauge may vary along a single line or even along a single edge of the stamp (read: "perf 14 to 15").

P 14 *irregular*: perforated 14 from a worn perforator, giving badly aligned holes irregularly spaced (read: "irregular perf 14").

P *comp(ound)* 14×15: two gauges in use but not necessarily on opposite sides of the stamp. It could be one side in one gauge and three in the other; or two adjacent sides with the same gauge. (Read: "perf compound of 14 and 15".) For three gauges or more, abbreviated as "P 12, 14½, 15 *or compound*" for example.

P 14, 14½: perforated approximately 14¼ (read: "perf 14 or 14½"). It does *not* mean two stamps, one perf 14 and the other perf 14½. This obsolescent notation is gradually being replaced in the Catalogue.

Imperf: imperforate (not perforated)

Imperf×P 14: imperforate at top ad bottom and perf 14 at sides.

P 14×*imperf*: perf 14 at top and bottom and imperforate at sides.

Such headings as "P 13×14 (*vert*) and P 14×13 (*horiz*)" indicate which perforations apply to which stamp format—vertical or horizontal.

Some stamps are additionally perforated so that a label or tab is detachable; others have been perforated for use as two halves. Listings are normally for whole stamps, unless stated otherwise.

Imperf×perf

Other terms. Perforation almost always gives circular holes; where other shapes have been used they are specified, e.g. square holes; lozenge perf. Interrupted perfs are brought about by the omission of pins at regular intervals. Perforations merely simulated by being printed as part of the design are of course ignored. With few exceptions, privately applied perforations are not listed.

In the 19th century perforations are often described as clean cut (clean, sharply incised holes), intermediate or rough (rough holes, imperfectly cut, often the result of blunt pins).

Perforation errors and varieties. Authenticated errors, where a stamp normally perforated is accidentally issued imperforate, are listed provided no traces of perforation (blind holes or indentations) remain. They must be provided as pairs, both stamps wholly imperforate, and are only priced in that form.

Stamps imperforate between stamp and sheet margin are not listed in this catalogue, but such errors on Great Britain stamps will be found in the *Great Britain Specialised Catalogue*.

Pairs described as "imperforate between" have the line of perforations between the two stamps omitted.

Imperf between (horiz pair): a horizontal pair of stamps with perfs all around the edges but none between the stamps.

Imperf between (vert pair): a vertical pair of stamps with perfs all around the edges but none between the stamps.

Imperf between   Imperf horizontally
(vertical pair)   (vertical pair)

Where several of the rows have escaped perforation the resulting varieties are listable. Thus:

Imperf vert (horiz pair): a horizontal pair of stamps perforated top and bottom; all three vertical directions are imperf—the two outer edges and between the stamps.

Imperf horiz (vert pair): a vertical pair perforated at left and right edges; all three horizontal directions are imperf—the top, bottom and between the stamps.

Straight edges. Large sheets cut up before issue to post offices can cause stamps with straight edges, i.e. imperf on one side or on two sides at right angles. They are not usually listable in this condition and are worth less than corresponding stamps properly perforated all round. This does not, however, apply to certain stamps, mainly from coils and booklets, where straight edges on various sides are the manufacturing norm affecting every stamp. The listings and notes make clear which sides are correctly imperf.

Malfunction. Varieties of double, misplaced or partial perforation caused by error or machine malfunction are not listable, neither are freaks, such as perforations placed diagonally from paper folds, nor missing holes caused by broken pins.

Types of perforating. Where necessary for classification, perforation types are distinguished.

These include:

Line perforation from one line of pins punching single rows of holes at a time.

Comb perforation from pins disposed across the sheet in comb formation, punching out holes at three sides of the stamp a row at a time.

Harrow perforation applied to a whole pane or sheet at one stroke.

Rotary perforation from toothed wheels operating across a sheet, then crosswise.

Sewing machine perforation. The resultant condition, clean-cut or rough, is distinguished where required.

Pin-perforation is the commonly applied term for pin-roulette in which, instead of being punched out, round holes are pricked by sharp-pointed pins and no paper is removed.

Mixed perforation occurs when stamps with defective perforations are re-perforated in a different gauge.

Punctured stamps. Perforation holes can be punched into the face of the stamp. Patterns of small holes, often in the shape of initial letters, are privately applied devices against pilferage. These (perfins) are outside the scope except for Australia, Canada, Cape of Good Hope, Papua and Sudan where they were used as official stamps by the national administration. Identification devices, when officially inspired, are listed or noted; they can be shapes, or letters or words formed from holes, sometimes converting one class of stamp into another.

Rouletting. In rouletting the paper is cut, for ease of separation, but none is removed. The gauge is measured, when needed, as for perforations. Traditional French terms descriptive of the type of cut are often used and types include:

Arc roulette (percé en arc). Cuts are minute, spaced arcs, each roughly a semicircle.

Cross roulette (percé en croix). Cuts are tiny diagonal crosses.

Line roulette (percé en ligne or *en ligne droite).* Short straight cuts parallel to the frame of the stamp. The commonest basic roulette. Where not further described, "roulette" means this type.

Rouletted in colour or coloured roulette (percé en lignes colorées or *en lignes de coleur).* Cuts with coloured edges, arising from notched rule inked simultaneously with the printing plate.

Saw-tooth roulette (percé en scie). Cuts applied zigzag fashion to resemble the teeth of a saw.

Serpentine roulette (percé en serpentin). Cuts as sharply wavy lines.

Zigzag roulette (percé en zigzags). Short straight cuts at angles in alternate directions, producing sharp points on separation. US usage favours "serrate(d) roulette" for this type.

Pin-roulette (originally *percé en points* and now *perforés trous d'epingle)* is commonly called pin-perforation in English.

4. Gum

All stamps listed are assumed to have gum of some kind; if they were issued without gum this is stated. Original gum (o.g.) means that which was present on the stamp as issued to the public. Deleterious climates and the presence of certain chemicals can cause gum to crack and, with early stamps, even make the paper deteriorate. Unscrupulous fakers are adept in removing it and regumming the stamp to meet the unreasoning demand often made for "full o.g." in cases where such a thing is virtually impossible.

The gum normally used on stamps has been gum arabic until the late 1960s when synthetic adhesives were introduced. Harrison and Sons Ltd for instance use *polyvinyl alcohol,* known to philatelists as PVA. This is almost invisible except for a slight yellowish tinge which was incorporated to make it possible to see that the stamps have been gummed. It has advantages in hot countries, as stamps do not curl and sheets are less likely to stick together. Gum arabic and PVA are not distinguished in the lists except that where a stamp exists with both forms this is indicated in footnotes. Our more specialised catalogues provide separate listing of gums for Great Britain.

Self-adhesive stamps are issued on backing paper, from which they are peeled before affixing to mail. Unused examples are priced as for backing paper intact, in which condition they are recommended to be kept. Used examples are best collected on cover or on piece.

5. Watermarks

Stamps are on unwatermarked paper except where the heading to the set says otherwise.

Detection. Watermarks are detected for Catalogue description by one of four methods: (1) holding stamps to the light; (2) laying stamps face down on a dark background; (3) adding a few drops of petroleum ether 40/60 to the stamp laid face down in a watermark tray; (4) by use of the Stanley Gibbons Detectamark, or other equipment, which work by revealing the thinning of the paper at the watermark. (Note that petroleum ether is highly inflammable in use and can damage photogravure stamps.)

Listable types. Stamps occurring on both watermarked and unwatermarked papers are different types and both receive full listing.

Single watermarks (devices occurring once on every stamp) can be modified in size and shape as between different issues; the types are noted but not usually separately listed. Fortuitous absence of watermark from a single stamp or its gross displacement would not be listable.

To overcome registration difficulties the device may be repeated at close intervals *(a multiple water-mark),* single stamps thus showing parts of several devices. Similarly, a *large sheet watermark* (or *all-over watermark)* covering numerous stamps can be used. We give informative notes and illustrations for them. The designs may be such that numbers of stamps in the sheet automatically lack watermark: this is not a listable variety. Multiple and all-over watermarks sometimes undergo modifications, but if the various types are difficult to distinguish from single stamps notes are given but not separate listings.

Papermakers' watermarks are noted where known but not listed separately, since most stamps in the sheet will lack them. Sheet watermarks which are nothing more than officially adopted papermakers' watermarks are, however, given normal listing.

Marginal watermarks, falling outside the pane of stamps, are ignored except where misplacement caused the adjoining row to be affected, in which case they may be footnoted.

Watermark errors and varieties. Watermark errors are recognised as of major importance. They comprise stamps intended to be on unwatermarked paper but issued watermarked by mistake, or stamps printed on paper with the wrong watermark. Varieties showing letters omitted from the watermark are also included, but broken or deformed bits on the dandy roll are not listed unless they represent repairs.

Watermark positions. The diagram shows how watermark position is described in the Catalogue. Paper has a side intended for printing and watermarks are usually impressed so that they read normally when looked through from that printed side. However, since philatelists customarily detect watermarks by looking at the back of the stamp the watermark diagram also makes clear what is actually seen.

Illustrations in the Catalogue are of watermarks in normal positions (from the front of the stamps) and are actual size where possible.

Differences in watermark position are collectable varieties. This Catalogue now lists inverted, sideways inverted and reversed watermark varieties on Commonwealth stamps from the 1860s onwards except where the watermark position is completely haphazard.

Great Britain inverted and sideways inverted watermarks can be found in the *Great Britain Specialised Catalogue* and the *Great Britain Concise Catalogue*.

Where a watermark comes indiscriminately in various positions our policy is to cover this by a general note: we do not give separate listings because the watermark position in these circumstances has no particular philatelic importance.

AS DESCRIBED (Read through front of stamp)		AS SEEN DURING WATERMARK DETECTION (Stamp face down and back examined
GvR	Normal	ꓤvӘ
ꓤvӘ	Inverted	Әʌꓤ
ꓤvӘ	Reversed	GvR
Әʌꓤ	Reversed and Inverted	ꓤʌӘ
GvR (rotated)	Sideways	ꓤvӘ (rotated)
GvR (rotated)	Sideways Inverted	ꓤvӘ (rotated)

Standard types of watermark. Some watermarks have been used generally for various British possessions rather than exclusively for a single colony. To avoid repetition the Catalogue classifies 11 general types, as under, with references in the headings throughout the listings being given either in words or in the form ("W w **9**") (meaning "watermark type w **9**"). In those cases where watermark illustrations appear in the listings themselves, the respective reference reads, for example, W **153**, thus indicating that the watermark will be found in the normal sequence of illustrations as (type) **153**.

The general types are as follows, with an example of each quoted.

W	Description	Example
w **1**	Large Star	St. Helena No. 1
w **2**	Small Star	Turks Is. No. 4
w **3**	Broad (pointed) Star	Grenada No. 24
w **4**	Crown (over) CC, small stamp	Antigua No. 13
w **5**	Crown (over) CC, large stamp	Antigua No. 31
w **6**	Crown (over) CA, small stamp	Antigua No. 21
w **7**	Crown CA (CA over Crown), large stamp	Sierra Leone No. 54
w **8**	Multiple Crown CA	Antigua No. 41
w **9**	Multiple Script CA	Seychelles No. 158
w **9a**	do. Error	Seychelles No. 158a
w **9b**	do. Error	Seychelles No. 158b
w **10**	V over Crown	N.S.W. No. 327
w **11**	Crown over A	N.S.W. No. 347

CC in these watermarks is an abbreviation for "Crown Colonies" and CA for "Crown Agents". Watermarks w **1**, w **2** and w **3** are on stamps printed by Perkins, Bacon; w **4** onwards on stamps from De La Rue and other printers.

w **1**
Large Star

w **2**
Small Star

w **3**
Broad-pointed Star

Watermark w **1**, *Large Star*, measures 15 to 16 mm across the star from point to point and about 27 mm from centre to centre vertically between stars in the sheet. It was made for long stamps like Ceylon 1857 and St. Helena 1856.

Watermark w **2**, *Small Star* is of similar design but measures 12 to 13½mm from point to point and 24 mm from centre to centre vertically. It was for use with ordinary-size stamps such as Grenada 1863–71.

When the Large Star watermark was used with the smaller stamps it only occasionally comes in the centre of the paper. It is frequently so misplaced as to show portions of two stars above and below and this eccentricity will very often help in determining the watermark.

Watermark w **3**, *Broad-pointed Star*, resembles w **1** but the points are broader.

w **4**
Crown (over) CC

w **5**
Crown (over) CC

Two *Crown (over) CC* watermarks were used: w **4** was for stamps of ordinary size and w **5** for those of larger size.

w **6**
Crown (over) CA

w **7**
CA over Crown

Two watermarks of *Crown CA* type were used, w **6** being for stamps of ordinary size. The other, w **7**, is properly described as *CA over Crown*. It was specially made for paper on which it was intended to print long fiscal stamps: that some were used postally accounts for the appearance of w **7** in the Catalogue. The watermark occupies twice the space of the ordinary Crown CA watermark, w **6**. Stamps of normal size printed on paper with w **7** watermark show it *sideways*; it takes a horizontal pair of stamps to show the entire watermark.

w **8**
Multiple Crown CA

w **9**
Multiple Script CA

Multiple watermarks began in 1904 with w **8**, *Multiple Crown CA*, changed from 1921 to w **9**, *Multiple Script CA*. On stamps of ordinary size portions of two or three watermarks appear and on the large-sized stamps a greater number can be observed. The change to letters in script character with w **9** was accompanied by a Crown of distinctly different shape.

It seems likely that there were at least two dandy rolls for each Crown Agents watermark in use at any one time with a reserve roll being employed when the normal one was withdrawn for maintenance or repair.

Both the Mult Crown CA and the Mult Script CA types exist with one or other of the letters omitted from individual impressions. It is possible that most of these occur from the reserve rolls as they have only been found on certain issues. The MCA watermark experienced such problems during the early 1920s and the Script over a longer period from the early 1940s until 1951.

During the 1920s damage must also have occurred on one of the Crowns as a substituted Crown has been found on certain issues. This is smaller than the normal and consists of an oval base joined to two upright ovals with a circle positioned between their upper ends. The upper line of the Crown's base is omitted, as are the left and right-hand circles at the top and also the cross over the centre circle.

Substituted Crown

The *Multiple Script CA* watermark, w **9**, is known with two errors, recurring among the 1950–52 printings of several territories. In the first a crown has fallen away from the dandy-roll that impresses the watermark into the paper pulp. It gives w **9a**, *Crown missing*, but this omission has been found in both "Crown only" (*illustrated*) and "Crown CA" rows. The resulting faulty paper was used for Bahamas, Johore, Seychelles and the postage due stamps of nine colonies

w **9a**: Error, Crown missing

w **9b**: Error, St. Edward's Crown

When the omission was noticed a second mishap occurred, which was to insert a wrong crown in the space, giving w **9b**, St. Edward's Crown. This produced varieties in Bahamas, Perlis, St. Kitts-Nevis and Singapore and the incorrect crown likewise occurs in (Crown only) and (Crown CA) rows.

w 10
V over Crown

w 11
Crown over A

Resuming the general types, two watermarks found in issues of several Australian States are: w **10**, *V over Crown*, and w **11**, *Crown over A*.

w 12
Multiple St. Edward's
Crown Block CA

w 13
Multiple PTM

The *Multiple St. Edward's Crown Block CA* watermark, w **12**, was introduced in 1957 and besides the change in the Crown (from that used in Multiple Crown Script CA, w **9**) the letters reverted to block capitals. The new watermark began to appear sideways in 1966 and these stamps are generally listed as separate sets.

The watermark w **13**, *Multiple PTM*, was introduced for new Malaysian issues in November 1961.

w 14
Multiple Crown CA Diagonal

By 1974 the two dandy-rolls the "upright" and the "sideways" for w **12** were wearing out; the Crown Agents therefore discontinued using the sideways watermark one and retained the other only as a stand-by. A new dandy-roll with the pattern of w **14**, *Multiple Crown CA Diagonal*, was introduced and first saw use with some Churchill Centenary issues.

The new watermark had the design arranged in gradually spiralling rows. It is improved in design to allow smooth passage over the paper (the gaps between letters and rows had caused jolts in previous dandy-rolls) and the sharp corners and angles, where fibres used to accumulate, have been eliminated by rounding.

This watermark had no "normal" sideways position amongst the different printers using it. To avoid confusion our more specialised listings do not rely on such terms as

"sideways inverted" but describe the direction in which the watermark points.

w 15
Multiple POST OFFICE

During 1981 w **15**, *Multiple POST OFFICE* was introduced for certain issues prepared by Philatelists Ltd, acting for various countries in the Indian Ocean, Pacific and West Indies.

w 16
Multiple Crown Script CA Diagonal

A new Crown Agents watermark was introduced during 1985, w **16**, *Multiple Crown Script CA Diagonal*. This was very similar to the previous w **14**, but showed "CA" in script rather than block letters. It was first used on the omnibus series of stamps commemorating the Life and Times of Queen Elizabeth the Queen Mother.

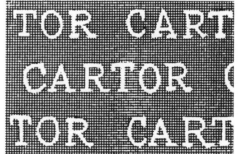

w 17
Multiple CARTOR

Watermark w **17**, *Multiple CARTOR*, was used from 1985 for issues printed by this French firm for countries which did not normally use the Crown Agents watermark.

w **18**

In 2008, following the closure of the Crown Agents Stamp Bureau, a new Multiple Crowns watermark, w **18** was introduced

In recent years the use of watermarks has, to a small extent, been superseded by fluorescent security markings. These are often more visible from the reverse of the stamp (Cook Islands from 1970 onwards), but have occurred printed over the design (Hong Kong Nos. 415/30). In 1982 the Crown Agents introduced a new stock paper, without watermark, known as "C-Kurity" on which a fluorescent pattern of blue rosettes is visible on the reverse, beneath the gum. This paper was used for issues from Gambia and Norfolk Island.

6. Colours

Stamps in two or three colours have these named in order of appearance, from the centre moving outwards. Four colours or more are usually listed as multicoloured.

In compound colour names the second is the predominant one, thus:

orange-red = a red tending towards orange;
red-orange = an orange containing more red
than usual.

Standard colours used. The 200 colours most used for stamp identification are given in the Stanley Gibbons Stamp Colour Key. The Catalogue has used the Stamp Colour Key as standard for describing new issues for some years. The names are also introduced as lists are rewritten, though exceptions are made for those early issues where traditional names have become universally established.

Determining colours. When comparing actual stamps with colour samples in the Stamp Colour Key, view in a good north daylight (or its best substitute; fluorescent "colour matching" light). Sunshine is not recommended. Choose a solid portion of the stamp design; if available, marginal markings such as solid bars of colour or colour check dots are helpful. Shading lines in the design can be misleading as they appear lighter than solid colour. Postmarked portions of a stamp appear darker than normal. If more than one colour is present, mask off the extraneous ones as the eye tends to mix them.

Errors of colour. Major colour errors in stamps or overprints which qualify for listing are: wrong colours; one colour inverted in relation to the rest; albinos (colourless impressions), where these have Expert Committee certificates; colours completely omitted, but only on unused stamps (if found on used stamps the information is footnoted) and with good credentials, missing colours being frequently faked.

Colours only partially omitted are not recognised, Colour shifts, however spectacular, are not listed.

Shades. Shades in philately refer to variations in the intensity of a colour or the presence of differing amounts of other colours. They are particularly significant when they can be linked to specific printings. In general, shades need to

be quite marked to fall within the scope of this Catalogue; it does not favour nowadays listing the often numerous shades of a stamp, but chooses a single applicable colour name which will indicate particular groups of outstanding shades. Furthermore, the listings refer to colours as issued; they may deteriorate into something different through the passage of time.

Modern colour printing by lithography is prone to marked differences of shade, even within a single run, and variations can occur within the same sheet. Such shades are not listed.

Aniline colours. An aniline colour meant originally one derived from coal-tar; it now refers more widely to colour of a particular brightness suffused on the surface of a stamp and showing through clearly on the back.

Colours of overprints and surcharges. All overprints and surcharges are in black unless stated otherwise in the heading or after the description of the stamp.

7. Specimen Stamps

Originally, stamps overprinted SPECIMEN were circulated to postmasters or kept in official records, but after the establishment of the Universal Postal Union supplies were sent to Berne for distribution to the postal administrations of member countries.

During the period 1884 to 1928 most of the stamps of British Crown Colonies required for this purpose were overprinted SPECIMEN in various shapes and sizes by their printers from typeset formes. Some locally produced provisionals were handstamped locally, as were sets prepared for presentation. From 1928 stamps were punched with holes forming the word SPECIMEN, each firm of printers using a different machine or machines. From 1948 the stamps supplied for UPU distribution were no longer punctured.

Stamps of some other Commonwealth territories were overprinted or handstamped locally, while stamps of Great Britain and those overprinted for use in overseas postal agencies (mostly of the higher denominations) bore SPECIMEN overprints and handstamps applied by the Inland Revenue or the Post Office.

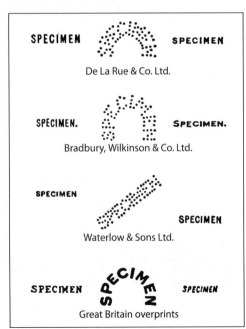

Some of the commoner types of overprints or punctures are illustrated here. Collectors are warned that dangerous forgeries of the punctured type exist.

The *Stanley Gibbons Commonwealth Catalogues* record those Specimen overprints or perforations intended for distribution by the UPU to member countries. In addition the Specimen overprints of Australia and its dependent territories, which were sold to collectors by the Post Office, are also included.

Various Perkins Bacon issues exist obliterated with a "CANCELLED" within an oval of bars handstamp.

Perkins Bacon "CANCELLED"
Handstamp

This was applied to six examples of those issues available in 1861 which were then given to members of Sir Rowland Hill's family. 75 different stamps (including four from Chile) are recorded with this handstamp although others may possibly exist. The unauthorised gift of these "CANCELLED" stamps to the Hill family was a major factor in the loss of the Agent General for the Crown Colonies (the forerunner of the Crown Agents) contracts by Perkins Bacon in the following year. Where examples of these scarce items are known to be in private hands the catalogue provides a price.

For full details of these stamps see *CANCELLED by Perkins Bacon* by Peter Jaffé (published by Spink in 1998).

All other Specimens are outside the scope of this volume.

Specimens are not quoted in Great Britain as they are fully listed in the Stanley Gibbons *Great Britain Specialised Catalogue*.

In specifying type of specimen for individual high-value stamps, "H/S" means handstamped, "Optd" is overprinted, "Perf" is punctured. Some sets occur mixed, e.g. "Optd/Perf". If unspecified, the type is apparent from the date or it is the same as for the lower values quoted as a set.

Prices. Prices for stamps up to £1 are quoted in sets; higher values are priced singly. Where specimens exist in more than one type the price quoted is for the cheapest. Specimen stamps have rarely survived even as pairs; these and strips of three, four or five are worth considerably more than singles.

8. Luminescence

Machines which sort mail electronically have been introduced in recent years. In consequence some countries have issued stamps on fluorescent or phosphorescent papers, while others have marked their stamps with phosphor bands.

The various papers can only be distinguished by ultraviolet lamps emitting particular wavelengths. They are separately listed only when the stamps have some other means of distinguishing them, visible without the use of these lamps. Where this is not so, the papers are recorded in footnotes or headings.

For this catalogue we do not consider it appropriate that collectors be compelled to have the use of an ultraviolet lamp before being able to identify stamps by

our listings. Some experience will also be found necessary in interpreting the results given by ultraviolet. Collectors using the lamps, nevertheless, should exercise great care in their use as exposure to their light is potentially dangerous to the eyes.

Phosphor bands are listable, since they are visible to the naked eye (by holding stamps at an angle to the light and looking along them, the bands appear dark). Stamps existing with or without phosphor bands or with differing numbers of bands are given separate listings. Varieties such as double bands, bands omitted, misplaced or printed on the back are not listed.

Detailed descriptions appear at appropriate places in the listings in explanation of luminescent papers; see, for example, Australia above No. 363, Canada above Nos. 472 and 611, Cook Is. above 249, etc.

For Great Britain, where since 1959 phosphors have played a prominent and intricate part in stamp issues, the main notes above Nos. 599 and 723 should be studied, as well as the footnotes to individual listings where appropriate. In general the classification is as follows.

Stamps with phosphor bands are those where a separate cylinder applies the phosphor after the stamps are printed. Issues with "all-over" phosphor have the "band" covering the entire stamp. Parts of the stamp covered by phosphor bands, or the entire surface for "all-over" phosphor versions, appear matt. Stamps on phosphorised paper have the phosphor added to the paper coating before the stamps are printed. Issues on this paper have a completely shiny surface.

Further particularisation of phosphor – their methods of printing and the colours they exhibit under ultraviolet – is outside the scope. The more specialised listings should be consulted for this information.

9. Coil Stamps

Stamps issued only in coil form are given full listing. If stamps are issued in both sheets and coils the coil stamps are listed separately only where there is some feature (e.g. perforation or watermark sideways) by which singles can be distinguished. Coil stamps containing different stamps *se-tenant* are also listed.

Coil join pairs are too random and too easily faked to permit of listing; similarly ignored are coil stamps which have accidentally suffered an extra row of perforations from the claw mechanism in a malfunctioning vending machine.

10. Stamp Booklets

Stamp booklets are now listed in this catalogue.

Single stamps from booklets are listed if they are distinguishable in some way (such as watermark or perforation) from similar sheet stamps.

Booklet panes are listed where they contain stamps of different denominations *se-tenant*, where stamp-size labels are included, or where such panes are otherwise identifiable. Booklet panes are placed in the listing under the lowest denomination present.

Particular perforations (straight edges) are covered by appropriate notes.

11. Miniature Sheets and Sheetlets

We distinguish between "miniature sheets" and "sheetlets" and this affects the catalogue numbering. An item in sheet form that is postally valid, containing a single stamp, pair, block or set of stamps, with wide, inscribed and/or decorative margins, is a miniature sheet if it is sold at post offices as an indivisible entity. As such the Catalogue allots a single MS number and describes what stamps make it up. The sheetlet or small sheet differs in that the individual stamps are intended to be purchased separately for postal purposes. For sheetlets, all the component postage stamps are numbered individually and the composition explained in a footnote. Note that the definitions refer to post office sale—not how items may be subsequently offered by stamp dealers.

12. Forgeries and Fakes

Forgeries. Where space permits, notes are considered if they can give a concise description that will permit unequivocal detection of a forgery. Generalised warnings, lacking detail, are not nowadays inserted, since their value to the collector is problematic.

Forged cancellations have also been applied to genuine stamps. This catalogue includes notes regarding those manufactured by "Madame Joseph", together with the cancellation dates known to exist. It should be remembered that these dates also exist as genuine cancellations.

For full details of these see *Madame Joseph Forged Postmarks* by Derek Worboys (published by the Royal Philatelic Society London and the British Philatelic Trust in 1994) or *Madame Joseph Revisited* by Brian Cartwright (published by the Royal Philatelic Society London in 2005).

Fakes. Unwitting fakes are numerous, particularly "new shades" which are colour changelings brought about by exposure to sunlight, soaking in water contaminated with dyes from adherent paper, contact with oil and dirt from a pocketbook, and so on. Fraudulent operators, in addition, can offer to arrange: removal of hinge marks; repairs of thins on white or coloured papers; replacement of missing margins or perforations; reperforating in true or false gauges; removal of fiscal cancellations; rejoining of severed pairs, strips and blocks; and (a major hazard) regumming. Collectors can only be urged to purchase from reputable sources and to insist upon Expert Committee certification where there is any kind of doubt.

The Catalogue can consider footnotes about fakes where these are specific enough to assist in detection.

ACKNOWLEDGEMENTS
We are grateful to individual collectors, members of the philatelic trade and specialist societies and study circles for their assistance in improving and extending the Stanley Gibbons range of catalogues. The addresses of societies and study circles relevant to this volume are:

Irish Philatelic Circle
Membership Secretary – Mr. B. Warren
2 Dargle Valley, Dublin 6
Ireland

Abbreviations

Printers

A.B.N. Co.	American Bank Note Co, New York.
B.A.B.N.	British American Bank Note Co. Ottawa
B.D.T.	B.D.T. International Security Printing Ltd, Dublin, Ireland
B.W.	Bradbury Wilkinson & Co, Ltd.
Cartor	Cartor S.A., La Loupe, France
C.B.N.	Canadian Bank Note Co, Ottawa.
Continental	Continental Bank Note Co. B.N. Co.
Courvoisier	Imprimerie Courvoisier S.A., La-Chaux-de-Fonds, Switzerland.
D.L.R.	De La Rue & Co, Ltd, London.
Enschedé	Joh. Enschedé en Zonen, Haarlem, Netherlands.
Format	Format International Security Printers Ltd., London
Harrison	Harrison & Sons, Ltd. London
J.W.	John Waddington Security Print Ltd., Leeds
P.B.	Perkins Bacon Ltd, London.
Questa	Questa Colour Security Printers Ltd, London
Walsall	Walsall Security Printers Ltd
Waterlow	Waterlow & Sons, Ltd, London.

General Abbreviations

Alph	Alphabet
Anniv	Anniversary
Comp	Compound (perforation)
Des	Designer; designed
Diag	Diagonal; diagonally
Eng	Engraver; engraved
F.C.	Fiscal Cancellation
H/S	Handstamped
Horiz	Horizontal; horizontally
Imp, Imperf	Imperforate
Inscr	Inscribed
L	Left
Litho	Lithographed
mm	Millimetres
MS	Miniature sheet
N.Y.	New York
Opt(d)	Overprint(ed)
P or P-c	Pen-cancelled
P, Pf or Perf	Perforated
Photo	Photogravure
Pl	Plate
Pr	Pair
Ptd	Printed
Ptg	Printing
R	Right
R.	Row

Recess	Recess-printed
Roto	Rotogravure
Roul	Rouletted
S	Specimen (overprint)
Surch	Surcharge(d)
T.C.	Telegraph Cancellation
T	Type
Typo	Typographed
Un	Unused
Us	Used
Vert	Vertical; vertically
W or wmk	Watermark
Wmk s	Watermark sideways

(†) = Does not exist

(–) (or blank price column) = Exists, or may exist, but no market price is known.

/ between colours means "on" and the colour following is that of the paper on which the stamp is printed.

Colours of Stamps

Bl (blue); blk (black); brn (brown); car, carm (carmine); choc (chocolate); clar (claret); emer (emerald); grn (green); ind (indigo); mag (magenta); mar (maroon); mult (multicoloured); mve (mauve); ol (olive); orge (orange); pk (pink); pur (purple); scar (scarlet); sep (sepia); turq (turquoise); ultram (ultramarine); verm (vermilion); vio (violet); yell (yellow).

Colour of Overprints and Surcharges

(B.) = blue, (Blk.) = black, (Br.) = brown, (C.) = carmine, (G.) = green, (Mag.) = magenta, (Mve.) = mauve, (Ol.) = olive, (O.) = orange, (P.) = purple, (Pk.) = pink, (R.) = red, (Sil.) = silver, (V.) = violet, (Vm.) or (Verm.) = vermilion, (W.) = white, (Y.) = yellow.

Arabic Numerals

As in the case of European figures, the details of the Arabic numerals vary in different stamp designs, but they should be readily recognised with the aid of this illustration.

٠	١	٢	٣	٤	٥	٦	٧	٨	٩
0	1	2	3	4	5	6	7	8	9

International Philatelic Glossary

English	French	German	Spanish	Italian
Agate	Agate	Achat	Agata	Agata
Air stamp	Timbre de la poste aérienne	Flugpostmarke	Sello de correo aéreo	Francobollo per posta aerea
Apple Green	Vert-pomme	Apfelgrün	Verde manzana	Verde mela
Barred	Annulé par barres	Balkenentwertung	Anulado con barras	Sbarrato
Bisected	Timbre coupé	Halbiert	Partido en dos	Frazionato
Bistre	Bistre	Bister	Bistre	Bistro
Bistre-brown	Brun-bistre	Bisterbraun	Castaño bistre	Bruno-bistro
Black	Noir	Schwarz	Negro	Nero
Blackish Brown	Brun-noir	Schwärzlichbraun	Castaño negruzco	Bruno nerastro
Blackish Green	Vert foncé	Schwärzlichgrün	Verde negruzco	Verde nerastro
Blackish Olive	Olive foncé	Schwärzlicholiv	Oliva negruzco	Oliva nerastro
Block of four	Bloc de quatre	Viererblock	Bloque de cuatro	Bloco di quattro
Blue	Bleu	Blau	Azul	Azzurro
Blue-green	Vert-bleu	Blaugrün	Verde azul	Verde azzuro
Bluish Violet	Violet bleuâtre	Bläulichviolett	Violeta azulado	Violtto azzurrastro
Booklet	Carnet	Heft	Cuadernillo	Libretto
Bright Blue	Bleu vif	Lebhaftblau	Azul vivo	Azzurro vivo
Bright Green	Vert vif	Lebhaftgrün	Verde vivo	Verde vivo
Bright Purple	Mauve vif	Lebhaftpurpur	Púrpura vivo	Porpora vivo
Bronze Green	Vert-bronze	Bronzegrün	Verde bronce	Verde bronzo
Brown	Brun	Braun	Castaño	Bruno
Brown-lake	Carmin-brun	Braunlack	Laca castaño	Lacca bruno
Brown-purple	Pourpre-brun	Braunpurpur	Púrpura castaño	Porpora bruno
Brown-red	Rouge-brun	Braunrot	Rojo castaño	Rosso bruno
Buff	Chamois	Sämisch	Anteado	Camoscio
Cancellation	Oblitération	Entwertung	Cancelación	Annullamento
Cancelled	Annulé	Gestempelt	Cancelado	Annullato
Carmine	Carmin	Karmin	Carmín	Carminio
Carmine-red	Rouge-carmin	Karminrot	Rojo carmín	Rosso carminio
Centred	Centré	Zentriert	Centrado	Centrato
Cerise	Rouge-cerise	Kirschrot	Color de ceresa	Color Ciliegia
Chalk-surfaced paper	Papier couché	Kreidepapier	Papel estucado	Carta gessata
Chalky Blue	Bleu terne	Kreideblau	Azul turbio	Azzurro smorto
Charity stamp	Timbre de bienfaisance	Wohltätigkeitsmarke	Sello de beneficenza	Francobollo di beneficenza
Chestnut	Marron	Kastanienbraun	Castaño rojo	Marrone
Chocolate	Chocolat	Schokolade	Chocolate	Cioccolato
Cinnamon	Cannelle	Zimtbraun	Canela	Cannella
Claret	Grenat	Weinrot	Rojo vinoso	Vinaccia
Cobalt	Cobalt	Kobalt	Cobalto	Cobalto
Colour	Couleur	Farbe	Color	Colore
Comb-perforation	Dentelure en peigne	Kammzähnung, Reihenzähnung	Dentado de peine	Dentellatura e pettine
Commemorative stamp	Timbre commémoratif	Gedenkmarke	Sello conmemorativo	Francobollo commemorativo
Crimson	Cramoisi	Karmesin	Carmesí	Cremisi
Deep Blue	Blue foncé	Dunkelblau	Azul oscuro	Azzurro scuro
Deep bluish Green	Vert-bleu foncé	Dunkelbläulichgrün	Verde azulado oscuro	Verde azzurro scuro
Design	Dessin	Markenbild	Diseño	Disegno
Die	Matrice	Urstempel. Type,	Cuño	Conio, Matrice

English	French	German	Spanish	Italian
		Platte		
Double	Double	Doppelt	Doble	Doppio
Drab	Olive terne	Trüboliv	Oliva turbio	Oliva smorto
Dull Green	Vert terne	Trübgrün	Verde turbio	Verde smorto
Dull purple	Mauve terne	Trübpurpur	Púrpura turbio	Porpora smorto
Embossing	Impression en relief	Prägedruck	Impresión en relieve	Impressione a relievo
Emerald	Vert-eméraude	Smaragdgrün	Esmeralda	Smeraldo
Engraved	Gravé	Graviert	Grabado	Inciso
Error	Erreur	Fehler, Fehldruck	Error	Errore
Essay	Essai	Probedruck	Ensayo	Saggio
Express letter stamp	Timbre pour lettres par exprès	Eilmarke	Sello de urgencia	Francobollo per espresso
Fiscal stamp	Timbre fiscal	Stempelmarke	Sello fiscal	Francobollo fiscale
Flesh	Chair	Fleischfarben	Carne	Carnicino
Forgery	Faux, Falsification	Fälschung	Falsificación	Falso, Falsificazione
Frame	Cadre	Rahmen	Marco	Cornice
Granite paper	Papier avec fragments de fils de soie	Faserpapier	Papel con filamentos	Carto con fili di seta
Green	Vert	Grün	Verde	Verde
Greenish Blue	Bleu verdâtre	Grünlichblau	Azul verdoso	Azzurro verdastro
Greenish Yellow	Jaune-vert	Grünlichgelb	Amarillo verdoso	Giallo verdastro
Grey	Gris	Grau	Gris	Grigio
Grey-blue	Bleu-gris	Graublau	Azul gris	Azzurro grigio
Grey-green	Vert gris	Graugrün	Verde gris	Verde grigio
Gum	Gomme	Gummi	Goma	Gomma
Gutter	Interpanneau	Zwischensteg	Espacio blanco entre dos grupos	Ponte
Imperforate	Non-dentelé	Geschnitten	Sin dentar	Non dentellato
Indigo	Indigo	Indigo	Azul indigo	Indaco
Inscription	Inscription	Inschrift	Inscripción	Dicitura
Inverted	Renversé	Kopfstehend	Invertido	Capovolto
Issue	Émission	Ausgabe	Emisión	Emissione
Laid	Vergé	Gestreift	Listado	Vergato
Lake	Lie de vin	Lackfarbe	Laca	Lacca
Lake-brown	Brun-carmin	Lackbraun	Castaño laca	Bruno lacca
Lavender	Bleu-lavande	Lavendel	Color de alhucema	Lavanda
Lemon	Jaune-citron	Zitrongelb	Limón	Limone
Light Blue	Bleu clair	Hellblau	Azul claro	Azzurro chiaro
Lilac	Lilas	Lila	Lila	Lilla
Line perforation	Dentelure en lignes	Linienzähnung	Dentado en linea	Dentellatura lineare
Lithography	Lithographie	Steindruck	Litografía	Litografia
Local	Timbre de poste locale	Lokalpostmarke	Emisión local	Emissione locale
Lozenge roulette	Percé en losanges	Rautenförmiger Durchstich	Picadura en rombos	Perforazione a losanghe
Magenta	Magenta	Magentarot	Magenta	Magenta
Margin	Marge	Rand	Borde	Margine
Maroon	Marron pourpré	Dunkelrotpurpur	Púrpura rojo oscuro	Marrone rossastro
Mauve	Mauve	Malvenfarbe	Malva	Malva
Multicoloured	Polychrome	Mehrfarbig	Multicolores	Policromo
Myrtle Green	Vert myrte	Myrtengrün	Verde mirto	Verde mirto
New Blue	Bleu ciel vif	Neublau	Azul nuevo	Azzurro nuovo
Newspaper stamp	Timbre pour journaux	Zeitungsmarke	Sello para periódicos	Francobollo per giornali
Obliteration	Oblitération	Abstempelung	Matasello	Annullamento
Obsolete	Hors (de) cours	Ausser Kurs	Fuera de curso	Fuori corso
Ochre	Ocre	Ocker	Ocre	Ocra

English	French	German	Spanish	Italian
Official stamp	Timbre de service	Dienstmarke	Sello de servicio	Francobollo di
Olive-brown	Brun-olive	Olivbraun	Castaño oliva	Bruno oliva
Olive-green	Vert-olive	Olivgrün	Verde oliva	Verde oliva
Olive-grey	Gris-olive	Olivgrau	Gris oliva	Grigio oliva
Olive-yellow	Jaune-olive	Olivgelb	Amarillo oliva	Giallo oliva
Orange	Orange	Orange	Naranja	Arancio
Orange-brown	Brun-orange	Orangebraun	Castaño naranja	Bruno arancio
Orange-red	Rouge-orange	Orangerot	Rojo naranja	Rosso arancio
Orange-yellow	Jaune-orange	Orangegelb	Amarillo naranja	Giallo arancio
Overprint	Surcharge	Aufdruck	Sobrecarga	Soprastampa
Pair	Paire	Paar	Pareja	Coppia
Pale	Pâle	Blass	Pálido	Pallido
Pane	Panneau	Gruppe	Grupo	Gruppo
Paper	Papier	Papier	Papel	Carta
Parcel post stamp	Timbre pour colis postaux	Paketmarke	Sello para paquete postal	Francobollo per pacchi postali
Pen-cancelled	Oblitéré à plume	Federzugentwertung	Cancelado a pluma	Annullato a penna
Percé en arc	Percé en arc	Bogenförmiger Durchstich	Picadura en forma de arco	Perforazione ad arco
Percé en scie	Percé en scie	Bogenförmiger Durchstich	Picado en sierra	Foratura a sega
Perforated	Dentelé	Gezähnt	Dentado	Dentellato
Perforation	Dentelure	Zähnung	Dentar	Dentellatura
Photogravure	Photogravure, Heliogravure	Rastertiefdruck	Fotograbado	Rotocalco
Pin perforation	Percé en points	In Punkten durchstochen	Horadado con alfileres	Perforato a punti
Plate	Planche	Platte	Plancha	Lastra, Tavola
Plum	Prune	Pflaumenfarbe	Color de ciruela	Prugna
Postage Due stamp	Timbre-taxe	Portomarke	Sello de tasa	Segnatasse
Postage stamp	Timbre-poste	Briefmarke, Freimarke, Postmarke	Sello de correos	Francobollo postale
Postal fiscal stamp	Timbre fiscal-postal	Stempelmarke als Postmarke verwendet	Sello fiscal-postal	Fiscale postale
Postmark	Oblitération postale	Poststempel	Matasello	Bollo
Printing	Impression, Tirage	Druck	Impresión	Stampa, Tiratura
Proof	Épreuve	Druckprobe	Prueba de impresión	Prova
Provisionals	Timbres provisoires	Provisorische Marken. Provisorien	Provisionales	Provvisori
Prussian Blue	Bleu de Prusse	Preussischblau	Azul de Prusia	Azzurro di Prussia
Purple	Pourpre	Purpur	Púrpura	Porpora
Purple-brown	Brun-pourpre	Purpurbraun	Castaño púrpura	Bruno porpora
Recess-printing	Impression en taille douce	Tiefdruck	Grabado	Incisione
Red	Rouge	Rot	Rojo	Rosso
Red-brown	Brun-rouge	Rotbraun	Castaño rojizo	Bruno rosso
Reddish Lilac	Lilas rougeâtre	Rötlichlila	Lila rojizo	Lilla rossastro
Reddish Purple	Poupre-rouge	Rötlichpurpur	Púrpura rojizo	Porpora rossastro
Reddish Violet	Violet rougeâtre	Rötlichviolett	Violeta rojizo	Violetto rossastro
Red-orange	Orange rougeâtre	Rotorange	Naranja rojizo	Arancio rosso
Registration stamp	Timbre pour lettre chargée (recommandée)	Einschreibemarke	Sello de certificado	Francobollo per raccomandate
Reprint	Réimpression	Neudruck	Reimpresión	Ristampa
Reversed	Retourné	Umgekehrt	Invertido	Rovesciato
Rose	Rose	Rosa	Rosa	Rosa
Rose-red	Rouge rosé	Rosarot	Rojo rosado	Rosso rosa
Rosine	Rose vif	Lebhaftrosa	Rosa vivo	Rosa vivo
Roulette	Percage	Durchstich	Picadura	Foratura
Rouletted	Percé	Durchstochen	Picado	Forato
Royal Blue	Bleu-roi	Königblau	Azul real	Azzurro reale

English	French	German	Spanish	Italian
Sage green	Vert-sauge	Salbeigrün	Verde salvia	Verde salvia
Salmon	Saumon	Lachs	Salmón	Salmone
Scarlet	Écarlate	Scharlach	Escarlata	Scarlatto
Sepia	Sépia	Sepia	Sepia	Seppia
Serpentine roulette	Percé en serpentin	Schlangenliniger Durchstich	Picado a serpentina	Perforazione a serpentina
Shade	Nuance	Tönung	Tono	Gradazione de colore
Sheet	Feuille	Bogen	Hoja	Foglio
Slate	Ardoise	Schiefer	Pizarra	Ardesia
Slate-blue	Bleu-ardoise	Schieferblau	Azul pizarra	Azzurro ardesia
Slate-green	Vert-ardoise	Schiefergrün	Verde pizarra	Verde ardesia
Slate-lilac	Lilas-gris	Schierferlila	Lila pizarra	Lilla ardesia
Slate-purple	Mauve-gris	Schieferpurpur	Púrpura pizarra	Porpora ardesia
Slate-violet	Violet-gris	Schieferviolett	Violeta pizarra	Violetto ardesia
Special delivery stamp	Timbre pour exprès	Eilmarke	Sello de urgencia	Francobollo per espressi
Specimen	Spécimen	Muster	Muestra	Saggio
Steel Blue	Bleu acier	Stahlblau	Azul acero	Azzurro acciaio
Strip	Bande	Streifen	Tira	Striscia
Surcharge	Surcharge	Aufdruck	Sobrecarga	Soprastampa
Tête-bêche	Tête-bêche	Kehrdruck	Tête-bêche	Tête-bêche
Tinted paper	Papier teinté	Getöntes Papier	Papel coloreado	Carta tinta
Too-late stamp	Timbre pour lettres en retard	Verspätungsmarke	Sello para cartas retardadas	Francobollo per le lettere in ritardo
Turquoise-blue	Bleu-turquoise	Türkisblau	Azul turquesa	Azzurro turchese
Turquoise-green	Vert-turquoise	Türkisgrün	Verde turquesa	Verde turchese
Typography	Typographie	Buchdruck	Tipografia	Tipografia
Ultramarine	Outremer	Ultramarin	Ultramar	Oltremare
Unused	Neuf	Ungebraucht	Nuevo	Nuovo
Used	Oblitéré, Usé	Gebraucht	Usado	Usato
Venetian Red	Rouge-brun terne	Venezianischrot	Rojo veneciano	Rosso veneziano
Vermilion	Vermillon	Zinnober	Cinabrio	Vermiglione
Violet	Violet	Violett	Violeta	Violetto
Violet-blue	Bleu-violet	Violettblau	Azul violeta	Azzurro violetto
Watermark	Filigrane	Wasserzeichen	Filigrana	Filigrana
Watermark sideways	Filigrane couché	Wasserzeichen liegend	Filigrana acostado	Filigrana coricata
Wove paper	Papier ordinaire, Papier uni	Einfaches Papier	Papel avitelado	Carta unita
Yellow	Jaune	Gelb	Amarillo	Giallo
Yellow-brown	Brun-jaune	Gelbbraun	Castaño amarillo	Bruno giallo
Yellow-green	Vert-jaune	Gelbgrün	Verde amarillo	Verde giallo
Yellow-olive	Olive-jaunâtre	Gelboliv	Oliva amarillo	Oliva giallastro
Yellow-orange	Orange jaunâtre	Gelborange	Naranja amarillo	Arancio giallastro
Zig-zag roulette	Percé en zigzag	Sägezahnartiger Durchstich	Picado en zigzag	Perforazione a zigzag

Guide to Entries

Ⓐ Country of Issue – When a country changes its name, the catalogue listing changes to reflect the name change, for example Namibia was formerly known as South West Africa, the stamps in Southern Africa are all listed under Namibia, but split into South West Africa and then Namibia.

Ⓑ Country Information – Brief geographical and historical details for the issuing country.

Ⓒ Currency – Details of the currency, and dates of earliest use where applicable, on the face value of the stamps.

Ⓓ Illustration – Generally, the first stamp in the set. Stamp illustrations are reduced to 75%, with overprints and surcharges shown actual size.

Ⓔ Illustration or Type Number – These numbers are used to help identify stamps, either in the listing, type column, design line or footnote, usually the first value in a set. These type numbers are in a bold type face – **123**; when bracketed (**123**) an overprint or a surcharge is indicated. Some type numbers include a lower-case letter – **123a**, this indicates they have been added to an existing set.

Ⓕ Date of issue – This is the date that the stamp/set of stamps was issued by the post office and was available for purchase. When a set of definitive stamps has been issued over several years the Year Date given is for the earliest issue. Commemorative sets are listed in chronological order. Stamps of the same design, or issue are usually grouped together, for example some of the New Zealand landscapes definitive series were first issued in 2003 but the set includes stamps issued to May 2007.

Ⓖ Number Prefix – Stamps other than definitives and commemoratives have a prefix letter before the catalogue number.
Their use is explained in the text: some examples are A for airmail, D for postage due and O for official stamps.

Ⓗ Footnote – Further information on background or key facts on issues.

Ⓘ Stanley Gibbons Catalogue number – This is a unique number for each stamp to help the collector identify stamps in the listing. The Stanley Gibbons numbering system is universally recognized as definitive.
Where insufficient numbers have been left to provide for additional stamps to a listing, some stamps will have a suffix letter after the catalogue number (for example 214a). If numbers have been left for additions to a set and not used they will be left vacant.
The separate type numbers (in bold) refer to illustrations (see **E**).

Ⓙ Colour – If a stamp is printed in three or fewer colours then the colours are listed, working from the centre of the stamp outwards (see **R**).

Ⓚ Design line – Further details on design variations

Ⓛ Key Type – Indicates a design type on which the stamp is based. These are the bold figures found below each illustration, for example listed in Cameroon, in the West Africa catalogue, is the Key type A and B showing the ex-Kaiser's yacht *Hohenzollern*. The type numbers are also given in bold in the second column of figures alongside the stamp description to indicate the design of each stamp. Where an issue comprises stamps of similar design, the corresponding type number should be taken as indicating the general design. Where there are blanks in the type number column it means that the type of the corresponding stamp

is that shown by the number in the type column of the same issue. A dash (–) in the type column means that the stamp is not illustrated. Where type numbers refer to stamps of another country, e.g. where stamps of one country are overprinted for use in another, this is always made clear in the text.

Ⓜ Coloured Papers – Stamps printed on coloured paper are shown – e.g. "brown/*yellow*" indicates brown printed on yellow paper.

Ⓝ Surcharges and Overprints – Usually described in the headings. Any actual wordings are shown in bold type. Descriptions clarify words and figures used in the overprint. Stamps with the same overprints in different colours are not listed separately. Numbers in brackets after the descriptions are the catalogue numbers of the non-overprinted stamps. The words "inscribed" or "inscription" refer to the wording incorporated in the design of a stamp and not surcharges or overprints.

Ⓞ Face value – This refers to the value of each stamp and is the price it was sold for at the Post Office when issued. Some modern stamps do not have their values in figures but instead it is shown as a letter, for example Great Britain use 1st or 2nd on their stamps as opposed to the actual value.

Ⓟ Catalogue Value – Mint/Unused. Prices quoted for Queen Victoria to King George V stamps are for lightly hinged examples.

Ⓠ Catalogue Value – Used. Prices generally refer to fine postally used examples. For certain issues they are for cancelled-to-order.

Prices
Prices are given in pence and pounds. Stamps worth £100 and over are shown in whole pounds:

Shown in Catalogue as	Explanation
10	10 pence
1.75	£1.75
15.00	£15
£150	£150
£2300	£2300

Prices assume stamps are in 'fine condition'; we may ask more for superb and less for those of lower quality. The minimum catalogue price quoted is 10p and is intended as a guide for catalogue users. The lowest price for individual stamps purchased from Stanley Gibbons is £1.
Prices quoted are for the cheapest variety of that particular stamp. Differences of watermark, perforation, or other details, often increase the value. Prices quoted for mint issues are for single examples, unless otherwise stated. Those in *se-tenant* pairs, strips, blocks or sheets may be worth more. Where no prices are listed it is either because the stamps are not known to exist (usually shown by a †) in that particular condition, or, more usually, because there is no reliable information on which to base their value.
All prices are subject to change without prior notice and we cannot guarantee to supply all stamps as priced. Prices quoted in advertisements are also subject to change without prior notice.

Ⓡ Multicoloured – Nearly all modern stamps are multicoloured (more than three colours); this is indicated in the heading, with a description of the stamp given in the listing.

Ⓢ Perforations – Please see page xiii for a detailed explanation of perforations.

(A) Country of issue ⟶

Bangladesh

(B) Country Information

In elections during December 1970 the Awami League party won all but two of the seats in the East Pakistan province and, in consequence, held a majority in the National Assembly. On 1 March 1971 the Federal Government postponed the sitting of the Assembly with the result that unrest spread throughout the eastern province. Pakistan army operations against the dissidents forced the leaders of the League to flee to India from where East Pakistan was proclaimed independent as Bangladesh. In early December the Indian army moved against Pakistan troops in Bangladesh and civilian government was re-established on 22 December 1971.

From 20 December 1971 various Pakistan issues were overprinted by local postmasters, mainly using handstamps. Their use was permitted until 30 April 1973. These are of philatelic interest, but are outside the scope of the catalogue.

(C) Currency ⟶ **(Currency. 100 paisa = 1 rupee)**

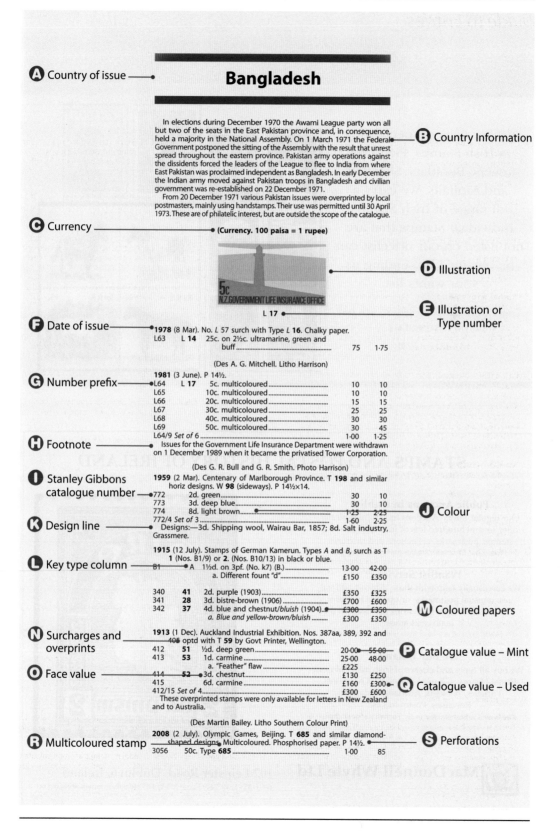

(D) Illustration

(E) Illustration or Type number

L 17

(F) Date of issue ⟶ **1978** (8 Mar). No. *L* 57 surch with Type *L* **16**. Chalky paper.

L63	L **14**	25c. on 2½c. ultramarine, green and buff		75	1·75

(Des A. G. Mitchell. Litho Harrison)

1981 (3 June). P 14½.

(G) Number prefix ⟶

L64	L **17**	5c. multicoloured	10	10
L65		10c. multicoloured	10	10
L66		20c. multicoloured	15	15
L67		30c. multicoloured	25	25
L68		40c. multicoloured	30	30
L69		50c. multicoloured	30	45
L64/9 *Set of 6*			1·00	1·25

(H) Footnote ⟶ Issues for the Government Life Insurance Department were withdrawn on 1 December 1989 when it became the privatised Tower Corporation.

(Des G. R. Bull and G. R. Smith. Photo Harrison)

1959 (2 Mar). Centenary of Marlborough Province. T **198** and similar horiz designs. W **98** (sideways). P 14½×14.

(I) Stanley Gibbons catalogue number ⟶

772		2d. green	30	10
773		3d. deep blue	30	10
774		8d. light brown	1·25	2·25
772/4 *Set of 3*			1·60	2·25

(J) Colour

(K) Design line ⟶ Designs:—3d. Shipping wool, Wairau Bar, 1857; 8d. Salt industry, Grassmere.

1915 (12 July). Stamps of German Kamerun. Types *A* and *B*, surch as T **1** (Nos. B1/9) or **2**. (Nos. B10/13) in black or blue.

(L) Key type column ⟶

B1	A	1½d. on 3pf. (No. k7) (B.)	13·00	42·00
		a. Different fount "d"	£150	£350

340	**41**	2d. purple (1903)	£350	£325
341	**28**	3d. bistre-brown (1906)	£700	£600
342	**37**	4d. blue and chestnut/*bluish* (1904)	£300	£350
		a. Blue and yellow-brown/*bluish*	£300	£350

(M) Coloured papers

(N) Surcharges and overprints ⟶ **1913** (1 Dec). Auckland Industrial Exhibition. Nos. 387aa, 389, 392 and 405 optd with T **59** by Govt Printer, Wellington.

412	**51**	½d. deep green	20·00	55·00
413	**53**	1d. carmine	25·00	48·00
		a. "Feather" flaw	£225	
414	**52**	3d. chestnut	£130	£250
415		6d. carmine	£160	£300
412/15 *Set of 4*			£300	£600

(P) Catalogue value – Mint

(O) Face value

(Q) Catalogue value – Used

These overprinted stamps were only available for letters in New Zealand and to Australia.

(Des Martin Bailey. Litho Southern Colour Print)

2008 (2 July). Olympic Games, Beijing. T **685** and similar diamond-shaped designs. Multicoloured. Phosphorised paper. P 14½.

(R) Multicoloured stamp ⟶

3056		50c. Type **685**	1·00	85

(S) Perforations

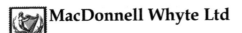

Ireland

104

105

106

107

108

Die I

Die II

Two Dies of the 2d.

Die I.—Inner frame-line at top and sides close to solid of background. Four complete lines of shading between top of head and oval frame-line. These four lines do not extend to the oval itself. White line round "TWOPENCE" thin.

Die II.—Inner frame-line further from solid of background. Three lines between top of head and extending to the oval. White line round "TWOPENCE" thicker.

109

100 Simple Cypher

110 Single Cypher

PROVISIONAL GOVERNMENT
16 January—6 December 1922
Stamps of Great Britain overprinted.

T **104/8**, W **100**; T **109**, W **110**

Rialtaſ
Sealaďać
na
hÉiſeann
1922
(1)

Rialtaſ
Sealaďać
na
hÉiſeann
1922.
(2)

Rialtaſ
Sealaďać
na   hÉiſeann
1922
(3)

("Provisional Government of Ireland, 1922")

1922 (17 Feb–July). T **104** to **108** (W **100**) and **109** of Great Britain overprinted in black.

(a) With T **1**, *by Dollard Printing House Ltd. Optd in black**

1	105	½d. green	2·25	40
		a. Opt inverted	£475	£600
		w. Wmk inverted	—	£600
2	104	1d. scarlet	3·50	60
		a. Opt inverted	£275	£350
		b. Opt double, both inverted, one albino	£350	
		c. Opt double	†	£1600
		w. Wmk inverted	—	£425
3		1d. carmine-red	10·00	2·25
4		2½d. bright blue	2·50	8·50
		a. Opt double, one albino	£475	
		b. Red opt (1 Apr)	2·50	4·00
5	106	3d. bluish violet	6·00	6·50
6		4d. grey-green	6·00	23·00
		a. Opt double, one albino	£475	
		b. Red opt (1 Apr)	9·50	16·00
		c. Carmine opt (July)	48·00	70·00
7	107	5d. yellow-brown	6·00	8·50
		x. Wmk reversed	—	£475
8	108	9d. agate	16·00	38·00
		a. Opt double, one albino	£375	
		b. Red opt (1 Apr)	17·00	19·00
		c. Carmine opt (July)	90·00	95·00
9		10d. turquoise-blue	11·00	65·00
1/9 *Set of 8 (cheapest)*			48·00	£110

*All values except 2½d. and 4d. are known with greyish black overprint, but these are difficult to distinguish.

The carmine overprints on the 4d. and 9d. may have been produced by Alex Thom & Co. Ltd. There was a further overprinting of the 2½d. at the same time, but this is difficult to distinguish.

The ½d. with red overprint is a trial or proof printing (*Price* £160).

Bogus inverted T **1** overprints exist on the 2d., 4d., 9d and 1s. values.

(b) With T **2**, *by Alex Thom & Co Ltd*

10	105	1½d. red-brown (*shades*)	3·00	1·75
		a. Error. ""PENCF"	£375	£325
		w. Wmk inverted	—	£375
		x. Wmk reversed	—	£375
12	106	2d. orange (Die I)	9·00	50
		a. Opt inverted	£200	£300
		w. Wmk inverted	—	£375
		x. Wmk reversed	£600	£375
13		2d. orange (Die II)	5·50	50
		a. Opt inverted	£400	£500
		w. Wmk inverted	—	£375
14	107	6d. reddish pur (*chalk-surfaced paper*)	20·00	26·00
		a. Deep reddish purple	25·00	30·00
15	108	1s. bistre-brown	13·00	15·00
10/15 *Set of 5*			45·00	40·00

Varieties occur throughout the T **2** overprint in the relative positions of the lines of the overprint, the "R" of "Rialtas" being over either the "Se" or "S" of "Sealadac" or intermediately.

*(c) With T **3** by Dollard Printing House Ltd*

17	**109**	2s.6d. sepia-brown	60·00	85·00
		a. Opt double, one albino	£1600	
18		2s.6d. reddish brown	75·00	95·00
19		5s. rose-carmine	90·00	£170
21		10s. dull grey-blue	£180	£375
17/21 Set of 3 (cheapest)			£300	£550

1922 (19 June–Aug). Optd as T **2**, in black, by Harrison & Sons, for use in horiz and vert coils.

26	**105**	½d. green	3·00	21·00
27	**104**	1d. scarlet	3·75	9·00
28	**105**	1½d. red-brown (21.6)	4·00	55·00
29	**106**	2d. bright orange (Die I)	22·00	50·00
29a		2d. bright orange (Die II) (August)	22·00	42·00
		ay. Wmk inverted and reversed	—	£400
26/9a Set of 5			50·00	£160

The Harrison overprint measures 15×17 mm (maximum) against the 14½×16 mm of T **2** (Thom printing) and is a much bolder black than the latter, while the individual letters are taller, the "i" of "Rialtas" being specially outstanding as it extends below the foot of the "R".

The "R" of "Rialtas" is always over the "Se" of "Sealadac".

1922. Optd by Thom.

*(a) As T **2** but bolder, in dull to shiny blue-black or red (June–Nov)*

30	**105**	½d. green	3·75	80
31	**104**	1d. scarlet	3·25	50
		a. "Q" for "O" (No. 357ab)	£1400	£1200
		b. Reversed "Q" for "O" (No. 357ac)	£375	£250
		w. Wmk inverted	†	£550
32	**105**	1½d. red-brown	4·00	4·50
		a. Chestnut	4·00	4·00
		y. Wmk inverted and reversed	†	£600
33	**106**	2d. orange (Die I)	18·00	1·50
34		2d. orange (Die II)	6·00	50
		y. Wmk inverted and reversed	£180	£150
35	**104**	2½d. blue (R.)	7·00	28·00
36	**106**	3d. violet	11·00	2·25
		a. Dull reddish violet	5·00	2·00
		y. Wmk inverted and reversed	£140	£140
37		4d. grey-green (R.)	4·50	10·00
38	**107**	5d. yellow-brown	5·50	11·00
39		6d. reddish pur (chalk-surfaced paper)	15·00	7·50
		a. Deep reddish purple	9·00	4·25
		w. Wmk inverted	£275	£140
		y. Wmk inverted and reversed	†	£350
40	**108**	9d. agate (R.)	14·00	27·00
41		9d. olive-green (R.)	6·00	50·00
42		10d. turquoise-blue	29·00	75·00
43		1s. bistre-brown	14·00	14·00
30/43 Set of 14			£110	£200

Both 2d. stamps exist with the overprint inverted but there remains some doubt as to whether they were issued.

These Thom printings are distinguishable from the Harrison printings by the size of the overprint, and from the previous Thom printings by the intensity and colour of the overprint, the latter being best seen when the stamp is looked through with a strong light behind it.

*(b) As with T **3**, but bolder, in shiny blue-black (Oct–Dec)*

44	**109**	2s.6d. sepia-brown	£250	£350
45		5s. rose-carmine	£275	£375
46		10s. dull grey-blue	£1000	£1400
44/6 Set of 3			£1400	£1900

The above differ from Nos. 17/21 not only in the bolder impression and colour of the ink but also in the "h" and "e" of "heireann" which are closer together and horizontally aligned.

Riαltαr
Seαlαραč
nα
hÉιρeαnn
1922.
(4)

SAoRstát
Éireαnn
1922
(5 Wide date) ("Irish Free State 1922")

1922 (21 Nov–Dec). Optd by Thom with T **4** (wider setting) in shiny blue-black.

47	**105**	½d. green	1·00	2·00
		a. Opt in dull black	£100	90·00
48	**104**	1d. scarlet	6·00	3·75
		w. Wmk inverted	†	£275
49	**105**	1½d. red-brown (4 Dec)	3·00	14·00
50	**106**	2d. orange (Die II)	9·00	7·00
51	**108**	1s. olive-bistre (4 Dec)	50·00	90·00
47/51 Set of 5			60·00	£100

The overprint T **4** measures 15¾ × 16 mm (maximum).

IRISH FREE STATE

6 December 1922—29 December 1937

1922 (Dec)–23.

*(a) Optd by Thom with T **5**, in dull to shiny blue-black or red*

52	**105**	½d. green	2·00	30

		a. No accent in "Saorstat"	£1400	£1000
		b. Accent inserted by hand	£100	£130
53	**104**	1d. scarlet	2·50	50
		aa. No accent in "Saorstat"	£17000	£10000
		a. No accent and final "t" missing	£15000	£8000
		b. Accent inserted by hand	£160	£180
		c. Accent and "t" inserted	£250	£300
		d. Accent and "at" inserted	£250	£300
		e. Reversed "Q" for "O" (No. 357ac)	£375	£250
		f. Opt triple, two albino	£600	
54	**105**	1½d. red-brown	3·50	8·50
55	**106**	2d. orange (Die II)	1·50	1·00
56	**104**	2½d. bright blue (R.) (6.1.23)	7·50	12·00
		a. No accent	£160	£200
57	**106**	3d. bluish violet (6.1.23)	4·75	11·00
		a. No accent	£325	£425
58		4d. grey-green (R.) (16.1.23)	4·75	12·00
		a. No accent	£180	£225
59	**107**	5d. yellow-brown	5·50	4·75
60		6d. reddish purple (chalk-surfaced paper) (shades)	3·75	2·00
		a. Accent inserted by hand	£850	£900
		y. Wmk inverted and reversed	85·00	70·00
61	**108**	9d. olive-green (R.)	9·00	5·50
		aa. Pale olive-green	13·00	12·00
		a. No accent	£275	£325
62		10d. turquoise-blue	23·00	75·00
63		1s. bistre-brown (shades)	8·00	11·00
		a. No accent	£12000	£12000
		b. Accent inserted by hand	£700	£800
64	**109**	2s.6d. chocolate-brown	48·00	70·00
		aa. Pale brown	48·00	70·00
		a. Major Re-entry (R. 1/2)	£1200	£1400
		b. No accent	£450	£600
		c. Accent reversed	£700	£850
65		5s. rose-carmine	85·00	£160
		a. No accent	£600	£900
		b. Accent reversed	£900	£1200
66		10s. dull grey-blue	£190	£350
		a. No accent	£3000	£4000
		b. Accent reversed	£4500	£5500
52/66 Set of 15			£350	£650

The "no accent" and "accent inserted" varieties on the ½d. to 1s. values occur on R. 15/12. On the 2s.6d. to 10s. values the "no accent" varieties occur on R. 3/2 and R. 8/2, the "accent reversed" on R. 7/4.

The accents inserted by hand are in dull black. The reversed accents are grave (thus "à") instead of acute ("á"). A variety with "S" of "Saorstát" directly over "é" of "éireann", instead of to left, may be found in all values except the 2½d. and 4d. In the 2s.6d., 5s. and 10s. it is very slightly to the left in the "S" over "é" variety, bringing the "á" of "Saorstát" directly above the last "n" of "éireann".

*(b) Optd with T **5**, in dull or shiny blue-black, by Harrison, for use in horiz or vert coils (7.3.23)*

67		½d. green	1·75	11·00
		a. Long "1" in "1922"	20·00	55·00
		y. Wmk inverted and reversed	†	—
68		1d. scarlet	6·00	21·00
		a. Long "1" in "1922"	75·00	£140
69		1½d. red-brown	6·50	50·00
		a. Long "1" in "1922"	85·00	£225
70		2d. orange (Die II)	9·50	17·00
		a. Long "1" in "1922"	35·00	60·00
		w. Wmk inverted	—	£300
67/70 Set of 4			21·00	90·00

In the Harrison overprint the characters are rather bolder than those of the Thom overprint, and the foot of the "1" of "1922" is usually rounded instead of square. The long "1" in "1922" has a serif at foot. The second "é" of "éireann" appears to be slightly raised.

PRINTERS. The following and all subsequent issues to No. 148 were printed at the Government Printing Works, Dublin, *unless otherwise stated.*

6 "Sword of Light"   **7** Map of Ireland   **8** Arms of Ireland

9 Celtic Cross   **10**

(Des J. J. O'Reilly (T **6**); J. Ingram (T **7**); Miss M. Girling (T **8**); and Miss L. Williams (T **9**). Typo. Plates made by Royal Mint, London)

1922 (6 Dec)–**34**. W **10**. P 15×14.

71	**6**	½d. bright green (20.4.23)	3·00	90
		a. Imperf × perf 14, Wmk sideways (11.34)	23·00	50·00
		w. Wmk inverted	40·00	25·00
72	**7**	1d. carmine (23.2.23)	2·00	10
		aw. Wmk inverted	38·00	10·00
		b. Perf 15 × imperf (single perf) (1933)	£100	£250
		bw. Ditto. Wmk inverted	£120	£250
		c. Perf 15 × imperf (7.34)	12·00	42·00
		d. Booklet pane. Three stamps plus three printed labels (21.8.31)	£450	£550
		dw. Wmk inverted	£450	£550
73		1½d. claret (2.2.23)	3·50	2·00
		w. Wmk inverted	£1300	£1100
74		2d. grey-green (6.12.22)	2·25	10
		a. Imperf × perf 14, Wmk sideways (11.34)	40·00	80·00
		b. Perf 15 × imperf (1934)	£13000	£1600
		w. Wmk inverted	35·00	10·00
		y. Wmk inverted and reversed	38·00	38·00
75	**8**	2½d. red-brown (7.9.23)	5·00	3·75
		w. Wmk inverted	60·00	27·00
76	**9**	3d. ultramarine (16.3.23)	2·50	1·75
		w. Wmk inverted	75·00	32·00
77	**8**	4d. slate-blue (28.9.23)	2·75	3·25
		w. Wmk inverted	£180	60·00
78	**6**	5d. deep violet (11.5.23)	9·50	6·50
79		6d. claret (21.12.23)	6·00	3·00
		w. Wmk inverted	£180	75·00
80	**8**	9d. deep violet (26.10.23)	15·00	5·50
81	**9**	10d. brown (11.5.23)	8·00	14·00
82	**6**	1s light blue (15.6.23)	16·00	4·50
		w. Wmk inverted	†	£1100
71/82 *Set of 12*			65·00	40·00

No. 72b is imperf vertically except for a single perf at each top corner. It was issued for use in automatic machines.

See also Nos. 111/22.

SAORSTÁT
ÉIReAnn
1922
(11 Narrow Date)   12 Daniel O'Connell

1925 (Aug)–**28**. T **109** of Great Britain (Bradbury, Wilkinson printing) optd at the Government Printing Works, Dublin or at Somerset House, London.

*(a) With T **11** in black or grey-black (25.8.25)*

83		2s.6d. chocolate-brown	40·00	£100
		a. Wide and narrow date (pair) (1927)	£300	£600
84		5s. rose-carmine	60·00	£150
		a. Wide and narrow date (pair) (1927)	£450	£950
85		10s. dull grey-blue	£150	£350
		a. Wide and narrow date (pair) (1927)	£1200	£2000
83/5 *Set of 3*			£225	£550

The varieties with wide and narrow date *se-tenant* are from what is known as the "composite setting," in which some stamps showed the wide date, as T **5**, while in others the figures were close together, as in T **11**.

Single examples of this printing with wide date may be distinguished from Nos. 64 to 66 by the colour of the ink, which is black or grey-black in the composite setting and blue-black in the Thom printing.

The type of the "composite" overprint usually shows distinct signs of wear.

*(b) As T **5** (wide date) in black (1927–28)*

86		2s.6d. chocolate-brown (9.12.27)	50·00	60·00
		a. Circumflex accent over "a"	£275	£375
		b. No accent over "a"	£450	£550
		c. Flat accent on "a"	£550	£650
87		5s. rose-carmine (2.28)	80·00	£100
		a. Circumflex accent over "a"	£425	£600
		c. Flat accent on "a"	£750	£900
88		10s. dull grey-blue (15.2.28)	£190	£225
		a. Circumflex accent over "a"	£1000	£1400
		c. Flat accent on "a"	£1700	£2000
86/8 *Set of 3*			£275	£350

This printing can be distinguished from the Thom overprints in dull black, by the clear, heavy impression (in deep black) which often shows in relief on the back of the stamp.

The variety showing a circumflex accent over the "a" occurred on R. 9/2. The overprint in this position finally deteriorated to such an extent that some examples of the 2s.6d. were without accent (No. 86b). A new cliché was then introduced with the accent virtually flat and which also showed damage to the "a" and the crossbar of the "t".

(Des L. Whelan. Typo)

1929 (22 June). Catholic Emancipation Centenary. W **10**. P 15×14.

89	**12**	2d. grey-green	70	45
90		3d. blue	4·25	11·00
91		9d. bright violet	4·25	5·00
89/91 *Set of 3*			8·25	15·00

13 Shannon Barrage   **14** Reaper

(Des E. L. Lawrenson. Typo)

1930 (15 Oct). Completion of Shannon Hydro-Electric Scheme. W **10**. P 15×14.

92	**13**	2d. agate	1·25	55

(T **14** and **15** des G. Atkinson. Typo)

1931 (12 June). Bicentenary of the Royal Dublin Society. W **10**. P 15×14.

93	**14**	2d. blue	1·00	30

15 The Cross of Cong   **16** Adoration of the Cross   **17** Hurler

1932 (12 May). International Eucharistic Congress. W **10**. P 15×14.

94	**15**	2d. grey-green	2·50	30
		w. Wmk inverted	†	—
95		3d. blue	3·75	6·50

(T **16** to **19** des R. J. King. Typo)

1933 (18 Sept). "Holy Year". W **10**. P 15×14.

96	**16**	2d. grey-green	2·25	15
		w. Wmk inverted	†	£600
97		3d. blue	4·00	2·50

1934 (27 July). Golden Jubilee of the Gaelic Athletic Association. W **10**. P 15×14.

98	**17**	2d. green	2·00	55
		w. Wmk inverted	†	£1000

1935 (Mar–July). T **109** of Great Britain (Waterlow re-engraved printings) optd as T **5** (wide date), at Somerset House, London.

99	**109**	2s.6d. chocolate (No. 450)	48·00	60·00
		a. Flat accent on "a" (R. 9/2)	£300	£300
100		5s. bright rose-red (No. 451)	90·00	90·00
		a. Flat accent on "a" (R. 9/2)	£425	£425
101		10s. indigo (No. 452)	£300	£325
		a. Flat accent on "a" (R. 9/2)	£1100	£1100
		b. Opt double	£7500	£4000
99/101 *Set of 3*			£400	£425

18 St. Patrick   **19** Ireland and New Constitution

1937 (8 Sept). W **10**. P 14×15.

102	**18**	2s.6d. emerald-green	£160	70·00
		w. Wmk inverted	£900	£400
103		5s. maroon	£180	£120
		w. Wmk inverted	£800	£400
104		10s. deep blue	£150	55·00
		w. Wmk inverted	£1200	£1400
102/4 *Set of 3*			£450	£200

See also Nos. 123/5.

EIRE

29 December 1937–17 April 1949

1937 (29 Dec). Constitution Day. W **10**. P 15×14.

105	**19**	2d. claret	2·00	20
		w. Wmk inverted	—	£350
106		3d. blue	5·00	3·75

For similar stamps see Nos. 176/7.

20 Father Mathew

(Des S. Keating. Typo)

1938 (1 July). Centenary of Temperance Crusade. W **10**. P 15×14.

107	**20**	2d. agate	2·50	50
		w. Wmk inverted	†	£400
108		3d. blue	12·00	6·50

21 George Washington, American Eagle and Irish Harp

22

(Des G. Atkinson. Typo)

1939 (1 Mar). 150th Anniv of U.S. Constitution and Installation of First U.S. President. W **10**. P 15×14.

109	**21**	2d. scarlet	2·75	1·00
110		3d. blue	4·00	5·50

> **SIZE OF WATERMARK.** T **22** can be found in various sizes from about 8 to 10 mm high. This is due to the use of two different dandy rolls supplied by different firms and to the effects of paper shrinkage and other factors such as pressure and machine speed.

White line above left value tablet joining horizontal line to ornament (R. 3/7)

1940–68. Typo. W **22**. P 15×14 or 14×15 (2s.6d. to 10s.).

111	**6**	½d. bright green (24.11.40)	3·00	40
		w. Wmk inverted	60·00	16·00
112	**7**	1d. carmine (26.10.40)	50	10
		aw. Wmk inverted	2·00	30
		b. From coils. Perf 14 × imperf (9.40)	60·00	65·00
		c. From coils. Perf 15 × imperf (20.3.46)	42·00	23·00
		cw. Wmk inverted	42·00	23·00
		d. Booklet pane. Three stamps plus three printed labels	£3250	
		dw. Wmk inverted	£3250	
113		1½d. claret (1.40)	19·00	30
		w. Wmk inverted	30·00	15·00
114		2d. grey-green (1.40)	50	10
		w. Wmk inverted	2·50	2·50
115	**8**	2½d. red-brown (3.41)	15·00	15
		w. Wmk inverted	24·00	6·50
116	**9**	3d. blue (12.40)	85	10
		w. Wmk inverted	4·00	2·00
117	**8**	4d. slate-blue (12.40)	55	10
		w. Wmk inverted	19·00	5·00
118	**6**	5d. deep violet (7.40)	1·00	10
		w. Wmk inverted	38·00	25·00
119		6d. claret (3.42)	2·75	50
		aw. Wmk inverted	27·00	10·00
		b. Chalk-surfaced paper (1967)	1·25	20
		bw. Wmk inverted	11·00	3·50
119c		8d. scarlet (12.9.49)	80	1·50
		cw. Wmk inverted	50·00	50·00
120	**8**	9d. deep violet (7.40)	1·50	80
		w. Wmk inverted	11·00	6·00
121	**9**	10d. brown (7.40)	75	80

121b		11d. rose (12.9.49)	2·25	3·25
122	**6**	1s. light blue (6.40)	70·00	18·00
		w. Wmk inverted	£1100	£275
123	**18**	2s.6d. emerald-green (10.2.43)	40·00	1·00
		aw. Wmk inverted	£100	35·00
		b. Chalk-surfaced paper (1967)	1·50	3·25
		bw. Wmk inverted	38·00	6·00
124		5s. maroon (15.12.42)	40·00	1·50
		a. Line flaw	£275	48·00
		bw. Wmk inverted	£225	55·00
		c. Chalk-surfaced paper (1968?)	13·00	4·25
		ca. Purple	4·00	9·50
		cb. Line flaw	£100	65·00
		cw. Wmk inverted	38·00	10·00
125		10s. deep blue (7.45)	60·00	6·00
		aw. Wmk inverted	£325	£110
		b. Chalk-surfaced paper (1968)	19·00	13·00
		ba. Blue (shades)	4·00	16·00
		bw. Wmk inverted		

111/25ba Set of 17 .... £110 30·00

There is a wide range of shades and also variations in paper used in this issue.

See also Nos. 227/8.

1941
I ℭℭUImᴺE AISÉIRℭE
1916

(**23** Trans "In memory of the rising of 1916")

24 Volunteer and G.P.O., Dublin

1941 (12 Apr). 25th Anniv of Easter Rising (1916). Provisional issue. T **7** and **9** (2d. in new colour), optd with T **23**.

126	**7**	2d. orange (G.)	2·00	1·00
127	**9**	3d. blue (V.)	27·00	11·00

(Des V. Brown. Typo)

1941 (27 Oct). 25th Anniv of Easter Rising (1916). Definitive issue. W **22**. P 15×14.

128	**24**	2½d. blue-black	3·25	1·25

25 Dr. Douglas Hyde

26 Sir William Rowan Hamilton

27 Bro. Michael O'Clery

(Des S. O'Sullivan. Typo)

1943 (31 July). 50th Anniv of Founding of Gaelic League. W **22**. P 15×14.

129	**25**	½d. green	1·25	70
130		2½d. claret	2·00	10
		w. Wmk inverted	†	£425

(Des S. O'Sullivan from a bust by Hogan. Typo)

1943 (13 Nov). Centenary of Announcement of Discovery of Quaternions. W **22**. P 15×14.

131	**26**	½d. green	75	70
132		2½d. brown	2·25	20

(Des R. J. King. Typo)

1944 (30 June). Tercentenary of Death of Michael O'Clery. (Commemorating the "Annals of the Four Masters"). W **22** (sideways*). P 14×15.

133	**27**	½d. emerald-green	10	10
		w. Wmk facing right	80	35
134		1s. red-brown	1·25	10
		w. Wmk facing right	3·75	2·00

*The normal sideways watermark shows the top of the e facing left, as seen from the back of the stamp.

Although issued as commemoratives these two stamps were kept in use as part of the current issue, replacing Nos. 111 and 122.

28 Edmund Ignatius Rice

29 "Youth Sowing Seeds of Freedom"

(Des S. O'Sullivan. Typo)

1944 (29 Aug). Death Centenary of Edmund Rice (founder of Irish Christian Brothers). W **22**. P 15×14.

135	**28**	2½d. slate	1·75	45
		w. Wmk inverted	†	£350

(Des R. J. King. Typo)

1945 (15 Sept). Centenary of Death of Thomas Davis (founder of Young Ireland Movement). W **22**. P 15×14.

136	**29**	2½d. blue	2·00	75
		w. Wmk inverted	—	£350
137		6d. claret	7·00	8·00

30 "Country and Homestead"

(Des R. J. King. Typo)

1946 (16 Sept). Birth Centenaries of Davitt and Parnell (land reformers). W **22**. P 15×14.

138	**30**	2½d. scarlet	2·50	25
139		3d. blue	3·50	4·25

31 Angel Victor over Rock of Cashel   **32** Over Lough Derg

33 Over Croagh Patrick   **34** Over Glendalough

(Des R. J. King. Recess Waterlow (1d. to 1s.3d. until 1961), D. L. R. (8d., 1s.3d. from 1961 and 1s.5d.))

1948 (7 Apr)–**65**. Air. T **31** and similar horiz designs. W **22**. P 15 (1s.5d.) or 15×14 (others).

140	**31**	1d. chocolate (4.4.49)	3·00	5·50
141	**32**	3d. blue	3·00	3·50
142	**33**	6d. magenta	1·00	2·50
142b	**32**	8d. lake-brown (13.12.54)	8·50	9·00
143	**34**	1s. green (4.4.49)	1·00	2·00
143a	**31**	1s.3d. red-orange (13.12.54)	8·50	1·50
		aw. Wmk inverted	£700	£425
143b		1s.5d. deep ultramarine (shades) (1.4.65)	4·00	2·00
140/3b	Set of 7		26·00	23·00

35 Theobald Wolfe Tone

(Des K. Uhlemann. Typo)

1948 (19 Nov). 150th Anniv of Insurrection. W **22**. P 15×14.

144	**35**	2½d. reddish purple	1·00	10
		w. Wmk inverted	†	—
145		3d. violet	3·25	4·25

REPUBLIC OF IRELAND

18 April 1949

36 Leinster House and Arms of Provinces   **37** J. C. Mangan

(Des Muriel Brandt. Typo)

1949 (21 Nov). International Recognition of Republic. W **22**. P 15×14.

146	**36**	2½d. reddish brown	2·00	10
		w. Wmk inverted	†	—
147		3d. bright blue	6·50	4·25

(Des R. J. King. Typo)

1949 (5 Dec). Death Centenary of James Clarence Mangan (poet). W **22**. P 15×14.

148	**37**	1d. green	1·50	35
		w. Wmk inverted	†	—

38 Statue of St. Peter, Rome

(Recess Waterlow & Sons)

1950 (11 Sept). Holy Year. W **22**. P 12½.

149	**38**	2½d. violet	1·00	40
150		3d. blue	8·00	12·00
151		9d. brown	8·00	15·00
149/51	Set of 3		15·00	25·00

PRINTERS. Nos. 152 to 200 were recess-printed by De La Rue & Co, Dublin, *unless otherwise stated*.

39 Thomas Moore   **40** Ireland at Home

(Eng W. Vacek)

1952 (10 Nov). Death Centenary of Thomas Moore (poet). W **22**. P 13.

152	**39**	2½d. reddish purple	1·00	10
		w. Wmk inverted	†	—
153		3½d. deep olive-green	1·75	4·25

(Des F. O'Ryan. Typo Government Printing Works, Dublin)

1953 (9 Feb). "An Tostal" (Ireland at Home) Festival. W **22** (sideways). P 14×15.

154	**40**	2½d. emerald-green	1·75	35
155		1s.4d. blue	19·00	29·00

41 Robert Emmet   **42** Madonna and Child (Della Robbia)   **43** Cardinal Newman (first Rector)

(Eng L. Downey)

1953 (21 Sept). 150th Death Anniv of Emmet (patriot). W **22**. P 13.

156	**41**	3d. deep bluish green	3·00	15
157		1s.3d. carmine	45·00	10·00

(Eng A. R. Lane)

1954 (24 May). Marian Year. W **22**. P 15.

158	**42**	3d. blue	1·00	10
159		5d. myrtle-green	2·00	3·25

(Des L. Whelan. Typo Govt Printing Works, Dublin)

1954 (19 July). Centenary of Founding of Catholic University of Ireland. W **22**. P 15×14.

160	**43**	2d. bright purple	2·00	10
		w. Wmk inverted	—	£350
161		1s.3d. blue	16·00	6·50

44 Statue of
Commodore Barry

(Des and eng H. Woyty-Wimmer)

1956 (16 Sept). Barry Commemoration. W **22**. P 15.

162	**44**	3d. slate-lilac	1·00	10
163		1s.3d. deep blue	4·50	8·00

45 John   **46** Thomas
Redmond   O'Crohan

1957 (11 June). Birth Centenary of John Redmond (politician). W **22**. P 14×15.

164	**45**	3d. deep blue	1·00	10
165		1s.3d. brown-purple	9·00	15·00

1957 (1 July). Birth Centenary of Thomas O'Crohan (author). W **22**. P 14×15.

166	**46**	2d. maroon	1·00	20
		w. Wmk inverted	†	£400
167		5d. violet	1·25	4·50

47 Admiral   **48** "Father   **49** Tom Clarke
Brown   Wadding" (Ribera)

(Des S. O'Sullivan. Typo Govt Printing Works, Dublin)

1957 (23 Sept). Death Centenary of Admiral William Brown. W **22**. P 15×14.

168	**47**	3d. blue	3·00	20
169		1s.3d. carmine	25·00	17·00

1957 (25 Nov). 300th Death Anniv of Father Luke Wadding (theologian). W **22**. P 15.

170	**48**	3d. deep blue	2·00	10
171		1s.3d. lake	15·00	8·50

1958 (28 July). Birth Centenary of Thomas J. ("Tom") Clarke (patriot). W **22**. P 15.

172	**49**	3d. deep green	2·00	10
173		1s.3d. red-brown	4·00	11·00

50 Mother Mary   **51** Arthur Guinness
Aikenhead

(Eng Waterlow. Recess Imprimerie Belge de Sécurité, Brussels subsidiary of Waterlow & Sons)

1958 (20 Oct). Death Centenary of Mother Mary Aikenhead (foundress of Irish Sisters of Charity). W **22**. P 15×14.

174	**50**	3d. Prussian blue	2·00	10
175		1s.3d. rose-carmine	11·00	8·00

(Typo Govt Printing Works, Dublin)

1958 (29 Dec). 21st Anniv of the Irish Constitution. W **22**. P 15×14.

176	**19**	3d. brown	1·00	10
177		5d. emerald-green	1·00	4·50

1959 (20 July). Bicentenary of Guinness Brewery. W **22**. P 15.

178	**51**	3d. brown-purple	3·00	10
179		1s.3d. blue	12·00	10·00

52 "The Flight of the Holy Family"

(Des K. Uhlemann)

1960 (20 June). World Refugee Year. W **22**. P 15.

180	**52**	3d. purple	40	10
181		1s.3d. sepia	60	3·75

53 Conference Emblem

(Des P. Rahikainen)

1960 (19 Sept). Europa. W **22**. P 15.

182	**53**	6d. light brown	5·50	1·00
183		1s.3d. violet	19·00	20·00

The ink of No. 183 is fugitive.

54 Dublin Airport, de Havilland   **55** St. Patrick
DH.84 Dragon Mk 2 *Iolar* and
Boeing 720

(Des J. Flanagan and D. R. Lowther)

1961 (26 June). 25th Anniv of Aer Lingus. W **22**. P 15.

184	**54**	6d. blue	1·75	3·75
		w. Wmk inverted		
185		1s.3d. green	2·25	5·50

(Recess B.W.)

1961 (25 Sept). Fifteenth Death Centenary of St. Patrick. W **22**. P 14½.

186	**55**	3d. blue	1·00	10
187		8d. purple	2·75	5·50
188		1s.3d. green	2·75	1·60
186/8	*Set of 3*		6·00	6·50

56 John O'Donovan and
Eugene O'Curry

(Recess B.W.)

1962 (26 Mar). Death Centenaries of O'Donovan and O'Curry (scholars). W **22**. P 15.

189	**56**	3d. carmine	30	10
190		1s.3d. purple	1·25	2·25

57 Europa "Tree"

(Des L. Weyer)

1962 (17 Sept). Europa. W **22**. P 15.

191	**57**	6d. carmine-red	70	1·00
192		1s.3d. turquoise	80	1·50

58 Campaign Emblem

(Des K. Uhlemann)

1963 (21 Mar). Freedom from Hunger. W **22**. P 15.

193	**58**	4d. deep violet	50	10
194		1s.3d. scarlet	2·75	2·75

59 "Co-operation"

(Des A. Holm)

1963 (16 Sept). Europa. W **22**. P 15.

195	**59**	6d. carmine	1·00	75
196		1s.3d. blue	3·25	3·75

60 Centenary Emblem

(Des P. Wildbur. Photo Harrison & Sons)

1963 (2 Dec). Centenary of Red Cross. W **22**. P 14½×14.

197	**60**	4d. red and grey	40	10
198		1s.3d. red, grey and light emerald	1·10	2·00

61 Wolfe Tone

(Des P. Wildbur)

1964 (13 Apr). Birth Bicentenary of Wolfe Tone (revolutionary). W **22**. P 15.

199	**61**	4d. black	50	10
200		1s.3d. ultramarine	1·90	2·00

62 Irish Pavilion at Fair   **63** Europa "Flower"

(Des A. Devane. Photo Harrison & Sons)

1964 (20 July). New York World's Fair. W **22**. P 14½×14.

201	**62**	5d. blue-grey, brown, violet and yellow-olive	50	10
		a. Brown omitted*	£6000	
202		1s.5d. blue-grey, brown, turquoise blue and light yellow-green	2·00	2·00

*No 201a comes from the top row of the sheet and shows part of the brown cross which would appear in the sheet margin. As the second horizontal row was normal it would appear that the brown cylinder was incorrectly registered.

(Des G. Bétemps. Photo Harrison)

1964 (14 Sept). Europa. W **22** (sideways). P 14×14½.

203	**63**	8d. olive-green and blue	1·50	1·25
204		1s.5d. red-brown and orange	6·00	3·25

64 "Waves of Communication"

(Des P. Wildbur. Photo Harrison)

1965 (17 May). I.T.U. Centenary. W **22**. P 14½×14.

205	**64**	3d. blue and green	30	10
206		8d. black and green	1·25	1·60

PRINTERS Nos. 207 onwards were photogravure-printed by the Stamping Branch of the Revenue Commissioners, Dublin, *unless otherwise stated.*

65 W. B. Yeats   **66** I.C.Y. Emblem
(poet)

(Des R. Kyne, from drawing by S. O'Sullivan)

1965 (14 June). Yeats' Birth Centenary. W **22** (sideways). P 15.

207	**65**	5d. black, orange-brown and deep green	30	10
208		1s.5d. black, grey-green and brown	2·25	1·75
		a. Brown omitted	£6000	

1965 (16 Aug). International Co-operation Year. W **22**. P 15.

209	**66**	3d. ultramarine and new blue	60	10
210		10d. deep brown and brown	1·00	3·25

67 Europa "Sprig"

(Des H. Karlsson)

1965 (27 Sept). Europa. W **22**. P 15.

211	**67**	8d. black and brown-red	1·50	1·00
212		1s.5d. purple and light turquoise-blue	7·00	3·50

68 James Connolly   **69** "Marching to Freedom"

(Des E. Delaney (No. 216), R. Kyne, after portraits by S. O'Sullivan (others))

1966 (12 Apr). 50th Anniv of Easter Rising. T **68/9** and similar horiz portraits. W **22**. P 15.

213		3d. black and greenish blue	75	10
		a. Horiz pair. Nos. 213/14	1·50	2·50
214		3d. black and bronze-green	75	10
215		5d. black and yellow-olive	75	10
		a. Horiz pair. Nos. 215/16	1·50	2·50
216		5d. black, orange and blue-green	75	10
217		7d. black and light orange-brown	75	2·25
		a. Horiz pair. Nos. 217/18	1·75	7·50
218		7d. black and blue-green	75	2·25
219		1s.5d. black and turquoise	75	1·50
		a. Horiz pair. Nos. 219/20	1·75	9·00
220		1s.5d. black and bright green	75	1·50
213/20 *Set of 8*			6·00	7·00

Designs:—No. 213, Type **68**; No. 214, Thomas J. Clarke; No. 215, P. H. Pearse; No. 216, Type **69**; No. 217, Eamonn Ceannt; No. 218, Sean MacDiarmada; No. 219, Thomas MacDonagh; No. 220, Joseph Plunkett.

Nos. 213/14, 215/16, 217/18 and 219/20 were each printed together, *se-tenant*, in horizontal pairs throughout the sheet.

76 R. Casement

77 Europa "Ship"

(Des R. Kyne)

1966 (3 Aug). 50th Death Anniv of Roger Casement (patriot). W **22** (sideways). P 15.

221	**76**	5d. black	15	10
222		1s. red-brown	40	50

(Des R. Kyne, after G. and J. Bender)

1966 (26 Sept). Europa. W **22** (sideways). P 15.

223	**77**	7d. emerald and orange	1·00	40
224		1s.5d. emerald and light grey	2·00	1·60

78 Interior of Abbey (from lithograph)

79 Cogwheels

1966 (8 Nov). 750th Anniv of Ballintubber Abbey. W **22**. P 15.

225	**78**	5d. red-brown	10	10
226		1s. black	20	25

1966–67. As Nos. 116, 118 but photo. Smaller design (17×21 *mm*). Chalk-surfaced paper. W **22**. P 15.

227	**9**	3d. blue (1.8.67)	40	15
228	**6**	5d. bright violet (1.12.66)	30	15
		w. Wmk inverted (from booklets)	1·75	1·50

No. 228 was only issued in booklets (Nos. SB16/17) at first but was released in sheets on 1.4.68 in a slightly brighter shade. In the sheet stamps the lines of shading are more regular.

(Des O. Bonnevalle)

1967 (2 May). Europa. W **22** (sideways). P 15.

229	**79**	7d. light emerald, gold and pale cream	60	50
230		1s.5d. carmine-red, gold and pale cream	1·90	1·75

80 Maple Leaves

(Des P. Hickey)

1967 (28 Aug). Canadian Centennial. W **22**. P 15.

231	**80**	5d. multicoloured	10	10
232		1s.5d. multicoloured	20	1·00

81 Rock of Cashel (from photo by Edwin Smith)

1967 (25 Sept). International Tourist Year. W **22** (inverted). P 15.

233	**81**	7d. sepia	15	20
234		10d. slate-blue	15	40

82 1c. Fenian Stamp Essay

83 24c. Fenian Stamp Essay

1967 (23 Oct). Centenary of Fenian Rising. W **22** (sideways). P 15.

235	**82**	5d. black and light green	10	10
236	**83**	1s. black and light pink	20	30

84 Jonathan Swift

85 Gulliver and Lilliputians

(Des M. Byrne)

1967 (30 Nov). 300th Birth Anniv of Jonathan Swift. W **22** (sideways). P 15.

237	**84**	3d. black and olive-grey	10	10
238	**85**	1s.5d. blackish brown and pale blue	20	30

86 Europa "Key"

(Des H. Schwarzenbach and M. Biggs)

1968 (29 Apr). Europa. W **22**. P 15.

239	**86**	7d. brown-red, gold and brown	50	50
240		1s.5d. new blue, gold and brown	75	1·00

87 St. Mary's Cathedral, Limerick

(Des from photo by J. J. Bambury. Recess B.W.)

1968 (26 Aug). 800th Anniv of St. Mary's Cathedral, Limerick. W **22**. P 15.

241	**87**	5d. Prussian blue	10	10
242		10d. yellow-green	20	60

88 Countess Markievicz

89 James Connolly

1968 (23 Sept). Birth Centenary of Countess Markievicz (patriot). W **22** (inverted on 1s.5d.). P 15.

243	**88**	3d. black	10	10
244		1s.5d. deep blue and blue	20	90

1968 (23 Sept). Birth Centenary of James Connolly (patriot). W **22** (sideways). P 15.

245	89	6d. deep brown and chocolate	20	75
246		1s. blackish green, apple-green and myrtle-green	20	10

90 Stylised Dog (brooch)

91 Stag

92 Winged Ox (Symbol of St. Luke)

93 Eagle (Symbol of St. John The Evangelist)

(Des H. Gerl)

1968–70. Pence values expressed with "p". W **22** (sideways* on ½d. to 1s.9d). P 15.

247	90	½d. red-orange (7.6.69)	10	30
248		1d. pale yellow-green (7.6.69)	15	10
		a. Coil stamp. Perf 14×15 (8.70?)	1·25	5·50
249		2d. light ochre (14.10.68)	50	10
		a. Coil stamp. Perf 14×15 (8.70?)	1·25	6·50
250		3d. blue (7.6.69)	35	10
		a. Coil stamp. Perf 14×15 (8.70?)	1·25	3·75
251		4d. deep brown-red (31.3.69)	30	10
252		5d. myrtle-green (31.3.69)	1·25	1·00
253		6d. bistre-brown (24.2.69)	30	10
		w. Wmk e facing right	5·50	3·25
254	91	7d. brown and yellow (7.6.69)	45	4·00
255		8d. chocolate and orange-brown (14.10.68)	45	3·25
256		9d. slate-blue and olive-green (24.2.69)	50	10
257		10d. chocolate and bluish violet (31.3.69)	1·50	3·25
258		1s. chocolate and red-brown (31.3.69)	40	10
259		1s.9d. black and lt turquoise-bl (24.2.69)	4·00	3·00
260	92	2s.6d. multicoloured (14.10.68)	1·75	30
261		5s. multicoloured (24.2.69)	3·00	3·50
262	93	10s. multicoloured (14.10.68)	4·75	4·75
247/62		Set of 16	17·00	21·00

*The normal sideways watermark shows the top of the "e" facing left, *as seen from the back of the stamp.*

The 1d., 2d., 3d., 5d., 6d., 9d., 1s. and 2s.6d. exist with PVA gum as well as gum arabic. The coil stamps exist on PVA only, and the rest on gum arabic only.

Stamps in similar designs were issued from 1974 to 1983.

94 Human Rights Emblem

95 Dail Eireann Assembly

1968 (4 Nov). Human Rights Year. W **22** (sideways). P 15.

263	94	5d. yellow, gold and black	15	10
264		7d. yellow, gold and red	15	40

(Des M. Byrne)

1969 (21 Jan). 50th Anniv of Dail Eireann (First National Parliament). W **22** (sideways). P 15×14½.

265	95	6d. myrtle-green	15	10
266		9d. Prussian blue	15	30

96 Colonnade

97 Quadruple I.L.O. Emblems

(Des L. Gasbarra and G. Belli; adapted Myra Maguire)

1969 (28 Apr). Europa. W **22**. P 15.

267	96	9d. grey, ochre and ultramarine	1·00	1·10
268		1s.9d. grey, gold and scarlet	1·25	1·75

(Des K. C. Dabczewski)

1969 (14 July). 50th Anniv of International Labour Organization. W **22** (sideways). P 15.

269	97	6d. black and grey	20	10
270		9d. black and yellow	20	25

98 "The Last Supper and Crucifixion" (Evie Hone Window, Eton Chapel)

(Des R. Kyne)

1969 (1 Sept). Contemporary Irish Art (1st issue). W **22** (sideways). P 15×14½.

271	98	1s. multicoloured	30	1·50

See also Nos. 280, 306, 317, 329, 362, 375, 398, 408, 452, 470 and 498.

99 Mahatma Gandhi

1969 (2 Oct). Birth Centenary of Mahatma Gandhi. W **22**. P 15.

272	99	6d. black and green	50	10
273		1s.9d. black and yellow	75	90

100 Symbolic Bird in Tree

(Des D. Harrington)

1970 (23 Feb). European Conservation Year. W **22**. P 15.

274	100	6d. bistre and black	20	10
275		9d. slate-violet and black	25	80

101 "Flaming Sun"

(Des L. le Brocquy)

1970 (4 May). Europa. W **22**. P 15.

276	**101**	6d. bright violet and silver	55	10
277		9d. brown and silver	90	1·25
278		1s.9d. deep olive-grey and silver	1·75	2·00
276/8	*Set of 3*		2·75	3·00

102 "Sailing Boats" (Peter Monamy)

(Des P. Wildbur and P. Scott)

1970 (13 July). 250th Anniv of Royal Cork Yacht Club. W **22**. P 15.

279	**102**	4d. multicoloured	15	10

103 "Madonna of Eire" (Mainie Jellett)

104 Thomas MacCurtain

1970 (1 Sept). Contemporary Irish Art (2nd issue) (sideways). W **22**. P 15.

280	**103**	1s. multicoloured	15	20

(Des P. Wildbur)

1970 (26 Oct). 50th Death Anniversaries of Irish Patriots. T **104** and similar vert design. W **22** (sideways). P 15.

281		9d. black, bluish violet and greyish black	1·00	25
		a. Pair. Nos. 281/2	2·00	2·50
282		9d. black, bluish violet and greyish black	1·00	25
283		2s.9d. black, new blue and greyish black	1·75	2·50
		a. Pair. Nos. 283/4	3·50	11·00
284		2s.9d. black, new blue and greyish black	1·75	2·50
281/4	*Set of 4*		5·00	5·00

Designs:—Nos. 281 and 283, Type **104**; others, Terence MacSwiney.

Nos. 281/2 and 283/4 were each printed together, *se-tenant*, in horizontal and vertical pairs throughout the sheet.

106 Kevin Barry

(Des P. Wildbur)

1970 (2 Nov). 50th Death Anniv of Kevin Barry (patriot). W **22** (inverted). P 15.

285	**106**	6d. olive-green	30	10
286		1s.2d. royal blue	40	1·10

106a Stylized Dog (Brooch)

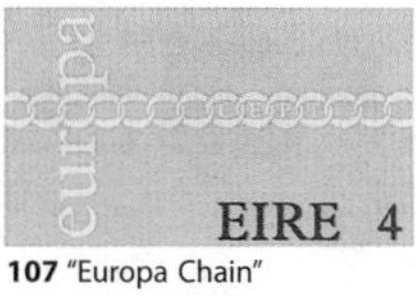

107 "Europa Chain"

Two types of 10p.:

I. Outline and markings of the ox in lilac.
II. Outline and markings in brown.

1971 (15 Feb)–**75**. Decimal Currency. Designs as Nos. 247/62 but with "p" omitted as in T **106a**. W **22** (sideways* on 10, 12, 20 and 50p.). P 15.

287	**106a**	½p. bright green	10	10
		a. Wmk sideways	4·50	10·00
		ab. Booklet pane of 6	25·00	
		aw. Wmk e facing right	4·50	10·00
		awb. Booklet pane of 6	25·00	
288	**106a**	1p. blue	40	10
		a. Coil stamp. Perf 14×14½	65	1·00
		b. Coil stamp. Nos. 288a, 289a, and 291a *se-tenant*	1·00	
		c. Wmk sideways	25	40
		ca. Booklet pane of 6	1·50	
		cb. Booklet pane. No. 288c×5 plus one *se-tenant* label (11.3.74)	1·00	
		cw. Wmk e facing right	25	40
		cwa. Booklet pane of 6	1·50	
		cwb. Booklet pane. No. 288cw×5 plus one *se-tenant* label (11.3.74)	1·00	
289		1½p. lake-brown	15	50
		a. Coil stamp. Perf 14×14½	20	50
		b. Coil strip. Nos. 289a, 291a, 294a and 290a *se-tenant* (24.2.72)	1·00	
		c. Coil strip. Nos. 289a×2, 290a and 295ab *se-tenant* (29.1.74)	1·00	
290		2p. myrtle-green	15	10
		a. Coil stamp. Perf 14×14½ (24.2.72)	20	60
		b. Wmk sideways (27.1.75)	25	50
		ba. Booklet pane. No. 290b×5 plus one *se-tenant* label.	1·00	
		bw. Wmk e facing right	25	50
		bwa. Booklet pane. No. 290bw ×5 plus one *se-tenant* label	1·00	
291		2½p. sepia	15	10
		a. Coil stamp. Perf 14×14½ (20.2.71)	30	85
		b. Wmk sideways	1·00	1·50
		ba. Booklet pane of 6	5·00	
		bw. Wmk e facing right	1·00	1·50
		bwa. Booklet pane of 6	5·00	
292		3p. cinnamon	15	10
293		3½p. orange-brown	25	10
294		4p. pale bluish violet	20	10
		a. Coil stamp. Perf 14×14½ (24.2.72)	70	60
295	**91**	5p. brown and yellow-olive	1·00	20
295a	**106a**	5p. bright yellow-green (29.1.74)	2·25	45
		ab. Coil stamp. Perf 14×14½ (29.1.74)	80	90
		ac. Wmk sideways (11.3.74)	55	80
		ad. Booklet pane. No. 295ac×5 plus one *se-tenant* label	3·00	
		ada. Booklet pane imperf vert	£2750	
		ae. Booklet pane. No. 295ac×6	5·00	
		awc. Wmk e facing right	55	80
		awd. Booklet pane. No. 295awc×5 plus one *se-tenant* label	3·00	
		awe. Booklet pane. No. 295awc×6	5·00	
296	**91**	6p. blackish brown and slate	3·50	1·75
296a		7p. indigo and olive-green (29.1.74)	4·25	45
297		7½p. chocolate and reddish lilac	50	1·40
298		9p. black and turquoise-green	1·00	45
299	**92**	10p. multicoloured (I)	15·00	10·00
299a		10p. multicoloured (II)	20·00	70
299b		12p. multicoloured (29.1.74)	60	1·50
300		20p. multicoloured	75	10
301	**93**	50p. multicoloured	2·00	75
287/301	*Set of 18*		28·00	8·00

Nos. 287a/awb, 288c/cwb, 290b/bwa, 291b/bwa and 295ac/awe come from booklets Nos. SB19/23. The sideways watermark has the top of the e pointing left, and the sideways inverted has it pointing right, *when seen from the back of the stamp*. Stamps with one, or two adjoining, sides imperf come from these booklets.

See also Nos. 339/59 and 478/83.

(Des H. Haflidason; adapted P. Wildbur)

1971 (3 May). Europa. W **22** (sideways). P 15.

302	**107**	4p. sepia and olive-yellow	75	10
303		6p. black and new blue	2·75	3·50

108 J. M. Synge

109 An Island Man (Jack B. Yeats)

(Des R. Kyne from a portrait by Jack B. Yeats)

1971 (19 July). Birth Centenary of J. M. Synge (playwright). W **22**. P 15.

304	**108**	4p. multicoloured		15	10
305		10p. multicoloured		60	80

(Des P. Wildbur)

1971 (30 Aug). Contemporary Irish Art (3rd issue). Birth Centenary of J. B. Yeats (artist). W **22**. P 15.

306	**109**	6p. multicoloured		55	55

110 Racial Harmony Symbol

111 "Madonna and Child" (statue by J. Hughes)

(Des P. Wildbur. Litho Harrison)

1971 (18 Oct). Racial Equality Year. No wmk. P 14×14½.

307	**110**	4p. red		20	10
308		10p. black		50	75

(Des R. Kyne)

1971 (15 Nov). Christmas. W **22**. P 15.

309	**111**	2½p. black, gold and deep bluish green		10	10
310		6p. black, gold and ultramarine		65	90

112 Heart

(Des L. le Brocquy)

1972 (7 Apr). World Health Day. W **22** (sideways). P 15.

311	**112**	2½p. gold and brown		30	15
312		12p. silver and grey		1·10	2·25

113 "Communications"

(Des P. Huovinen and P. Wildbur)

1972 (1 May). Europa. W **22** (sideways). P 15.

313	**113**	4p. orange, black and silver		2·50	25
314		6p. blue, black and silver		7·50	4·75

114 Dove and Moon   **115** "Black Lake" (Gerard Dillon)

(Des P. Scott)

1972 (1 June). The Patriot Dead, 1922–23. W **22**. P 15.

315	**114**	4p. grey-blue, light orange and deep blue		10	10
316		6p. dp yellow-grn, lemon and dp dull grn		65	50

(Des P. Wildbur)

1972 (10 July). Contemporary Irish Art (4th issue). W **22** (sideways). P 15.

317	**115**	3p. multicoloured		60	35

116 "Horseman" (Carved Slab)

117 Madonna and Child (from Book of Kells)

118 2d. Stamp of 1922

(Des P. Scott)

1972 (28 Aug). 50th Anniv of Olympic Council of Ireland. W **22**. P 15.

318	**116**	3p. bright yellow, black and gold		15	10
319		6p. salmon, black and gold		55	90

> **WATERMARK.** All issues from here onwards are on unwatermarked paper.

(Des P. Scott)

1972 (16 Oct). Christmas. P 15.

320	**117**	2½p. multicoloured (shades)		10	10
321		4p. multicoloured		25	10
322		12p. multicoloured		1·00	1·00
320/2 *Set of 3*				1·25	1·10

(Des Stamping Branch of the Revenue Commissioners, Dublin)

1972 (6 Dec). 50th Anniv of the First Irish Postage Stamp. P 15.

323	**118**	6p. light grey and grey-green		60	60
MS324 72×104 mm. No. 323×4				3·75	7·50

119 Celtic Head Motif

(Des L. le Brocquy)

1973 (1 Jan). Entry into European Communities. P 15.

325	**119**	6p. multicoloured		45	70
326		12p. multicoloured		65	90

120 Europa "Posthorn"

(Des L. Anisdahl; adapted R. Kyne)

1973 (30 Apr). Europa. P 15.

327	**120**	4p. bright blue		1·75	10
328		6p. black		4·25	3·25

121 "Berlin Blues II" (W. Scott)   **122** Weather Map

(Adapted by R. Scott)

1973 (9 Aug). Contemporary Irish Art (5th issue). P 15×14½.

329	**121**	5p. ultramarine and grey-black		40	30

(Des R. Ballagh)

1973 (4 Sept). I.M.O./W.M.O. Centenary. P 14½×15.

330	**122**	3½p. multicoloured		30	10
331		12p. multicoloured		1·10	2·00

123 Tractor ploughing

(Des P. Scott)

1973 (5 Oct). World Ploughing Championships, Wellington Bridge.
P 15×14½.

332	**123**	5p. multicoloured	15	10
333		7p. multicoloured	1·00	50

124 "Flight into
Egypt" (Jan de Cock)

125 Daunt Island Lightship
and *Mary Stanford* (Ballycotton
lifeboat), 1936

(Des D. Kiely. Litho ("EIRE" and face value) and photo (3½p) or photo
(12p.))

1973 (1 Nov). Christmas. P 15.

334	**124**	3½p. multicoloured	15	10
335		12p. multicoloured	1·10	1·50

(Des M. Byrne from painting by B. Gribble)

1974 (28 Mar). 150th Anniv of Royal National Lifeboat Institution.
P 15×14½.

| 336 | **125** | 5p. multicoloured | 30 | 30 |

126 "Edmund Burke",
(statue by J. H. Foley)

(Des P. Wildbur)

1974 (29 Apr). Europa. P 14½×15.

337	**126**	5p. black and pale violet-blue	1·50	10
338		7p. black and light emerald	5·00	2·50

Two types of 50p.:

Type I. Fine screen (Cyl 1)

Type II. Coarse screen (Cyl 2)

1974–83. Designs as Nos. 287 etc. No wmk. P 15.

339	106a	½p. bright green (5.6.78)	30	10
340		1p. blue (21.2.75)	10	10
		a. Coil stamp. Perf 14×14½ (21.3.77)	1·00	1·50
		b. Coil strip. Nos. 340a, 341a×2 and 344a *se-tenant* (21.3.77)	2·50	
341		2p. myrtle-green (7.4.76)	10	10
		a. Coil stamp. Perf 14×14½ (21.3.77)	40	50
342		3p. cinnamon (21.2.75)	10	10
343		3½p. orange-brown (9.10.74)	2·75	4·00
344		5p. bright yellow-green (16.8.74)	60	10
		a. Coil stamp. Perf 14×14½ (21.3.77)	1·40	85
345	91	6p. blackish brn and slate (16.10.74)	70	2·25
346	106a	6p. slate (17.6.75)	20	10
347	91	7p. indigo and olive-green (27.9.74).	70	35
348	106a	7p. deep yellow-green (17.6.75)	35	10
		a. Booklet pane. No. 348×5 plus *se-tenant* label (21.3.77)	7·00	
349	91	8p. dp brown and dp orge-brn (17.6.75)	60	50
350	106a	8p. chestnut (14.7.76)	30	10
351	91	9p. black and turquoise-green (12.74)	70	30
352	106a	9p. greenish slate (14.7.76)	30	10
352a		9½p. vermilion (3.12.79)	35	20
353	92	10p. multicoloured (II) (12.74)	1·25	30
354	91	10p. black and violet-blue (14.7.76)	70	10
354a	106a	10p. deep mauve (8.6.77)	70	10
355	91	11p. black and rose-carmine (14.7.76)	45	1·25
355a		12p. black and bright green (8.6.77)	55	10
355b	106a	12p. yellowish green (26.3.80)	30	10
355c	91	13p. reddish brn and red-brn (26.3.80)	40	2·00
356	92	15p. multicoloured (17.6.75)	55	1·00
356a	106a	15p. ultramarine (10.7.80)	40	10
356b	91	16p. black and dull yellow-grn (10.7.80).	40	1·00
356c	92	17p. multicoloured (8.6.77)	50	1·75
357		20p. multicoloured (13.6.74)	50	15
358	93	50p. multicoloured (I) (12.74)	1·00	30
		a. Type II (1983)	1·75	2·50
359		£1 multicoloured (17.6.75)	1·75	30
339/59 *Set of 29*			16·00	14·50

For 18p., 19p., 22p., 24p., 26p. and 29p. values printed by
lithography, see Nos. 478/83.

Stamps with one or two sides imperf come from pane No. 348a
from booklet No. SB24.

127 "Oliver Goldsmith"
(statue by J. H. Foley)

128 "Kitchen Table"
(Norah McGuiness)

(Des P. Wildbur)

1974 (24 June). Death Bicentenary of Oliver Goldsmith (writer).
P 14½×15.

360	**127**	3½p. black and olive-yellow	25	10
361		12p. black and bright yellowish green ..	75	1·00

(Design adapted by Norah McGuiness. Photo Harrison)

1974 (19 Aug.). Contemporary Irish Art (6th issue). P 14×14½.

| 362 | **128** | 5p. multicoloured | 35 | 30 |

129 Rugby Players

130 U.P.U. "Postmark"

(Design adapted from Irish Press photograph. Eng C. Slania Recess (3½p.) or recess and photo (12p.) Harrison)

1974 (9 Sept.). Centenary of Irish Rugby Football Union. P 14½×14.

363	**129**	3½p. greenish black	50	10
		a. Deep greenish blue	6·00	3·50
364		12p. multicoloured	2·00	2·75

No. 363a is from a second printing using a recut plate on which the engraving was deeper.

(Des R. Ballagh)

1974 (9 Oct.). Centenary of Universal Postal Union. P 14½×15.

365	**130**	5p. light yellowish green and black	25	10
366		7p. light ultramarine and black	35	55

131 "Madonna and Child" (Bellini)

132 "Peace"

(Des P. Wildbur)

1974 (14 Nov.). Christmas. P 14½×15.

367	**131**	5p. multicoloured	15	10
368		15p. multicoloured	60	90

(Des Alexandra Wejchert)

1975 (24 Mar.). International Women's Year. P 14½×15.

369	**132**	8p. brt reddish purple and ultramarine	25	75
370		15p. ultramarine and bright green	50	1·25

133 "Castletown Hunt" (R. Healy)

(Des R. Kyne)

1975 (28 Apr.). Europa. P 15×14½.

371	**133**	7p. grey-black	1·75	15
372		9p. dull blue-green	5·00	2·50

134 Putting

(Des from photographs by J. McManus. Litho ("EIRE" and face value) and photo).

1975 (26 June). Ninth European Amateur Golf Team Championship, Killarney. P 15×14½.

373	**134**	6p. multicoloured (shades)	75	45
374	–	9p. multicoloured (shades)	1·50	1·50

The 9p. is similar to T **134** but shows a different view of the putting green.

135 "Bird of Prey" (sculpture by Oisin Kelly)

(Design adapted by the artist)

1975 (28 July). Contemporary Irish Art (7th issue). P 15×14½.

375	**135**	15p. yellow-brown	75	75

136 Nano Nagle (founder) and Waifs

137 Tower of St. Anne's Church, Shandon

(Des Kilkenny Design Workshops)

1975 (1 Sept.). Bicentenary of Presentation Order of Nuns. P 14½×15.

376	**136**	5p. black and pale blue	20	10
377		7p. black and light stone	30	30

(Des P. Scott)

1975 (6 Oct.). European Architectural Heritage Year. T **137** and similar vert design. P 12½.

378	**137**	5p. blackish brown	20	10
379		6p. multicoloured	40	85
380	–	7p. steel-blue	40	10
381	–	9p. multicoloured	40	80
378/81	Set of 4		1·25	1·60

Design:—Nos. 380/1, Interior of Holycross Abbey, Co. Tipperary.

138 St. Oliver Plunkett (commemorative medal by Imogen Stuart)

139 "Madonna and Child" (Fro Filippo Lippi)

(Design adapted by the artist. Recess Harrison)

1975 (13 Oct.). Canonisation of Oliver Plunkett. P 14×14½.

382	**138**	7p. black	15	10
383		15p. chestnut	55	45

(Des P. Wildbur)

1975 (13 Nov.). Christmas. P 15.

384	**139**	5p. multicoloured	15	10
385		7p. multicoloured	20	10
386		10p. multicoloured	75	60
384/6	Set of 3		1·00	65

140 James Larkin (from a drawing by Sean O'Sullivan)

141 Alexander Graham Bell

(Des P. Wildbur. Litho)

1976 (21 Jan). Birth Centenary of James Larkin (Trade Union leader). P 14½×15.

387	**140**	7p. deep bluish green and pale grey ..	20	10
388		11p. sepia and yellow-ochre....................	40	55

(Des R. Ballagh)

1976 (10 Mar). Telephone Centenary. P 14½×15.

389	**141**	9p. multicoloured.......................................	20	10
390		15p. multicoloured.....................................	45	50

142 1847 Benjamin Franklin Essay

(Des L. le Brocquy; graphics by P. Wildbur. Litho Irish Security Stamp Printing Ltd)

1976 (17 May). Bicentenary of American Revolution. T **142** and similar horiz designs. P 14½×14.

391	7p. ultramarine, light red and silver...............	20	10
	a. Silver (inscr) omitted	†	£1700
392	8p. ultramarine, light red and silver...............	25	1·10
393	9p. violet-blue, orange and silver..................	25	10
394	15p. light rose-red, grey-blue and silver........	45	75
	a. Silver (face-value and inscr) omitted......	£900	£1000
391/4 *Set of 4*		1·00	1·90
MS395 95×75 mm. Nos. 391/4		2·75	8·00
	a. Silver omitted		£10000

Designs:—7p. Thirteen stars; 8p. Fifty stars; 9, 15p. Type **142**.
No. **MS**395 exists with the sheet margins overprinted in blue to commemorate "Stampa 76", the Irish National Stamp Exhibition.

143 Spirit Barrel

(Des P. Hickey)

1976 (1 July). Europa. Irish Delft. T **143** and similar horiz design. Multicoloured. P 15×14.

396	9p. Type **143**	1·25	20
397	11p. Dish..	2·75	1·60

144 "The Lobster Pots, West of Ireland" (Paul Henry)

(Des R. McGrath)

1976 (30 Aug). Contemporary Irish Art (8th issue). P 15.

398	**144**	15p. multicoloured	60	60

145 Radio Waves

(Des G. Shepherd and A. O'Donnell. Litho De La Rue Smurfit Ltd, Dublin)

1976 (5 Oct). 50th Anniv of Irish Broadcasting Service. T **145** and similar vert design. Chalk-surfaced paper. P 14½×14 (9p.) or 14×14½ (11p.).

399	9p. light new blue and bottle-green	20	10
400	11p. agate, orange-red and light new blue ..	60	1·00

Design:—11p. Transmitter, radio waves and globe.

146 "The Nativity" (Lorenzo Monaco)

(Des R. McGrath)

1976 (11 Nov). Christmas. P 15×14½.

401	**146**	7p. multicoloured....................................	15	10
402		9p. multicoloured....................................	15	10
403		15p. multicoloured..................................	55	55
401/3 *Set of 3*			75	65

147 16th Century Manuscript

(Des P. Hickey)

1977 (9 May). Centenaries of National Library (8p.) and National Museum (10p.). T **147** and similar horiz design. Multicoloured. P 15×14½.

404	8p. Type **147**	30	30
405	10p. Prehistoric stone............................	40	35

148 Ballynahinch, Galway

149 "Head" (Louis le Brocquy)

(Des E. van der Grijn. Litho Irish Security Stamp Printing Ltd)

1977 (27 June). Europa. T **148** and similar vert design. Multicoloured. P 14×15.

406	10p. Type **148**	1·50	25
407	12p. Lough Tay, Wicklow.......................	4·50	1·50

(Design adapted by the artist. Litho Irish Security Stamp Ptg Ltd)

1977 (8 Aug). Contemporary Irish Art (9th issue). P 14×14½.

408	**149**	17p. multicoloured	65	75

150 Guide and Tents

151 "The Shanachie" (drawing by Jack B. Yeats)

(Des R. Ballagh)

1977 (22 Aug). Scouting and Guiding. T **150** and similar horiz design. Multicoloured. P 15×14½.

409	**150**	8p. Type **150**	30	10
410		17p. Tent and Scout saluting............................	80	1·50

(Des L. Miller (10p.), R. Ballagh (12p.). Litho Irish Security Stamp Printing Ltd)

1977 (12 Sept.). Anniversaries. T **151** and similar horiz design. P 14×14½ (10p.) or 14½×14 (12p.).

411	10p. black..	35	15
412	12p. black..	45	1·00

Designs and events:—10p. Type **151** (Golden Jubilee of Irish Folklore Society); 12p. The philosopher Eriugena (1100th death anniv).

152 "Electricity" (Golden Jubilee of Electricity Supply Board)

(Des R. Ballagh (10p.), P. Hickey (12p.), B. Blackshaw (17p.). Photo Stamping Branch of the Revenue Commissioners (12p.); Litho Irish Security Stamp Ptg Ltd (others))

1977 (10 Oct). Golden Jubilees. T **152** and similar horiz designs. P 15×14½ (12p.) or 15×14 (others).

413	10p. multicoloured	15	10
414	12p. multicoloured	30	1·40
415	17p. grey-black and grey-brown	65	35
413/15 Set of 3		1·00	1·60

Designs:—12p. Bulls (from contemporary coinage) (Jubilee of Agricultural Credit Corporation); 17p. Greyhound (Jubilee of greyhound track racing).

153 "The Holy Family" (Giorgione)

154 Junkers W.33 *Bremen* in Flight

(Des R. McGrath)

1977 (3 Nov). Christmas. P 14½×15.

416	**153**	8p. multicoloured	20	10
417		10p. multicoloured	20	10
418		17p. multicoloured	75	1·25
416/18 Set of 3			1·00	1·25

(Des R. Ballagh. Litho Irish Security Stamp Ptg Ltd)

1978 (13 Apr). 50th Anniv of First East-West Transatlantic Flight. P 14×14½.

419	**154**	10p. bright blue and black	20	15
420		17p. olive-brown and black	35	1·10

The 17p. is as T **154** but shows a different sky and sea.

155 Spring Gentian

156 Catherine McAuley

(Des Wendy Walsh. Litho Irish Security Stamp Ptg Ltd)

1978 (12 June). Wild Flowers. T **155** and similar vert designs. Multicoloured. P 14×15.

421	8p. Type **155**	25	40
422	10p. Strawberry tree	25	15
423	11p. Large-flowered Butterwort	25	50
424	17p. St. Dabeoc's Heath	45	2·00
421/4 Set of 4		1·10	2·75

(Des R. Ballagh (10p.), R. Kyne (11p.), E. van der Grijn (17p.). Litho Irish Security Stamp Ptg Ltd)

1978 (18 Sept.). Anniversaries and Events. T **156** and similar multicoloured designs. P 14½×14 (11p.) or 14×14½ (others).

425	10p. Type **156**	25	10
426	11p. Doctor performing vaccination (*horiz*)	35	80
427	17p. "Self Portrait"	55	1·10
425/7 Set of 3		1·00	1·75

Events:—10p. Birth bicentenary of Catherine McAuley (founder of Sisters of Mercy); 11p. Global eradication of Smallpox; 17p. Birth centenary of Sir William Orpen (painter).

157 Diagram of Drilling Rig

158 Farthing

(Des R. Ballagh. Litho Irish Security Stamp Ptg Ltd)

1978 (18 Oct). Arrival Onshore of Natural Gas. P 14×14½.

428	**157**	10p. maroon, turquoise-green and bistre	30	30

(Des P. Wildbur and R. Mercer)

1978 (26 Oct). 50th Anniv of Irish Currency. T **158** and similar horiz designs. P 15×14½.

429	8p. black, copper and deep bluish green	20	20
430	10p. black, silver and blue-green	25	10
431	11p. black, copper and chocolate	30	50
432	17p. black, silver and deep blue	40	1·00
429/32 Set of 4		1·00	1·60

Designs:—10p. Florin; 11p. Penny; 17p. Half-crown.

159 "The Virgin and Child" (Guercino)

160 Conolly Folly, Castletown

(Des P. Wildbur)

1978 (16 Nov). Christmas. P 14½×15.

433	**159**	8p. purple-brown, gold and pale turquoise-green	15	10
434		10p. purple-brown, chocolate and pale turquoise-green	15	10
435		17p. purple-brown, deep blue-green and pale turquoise-green	45	1·40
433/5 Set of 3			65	1·40

(Des R. McGrath)

1978 (6 Dec). Europa. Architecture. T **160** and similar horiz design. P 15×14½.

436	10p. lake-brown and red-brown	1·50	15
437	11p. green and deep green	1·50	1·75

Design:—11p. Dromoland Belvedere.

161 Athletes in Cross-country Race

162 "European Communities" (in languages of member nations)

(Des R. Mercer. Litho Irish Security Stamp Ptg Ltd)

1979 (20 Aug). Seventh World Cross-country Championships, Limerick. P 14½×14.

438	**161**	8p. multicoloured	20	30

(Des P. Wildbur)

1979 (20 Aug). First Direct Elections to European Assembly. P 14½×15.
439 **162** 10p. dull turquoise-green............................ 15 15
440 11p. reddish violet... 15 35

163 Sir Rowland Hill

(Des C. Harrison. Litho Irish Security Stamp Ptg Ltd)

1979 (20 Aug). Death Centenary of Sir Rowland Hill. P 14×14½.
441 **163** 17p. black, brownish grey and red.......... 30 60

164 Winter Wren (*Troglodytes troglodytes*)

(Des Wendy Walsh. Litho Irish Security Stamp Ptg Ltd)

1979 (30 Aug). Birds. T **164** and similar horiz designs. Multicoloured. P 14½×14.
442 8p. Type **164** 40 80
443 10p. Great Crested Grebe (*Podiceps cristatus*). 40 15
444 11p. White-fronted Goose (*Anser albifrons flavirostris*) 45 80
445 17p. Peregrine Falcon (*Falco peregrinus*) .... 70 2·00
442/5 Set of 4 .... 1·75 3·25

165 "A Happy Flower" (David Gallagher)

(Des P. Wildbur. Litho Irish Security Stamp Ptg Ltd)

1979 (13 Sept). International Year of the Child. Paintings by Children. T **165** and similar multicoloured designs. P 14×14½ (11p.) or 14½×14 (others).
446 10p. Type **165** 20 10
447 11p. "Myself and My Skipping Rope" (Lucy Norman) (*vert*)............... 25 60
448 17p. "Swans on a Lake" (Nicola O'Dwyer) 35 85
446/8 Set of 3 .... 70 1·40

166 Pope John Paul II   **167** Brother and Child

(Des P. Byrne. Litho Irish Security Stamp Ptg Ltd)

1979 (29 Sept). Visit of Pope John Paul II. P 14½×14.
449 **166** 12p. multicoloured.................................... 30 20

(Des R. Kyne (9½p.), P. Scott (11p.), R. Mercer (20p.). Photo Stamping Branch of the Revenue Commissioners, Dublin (11p.), Litho Irish Security Stamp Ptg Ltd (others).

1979 (4 Oct). Commemorations. T **167** and similar designs. P 14½×14 (9½p.), 14½×15 (11p.) or 14×14½ (others).
450 9½p. black and pale claret.................................. 20 10

451 11p. black, reddish orange and bright blue.. 20 70
452 20p. multicoloured... 40 1·40
450/2 Set of 3 .... 70 2·00
Designs and commemorations: Horiz—9½p. Type **167** (Centenary of Hospitaller Order of St. John of God in Ireland); 20p. "Seated Figure" (sculpture by F. E. McWilliam) (Contemporary Irish Art (10th issue)). Vert—11p. Windmill and Sun (International Energy Conservation Month).

168 Patrick Pearse, "Liberty" and General Post Office, Dublin   **169** Madonna and Child (panel painting from Domnach Airgid Shrine)

(Des R. Ballagh)

1979 (10 Nov). Birth Centenary of Patrick Pearse (patriot). P 15×14½.
453 **168** 12p. multicoloured.................................... 30 15

(Des Ewa Gargulinska)

1979 (15 Nov). Christmas. P 14½×15.
454 **169** 9½p. multicoloured.................................... 15 10
455 20p. multicoloured... 30 55

170 Bianconi Long Car, 1836   **171** John Baptist de la Salle (founder)

(Des P. Wildbur. Litho Irish Security Stamp Ptg Ltd)

1979 (6 Dec). Europa. Communications. T **170** and similar horiz design. Multicoloured. P 14½×14.
456 12p. Type **170** .... 1·25 30
457 13p. Transatlantic cable, Valentia, 1866........... 1·75 1·40

(Des P. Wildbur. Litho Irish Security Stamp Ptg Ltd)

1980 (19 Mar). Centenary of arrival of De La Salle Order. P 14×14½.
458 **171** 12p. multicoloured.................................... 30 30

172 George Bernard Shaw   **173** Stoat

(Des P. Byrne. Litho Irish Security Stamp Ptg Ltd)

1980 (7 May). Europa. Personalities. T **172** and similar multicoloured design. P 14×14½.
459 12p. Type **172** .... 1·25 50
460 13p. Oscar Wilde (29×40 *mm*)......................... 2·00 2·50

(Des Wendy Walsh. Litho Irish Security Stamp Ptg Ltd)

1980 (30 July). Wildlife. T **173** and similar vert designs. Multicoloured. P 14×14½.

461	12p. Type **173**	25	40
462	15p. Arctic Hare	25	15
463	16p. Red Fox	25	80
464	25p. Red Deer	35	1·60
461/4 Set of 4		1·00	2·75
MS465 73×97 mm. Nos. 461/4		1·00	2·75

No. **MS**465 exists with the sheet margins overprinted to commemorate "STAMPA 80", the Irish National Stamp Exhibition, in black or red, and for the Dublin Stamp Show, 1992, in red.

174 Playing Bodhran and Whistle   **175** Sean O'Casey

(Des J. Dixon and P. Wildbur. Litho Irish Security Stamp Ptg Ltd)

1980 (25 Sept). Traditional Music and Dance. T **174** and similar vert designs. Multicoloured. P 14×14½.

466	12p. Type **174**	15	10
467	15p. Playing Uilleann pipes	20	15
468	25p. Dancing	35	1·10
466/8 Set of 3		65	1·25

(Des P. Wildbur (12p.), P. Scott (25p.). Litho Irish Security Stamp Ptg Ltd)

1980 (23 Oct). Commemorations. T **175** and similar vert design. P 14×14½.

469	12p. multicoloured	20	10
470	25p. black, buff and drab	35	1·00

Designs and commemorations:—12p. Type **175** (Birth centenary of Sean O'Casey (playwright)); 25p. "Gold Painting No. 57" (Patrick Scott) (Contemporary Irish Art (11th issue)).

176 Nativity Scene (painting by Geraldine McNulty)   **177** Boyle Air-pump, 1659

(Des P. Wildbur)

1980 (13 Nov). Christmas. P 14½×15.

471	**176** 12p. multicoloured	15	10
472	15p. multicoloured	20	10
473	25p. multicoloured	40	1·25
471/3 Set of 3		65	1·25

(Des P. Wildbur. Litho Irish Security Stamp Ptg Ltd)

1981 (12 Mar). Irish Science and Technology. T **177** and similar vert designs. Multicoloured. P 14×14½.

474	12p. Type **177**	20	10
475	15p. Ferguson tractor, 1936	25	10
476	16p. Parsons turbine, 1884	30	90
477	25p. Holland submarine, 1878	35	1·25
474/7 Set of 4		1·00	2·10

(Litho Irish Security Stamp Ptg Ltd)

1981 (27 Apr)–**82**. No wmk. P 14×14½.

478	**106a**	18p. dull claret	45	50
479		19p. light blue	55	2·25
480		22p. dull turquoise-blue (1.9.81)	65	10
481		24p. drab (29.10.81)	1·25	2·00
482		26p. blue-green (1.4.82)	1·50	40
483		29p. purple (1.4.82)	2·00	3·25
478/83 Set of 6			5·75	7·75

178 "The Legend of the Cock and the Pot"   **179** Cycling

(Des P. Byrne. Litho Irish Security Stamp Ptg Ltd)

1981 (4 May). Europa. Folklore. Paintings by Maria Simonds-Gooding T **178** and similar vert design. P 14×14½.

491	18p. black, orange-yellow and carmine	1·25	10
492	19p. black, yellow-orange and yellow	2·25	1·50

Design:—19p. "The Angel with the Scales of Judgement".

(Des R. Ballagh. Litho Irish Security Stamp Ptg Ltd)

1981 (24 June). 50th Anniv of "An Óige" (Irish Youth Hostel Association). T **179** and similar multicoloured designs. P 14×14½ (15, 30p.) or 14½×14 (others).

493	15p. Type **179**	25	40
494	18p. Hill-walking (horiz)	25	10
495	19p. Mountaineering (horiz)	25	95
496	30p. Rock-climbing	40	95
493/6 Set of 4		1·00	2·10

180 Jeremiah O'Donovan Rossa   **181** "Railway Embankment" (W. J. Leech)

(Des C. Harrison. Litho Irish Security Stamp Ptg Ltd)

1981 (31 Aug). 150th Birth Anniv of Jeremiah O'Donovan Rossa (politician). P 14×14½.

497	**180** 15p. multicoloured	40	30

(Des P. Wildbur. Litho Irish Security Stamp Ptg Ltd)

1981 (31 Aug). Contemporary Irish Art (12th issue). P 14½×14.

498	**181** 30p. multicoloured	1·00	70

182 James Hoban and White House   **183** "Arkle" (steeplechaser)

(Des B. Thompson. Litho Irish Security Stamp Ptg Ltd)

1981 (29 Sept). 150th Death Anniv of James Hoban (White House architect). P 14½×14.

499	**182** 18p. multicoloured	50	30

A stamp in a similar design was issued by the United States.

(Des Wendy Walsh and P. Wildbur. Litho Irish Security Stamp Ptg Ltd)

1981 (23 Oct). Famous Irish Horses. T **183** and similar horiz designs. Multicoloured. Ordinary paper (18p.) or chalk-surfaced paper (others). P 14½×14.

500	18p. Type **183**	65	1·25
	a. Pair. Nos. 500/1	1·25	2·50
501	18p. "Boomerang" (showjumper)	65	1·25
502	22p. "King of Diamonds" (Draught horse)	65	30
503	24p. "Ballymoss" (flatracer)	65	85
504	36p. "Coosheen Finn" (Connemara pony)	70	1·10
500/4 Set of 5		3·00	4·25

The 18p. values were printed together, se-tenant, in horizontal and vertical pairs throughout the sheet.

184 "Nativity" (F. Barocci)

185 Eviction Scene

(Des P. Wildbur. Litho Irish Security Stamp Ptg Ltd)

1981 (19 Nov). Christmas. Chalk-surfaced paper. P 14×14½.

505	**184**	18p. multicoloured	30	10
506		22p. multicoloured	35	10
507		36p. multicoloured	1·00	1·50
505/7 *Set of 3*			1·50	1·50

(Des R. Mercer (18p.), P. Wildbur (22p.). Litho Irish Security Stamp Ptg Ltd)

1981 (10 Dec). Anniversaries. T **185** and similar multicoloured design. Chalk-surfaced paper. P 14×14½ (18p.) or 14½×14 (22p.).

508	18p. Type **185**		50	25
509	22p. Royal Dublin Society emblem (*horiz*).....		50	30

Anniversaries—18p. Centenary of Land Law (Ireland) Act; 22p. 250th anniv of Royal Dublin Society (organization for the advancement of agriculture, industry, art and science).

186 Upper Lake, Killarney National Park

187 "The Stigmatization of St Francis" (Sassetta)

(Des P. Wildbur. Litho Irish Security Stamp Ptg Ltd)

1982 (26 Feb). 50th Anniv of Killarney National Park. T **186** and similar horiz design. Multicoloured. P 14½×14.

510	18p. Type **186**		40	20
511	36p. Eagle's Nest		85	1·60

(Des P. Wildbur (22p.), M. Craig (24p.). Litho Irish Security Stamp Ptg Ltd)

1982 (2 Apr). Religious Anniversaries. T **187** and similar horiz design. Chalk-surfaced paper. P 14×14½ (22p.) or 14½×14 (24p.).

512	22p. multicoloured		40	15
513	24p. olive-brown		60	1·10

Designs and anniversaries:—22p. Type **187** (800th birth anniv of St Francis of Assisi (founder of Franciscan Order)); 24p. Francis Makemie (founder of American Presbyterianism) and old Presbyterian Church, Ramelton, Co Donegal (300th anniv of ordination).

188 The Great Famine, 1845–1850

189 Pádraic O' Conaire (writer) (Birth Centenary)

(Des P. Wildbur. Litho Irish Security Stamp Ptg Ltd)

1982 (4 May). Europa. Historic Events. T **188** and similar design. Chalk-surfaced paper. P 14×14½ (26p.) or 14½×14 (29p.).

514	26p. black and stone		3·50	50
515	29p. multicoloured		6·50	7·50

Design: Horiz—29p. The coming of Christianity to Ireland.

(Des P. Wildbur. Litho Irish Security Stamp Ptg Ltd)

1982 (16 June). Anniversaries of Cultural Figures. T **189** and similar vert designs. Chalk-surfaced paper. P 14×14½.

516	22p. black and light blue		25	30
517	26p. black and sepia		50	30
518	29p. black and blue		50	1·75
519	44p. black and greenish grey		55	1·60
516/19 *Set of 4*			1·60	3·50

Designs and anniversaries—26p. James Joyce (writer) (Birth centenary); 29p. John Field (musician) (Birth bicentenary); 44p. Charles Kickham (writer) (Death centenary).

190 Porbeagle Shark (*Lamna nasus*)

191 St. Patrick (Galway hooker)

(Des Wendy Walsh and P. Wildbur. Litho Irish Security Stamp Ptg Ltd)

1982 (29 July). Marine Life. T **190** and similar horiz designs. Multicoloured. Chalk-surfaced paper. P 14½×14.

520	22p. Type **190**		50	1·25
521	22p. Common European Oyster (*Ostrea edulis*)		50	1·25
522	26p. Atlantic Salmon (*Salmo salar*)		60	30
523	29p. Dublin Bay Prawn (*Nephrops norvegicus*)		60	1·75
520/3 *Set of 4*			2·00	4·00

(Des P. Wildbur. Litho Irish Security Stamp Ptg Ltd)

1982 (21 Sept). Irish Boats. T **191** and similar multicoloured designs. Ordinary paper (26p.) or chalk-surfaced paper (others). P 14×14½ (Nos. 524 and 527) or 14½×14 (others).

524	22p. Type **191**		50	1·25
525	22p. Currach (*horiz*)		50	1·25
526	26p. *Asgard II* (cadet brigantine) (*horiz*)		60	30
527	29p. Howth 17 foot yacht		60	1·75
524/7 *Set of 4*			2·00	4·00

192 "Irish House of Commons" (painting by Francis Wheatley)

(Des P. Wildbur (22p.) or R. Ballagh (26p.). Litho Irish Security Stamp Ptg Ltd)

1982 (14 Oct). Bicentenary of Grattan's Parliament (22p.) and Birth Centenary of Eamon de Valera (26p.). T **192** and similar multicoloured design. P 14½×14 (22p.) or 14×14½ (26p.).

528	22p. Type **192**		35	1·25
529	26p. Eamon de Valera (*vert*)		40	40

193 "Madonna and Child" (sculpture)

194 Aughnanure Castle

(Des P. Wildbur. Litho Irish Security Stamp Ptg Ltd)

1982 (11 Nov). Christmas. P 14×14½.

530	**193**	22p. multicoloured	30	90
531		26p. multicoloured	30	35

(Des M. Craig and P. Wildbur. Litho Irish Security Stamp Ptg Ltd)

1982 (15 Dec)–**90**. Irish Architecture. T **194** and similar designs. Chalk-surfaced paper (24, 28, 32, 37, 39, 46p., £1 (No. 550b), £2) or ordinary paper (others). P 15×14 (15, 20, 22, 23, 24, 26, 39, 46, 50p., £1 (No. 550), £2, £5) or 14×15 (others).

532	1p. dull violet-blue (6.7.83)	10	10
	a. Chalk-surfaced paper (9.87)	50	50
533	2p. deep yellow-green (6.7.83)	20	10
	a. Chalk-surfaced paper (27.6.85)	50	40
	ab. Booklet pane. Nos. 533a and 545a, each×2	4·00	
	ac. Booklet pane. Nos. 533a, 543a and 545a, each×4	5·50	
	ad. Booklet pane. Nos. 533a×2, 535b×3, 544a×3 and 545c×4 (8.9.86)	5·50	
	ae. Booklet pane. Nos. 533a×4, 535b, 544a×2 and 545c×5 (24.11.88)	5·00	
534	3p. black (6.7.83)	20	10
	a. Chalk-surfaced paper (2.88)	1·00	1·25
535	4p. maroon (16.3.83)	20	10
	a. Booklet pane. Nos. 535×3, 543×4 and 1 label (15.8.83)	2·00	
	b. Chalk-surfaced paper (9.7.84)	40	40
	ba. Booklet pane. Nos. 535b×3, 543a×5 and 545a×4	4·00	
	c. Perf 13½ (3.5.90)	1·75	3·50
	ca. Booklet pane. Nos. 535c×3, 545b, 752ab×2 and 754ab×2	6·00	
536	5p. olive-sepia (6.7.83)	30	10
	a. Chalk-surfaced paper (8.87)	1·00	35
537	6p. deep grey-blue (16.3.83)	30	15
	a. Chalk-surfaced paper (11.85)	2·00	2·00
538	7p. dull yellow-green (16.3.83)	30	1·25
	a. Chalk-surfaced paper (3.88)	2·50	3·50
539	10p. black (6.7.83)	30	10
	a. Chalk-surfaced paper (3.87)	1·00	40
540	12p. purple-brown (6.7.83)	30	2·00
	a. Chalk-surfaced paper (5.87)	4·50	6·50
541	15p. deep yellow-green (6.7.83)	45	35
542	20p. deep brown-purple (16.3.83)	50	45
	a. Chalk-surfaced paper (12.84)	1·75	2·00
543	22p. chalky blue	50	10
	a. Chalk-surfaced paper (9.7.84)	75	60
544	23p. yellow-green (16.3.83)	85	1·25
544a	24p. bistre-brown (27.6.85)	1·25	35
	ab. Ordinary paper (9.87)	5·50	2·75
545	26p. blackish brown	75	10
	a. Chalk-surfaced paper (9.7.84)	75	30
	b. Perf 13½ (3.5.90)	3·00	6·50
545c	28p. maroon (27.6.85)	75	45
	ca. Ordinary paper (10.87)	9·00	9·00
546	29p. deep yellow-green	70	2·00
547	30p. black (16.3.83)	70	30
	a. Chalk-surfaced paper (3.87)	1·00	50
	b. Perf 13½ (3.5.90)	3·75	6·50
	ba. Booklet pane. Nos. 547b, 754ab and 774a/5a	6·00	
	bb. Booklet pane. Nos. 547b×2, 754ab×2 and 774a	6·00	
547c	32p. bistre-brown (1.5.86)	2·50	3·00
	ca. Ordinary paper (9.90)	6·00	7·50
547d	37p. chalky blue (27.6.85)	1·00	2·75
547e	39p. maroon (1.5.86)	2·50	2·75
548	44p. black and grey	1·00	1·00
	a. Chalk-surfaced paper (4.85)	3·25	3·00
548b	46p. olive-green and brownish grey (1.5.86)	6·50	2·00
	ba. Ordinary paper (9.87)	35·00	30·00
549	50p. dull ultramarine and grey (16.3.83)	1·75	65
	a. Chalk-surfaced paper (12.84)	2·50	1·00
550	£1 bistre-brown and grey	7·00	4·00
	a. Chalk-surfaced paper (9.84)	10·00	8·00
550b	£1 chalky blue and brownish grey (27.6.85)	5·00	1·25
	ba. Ordinary paper (1.88)	17·00	17·00
550c	£2 grey-olive and black (26.7.88)	6·50	5·50
551	£5 crimson and grey	12·00	6·00
	a. Chalk-surfaced paper (8.87)	32·00	32·00
532/51 Set of 28		48·00	35·00

Designs: Horiz (as T **194**)—1p. to 5p. Central Pavilion, Dublin Botanic Gardens; 6p. to 12p. Dr. Steevens' Hospital, Dublin; 28p. to 37p. St. MacDara's Church. (40×24 mm)—46p., £1 (No. 550) Cahir Castle; 50p., £2 Casino, Marino; £5 Central Bus Station, Dublin. Vert (as T **194**)—15p. to 22p. Type **194**; 23p. to 26p., Cormac's Chapel. (24×40 mm)—44p., £1 (No. 550b) Killarney Cathedral.

The following stamps first appeared in booklet panes, but were later issued in sheets: Nos. 533a (7.86), 535b (7.85), 543a (10.84) and 545a (1.85).

Nos. 533ab/ae and 535a/ba show the horizontal edges of the panes imperforate so that 2, 22 and 26p. values from them exist imperforate at top, bottom, left or right, the 4p. at top or bottom the 24p. at right and the 28p. at top.

No. 535ba comes from a £2 Discount booklet, No. SB26, and shows "Booklet Stamp" printed over the gum on the reverse of each stamp.

Nos. 535c, 545b and 547b are on ordinary paper and come from the 1990 150th Anniversary of the Penny Black £6 booklet, No. SB35. Examples of Nos. 535c, 545b and 752ab from the right-hand column of booklet pane No. 535ca are imperforate at right (4p.) or top (others). In booklet pane No. 547bb, Nos. 547b and 754ab are imperforate at right.

Booklet pane No. 547ba exists with the margins overprinted to commemorate "New Zealand 1990" International Stamp Exhibition Auckland, and No. 547bb with the margins overprinted in blue for "STAMPA 90", the Irish National Stamp Exhibition.

Nos. 550/a were withdrawn without warning on 14 November 1984 after the authorities had discovered forged examples of the £1 stamp used in P.O. savings books. Such forgeries, which it is believed were not used for postal purposes, are line perforated 14.75 or 12 instead of the 14.75×14 comb perforation of the genuine and also show the foot of the "1" rounded instead of square.

195 Ouzel Galley Goblet   **196** Padraig O Siochfhradha (writer and teacher) (Birth cent)

(Des P. Wildbur (22p.), C. Harrison (26p.). Litho Irish Security Stamp Ptg Ltd)

1983 (23 Feb). Bicentenaries of Dublin Chamber of Commerce (22p.) and Bank of Ireland (26p.). T **195** and similar multicoloured design. P 14×14½ (22p.) or 14½×14 (26p.).

552	22p. Type **195**	30	90
553	26p. Bank of Ireland building (horiz)	35	35

(Des C. Harrison (26p.), R. Ballagh (29p.). Litho Irish Security Stamp Ptg Ltd)

1983 (7 Apr). Anniversaries. T **196** and similar vert design. Multicoloured. P 14×14½.

554	26p. Type **196**	50	75
555	29p. Young Boys' Brigade member (Centenary)	90	1·50

197 Neolithic Carved Pattern, Newgrange Tomb

(Des L. le Brocquy (26p.). P. Wildbur (29p.). Litho Irish Security Stamp Ptg Ltd)

1983 (4 May). Europa. T **197** and similar horiz design. P 14½×14.

556	26p. grey-black and gold	2·50	50
557	29p. black, blackish brown and gold	7·00	5·50

Design:—29p. Sir William Rowan Hamilton's formulae for the multiplication of quaternions.

198 Kerry Blue Terrier

(Des Wendy Walsh and L. Miller. Litho Irish Security Stamp Ptg Ltd)

1983 (23 June). Irish Dogs. T **198** and similar horiz designs. Multicoloured. P 14½×14.

558	22p. Type **198**	65	35
559	26p. Irish Wolfhound	70	45
560	26p. Irish Water Spaniel	70	45
561	29p. Irish Terrier	75	2·25
562	44p. Irish Setters	1·25	2·50
558/62 Set of 5		3·50	5·50
MS563 142×80 mm. Nos. 558/62		6·00	8·00

No. **MS**563 exists with the sheet margins overprinted in blue to commemorate "STAMPA 83", the Irish National Stamp Exhibition.

199 Animals (Irish Society for the Prevention of Cruelty to Animals)

200 Postman with Bicycle

(Des Wendy Walsh (No. 564), B. Murphy (No. 566), K. Uhlemann (No. 567), R. Ballagh (others). Litho Irish Security Stamp Ptg Ltd)

1983 (11 Aug). Anniversaries and Commemorations. T **199** and similar designs. P 14½×14 (Nos. 564, 566) or 14×14½ (others).

564	**199**	22p. multicoloured	1·25	1·00
565		22p. multicoloured	50	1·00
566		26p. multicoloured	50	60
567		26p. multicoloured	50	60
568		44p. grey-blue and black	75	2·00
564/8 *Set of 5*			3·25	4·75

Designs: Vert—No. 565, Sean Mac Diarmada (patriot) (Birth cent); No. 567, "St. Vincent de Paul in the Streets of Paris" (150th anniv of Society of St. Vincent de Paul); No. 568, "Andrew Jackson" (Frank McKelvey) (President of the United States). Horiz—No. 566, "100" (Centenary of Industrial Credit Company).

(Des R. Ballagh. Litho Irish Security Stamp Ptg Ltd)

1983 (15 Sept). World Communications Year. T **200** and similar vert design. Multicoloured. P 14×14½.

569	22p. Type **200**	1·40	75
570	29p. Dish antenna	90	2·00

201 Weaving

202 "La Natividad" (R. van der Weyden)

(Des R. Mercer. Litho Irish Security Stamp Ptg Ltd)

1983 (13 Oct). Irish Handicrafts. T **201** and similar vert designs. Multicoloured. P 14×14½.

571	22p. Type **201**	65	50
572	26p. Basketmaking	65	35
573	29p. Irish crochet	75	1·25
574	44p. Harpmaking	1·25	2·50
571/4 *Set of 4*		3·00	4·25

(Des and litho Irish Security Stamp Ptg Ltd)

1983 (30 Nov). Christmas. P 14×14½.

575	**202**	22p. multicoloured	40	30
576		26p. multicoloured	60	30

203 Dublin and Kingstown Railway Steam Locomotive *Princess*

(Des C. Rycroft. Litho Irish Security Stamp Ptg Ltd)

1984 (30 Jan). 150th Anniv of Irish Railways. T **203** and similar horiz designs. Multicoloured. Ordinary paper (23p., 26p. and **MS**581) or chalk-surfaced paper (others). P 15×14.

577	23p. Type **203**	75	1·25
578	26p. Great Southern Railway steam locomotive *Macha*	75	35
579	29p. Great Northern Railway steam locomotive No. 87 *Kestrel*	85	1·75
580	44p. Coras Iompair Eireann two-car electric unit	1·10	2·25

577/80 *Set of 4*		3·00	5·00
MS581 129×77 mm. Nos. 577/80		3·75	5·00

No. **MS**581 exists with the sheet margins overprinted in black to commemorate "STAMPA 84", the Irish National Stamp Exhibition.

204 *Sorbus hibernica*

(Des Wendy Walsh and P. Wildbur. Litho Irish Security Stamp Ptg Ltd)

1984 (1 Mar). Irish Trees. T **204** and similar horiz. designs. Multicoloured. P 15×14.

582	22p. Type **204**	55	70
583	26p. *Taxus baccata fastigiata*	60	30
584	29p. *Salix hibernica*	70	1·75
585	44p. *Betula pubescens*	1·00	2·50
582/5 *Set of 4*		2·50	4·75

205 St. Vincent's Hospital, Dublin

(Des B. Donegan, adapted by C. Vis (26p.), B. Murphy (44p.). Litho Irish Security Stamp Ptg Ltd)

1984 (12 Apr). 150th Anniv of St. Vincent's Hospital and Bicentenary of Royal College of Surgeons. T **205** and similar horiz design. Multicoloured. P 15×14.

586	26p. Type **205**	75	30
587	44p. Royal College and logo	1·25	1·50

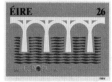

206 C.E.P.T. 25th Anniversary Logo

(Des J. Larriviére. Litho Irish Security Stamp Ptg Ltd)

1984 (10 May). Europa. P 15×14.

588	**206**	26p. blue, deep dull blue and black	2·50	50
589		29p. light green, blue-green and black.	5·00	4·25

207 Flags on Ballot Box

(Des R. Ballagh. Litho Irish Security Stamp Ptg Ltd)

1984 (10 May). Second Direct Elections to European Assembly. P 15×14.

590	**207**	26p. multicoloured	1·00	70

208 John McCormack

209 Hammer-throwing

(Des R. Mercer and J. Sharpe. Litho Irish Security Stamp Ptg Ltd)

1984 (6 June). Birth Centenary of John McCormack (tenor). P 14×15.
591   **208**   22p. multicoloured.............................. 50   70

(Des L. le Brocquy and P. Wildbur. Litho Irish Security Stamp Ptg Ltd)

1984 (21 June). Olympic Games, Los Angeles. T **209** and similar horiz designs. P 15×14.
592   22p. deep mauve, black and gold.................... 35   80
593   26p. violet, black and gold............................ 40   65
594   29p. bright blue, black and gold 60   1·25
592/4 *Set of 3* .... 1·25   2·50
    Designs:—26p. Hurdling; 29p. Running.

210 Hurling

211 Galway Mayoral Chain (500th Anniv of Mayoral Charter)

(Des C. Harrison. Litho Irish Security Stamp Ptg Ltd)

1984 (23 Aug). Centenary of Gaelic Athletic Association. T **210** and similar multicoloured design. P 15×14 (22p.) or 14×15 (26p.).
595   22p. Type **210** 50   90
596   26p. Irish football (*vert*)............................ 60   90

(Des P. Wildbur. Litho Irish Security Stamp Ptg Ltd)

1984 (18 Sept). Anniversaries. T **211** and similar multicoloured design. P 14×15 (26p.) or 15×14 (44p.).
597   26p. Type **211** 35   50
598   44p. St Brendan (from 15th-cent Bodleian manuscript) (1500th birth anniv) (*horiz*). 75   1·50

212 Hands passing Letter

(Litho Irish Security Stamp Ptg Ltd)

1984 (19 Oct). Bicentenary of the Irish Post Office. P 15×14.
599   **212**   26p. multicoloured........................... 60   70

213 "Virgin and Child" (Sassoferrato)

214 "Love" and Heart-shaped Balloon

(Des O'Connor O'Sullivan Advertising (17p.), P. Wildbur (others). Litho Irish Security Stamp Ptg Ltd)

1984 (26 Nov). Christmas. T **213** and similar multicoloured design. Chalk-surfaced paper. P 15×14 (17p.) or 14×15 (others).
600   17p. Christmas star (*horiz*)..................... 45   80
601   22p. Type **213** 45   1·25
602   26p. Type **213** 65   40
600/2 *Set of 3* .... 1·40   2·25
    No. 600 represented a special concession rate for Christmas card postings to addresses within Ireland and Great Britain between 26 November and 8 December 1984.

(Des Susan Dubsky (22p.), Patricia Jorgensen (26p.). Litho Irish Security Stamp Ptg Ltd)

1985 (31 Jan). Greetings Stamps. T **214** and similar multicoloured design. Chalk-surfaced paper. P 15×14 (22p.) or 14×15 (26p.).
603   22p. Type **214** 50   75
604   26p. Bouquet of hearts and flowers (*vert*).... 60   75

215 Dunsink Observatory (Bicentenary)   **216** *Polyommatus icarus*

(Des R. Ballagh (22, 44p.) K. Thomson (26p.), M. Lunt (37p.). Litho Irish Security Stamp Ptg Ltd)

1985 (14 Mar). Anniversaries. T **215** and similar designs. Multicoloured. Chalk-surfaced paper. P 15×14 (26p.) or 14×15 (others).
605   22p. Type **215** 60   50
606   26p. "A Landscape at Tivoli, Cork, with Boats" (Nathaniel Grogan) (800th anniv of City of Cork) (*horiz*)....................... 60   30
607   37p. Royal Irish Academy (Bicentenary).......... 80   1·75
608   44p. Richard Crosbie's balloon flight (Bicentenary of first aeronautic flight by an Irishman)................................. 1·00   1·75
605/8 *Set of 4* .... 2·75   3·75

(Des I. Loe. Litho Irish Security Stamp Ptg Ltd)

1985 (11 Apr). Butterflies. T **216** and similar vert designs. Multicoloured. Chalk-surfaced paper. P 14×15.
609   22p. Type **216** .... 1·25   1·00
610   26p. *Vanessa atalanta*............................. 1·25   70
611   28p. *Gonepteryx rhamni*........................... 1·50   2·75
612   44p. *Eurodryas aurinia*............................. 1·60   3·25
609/12 *Set of 4*... 5·00   7·00

217 Charles Villiers Stanford (composer)

(Des P. Hickey and J. Farrar. Litho Irish Security Stamp Ptg Ltd)

1985 (16 May). Europa. Irish Composers. T **217** and similar horiz design. Multicoloured. Chalk-surfaced paper. P 15×14.
613   26p. Type **217** .... 2·50   50
614   37p. Turlough Carolan (composer and lyricist)... 5·50   6·00

218 George Frederick Handel   **219** U.N. Patrol of Irish Soldiers, Congo, 1960 (25th Anniv. of Irish Participation in U.N. Peace-keeping Force)

(Des K. Uhlemann and J. Farrar. Litho Irish Security Stamp Ptg Ltd)

1985 (16 May). European Music Year. Composers. T **218** and similar vert designs. Multicoloured. Chalk-surfaced paper. P 14×15.
615   22p. Type **218** .... 1·25   2·50
     a. Pair. Nos. 615/16....................... 2·50   5·00
616   22p. Guiseppe Domenico Scarlatti................ 1·25   2·50
617   26p. Johann Sebastian Bach .... 1·50   50
615/17 *Set of 3* .... 3·50   5·00
    Nos. 615/16 were printed together, *se-tenant*, in horizontal and vertical pairs throughout the sheet.

(Des B. Donegan and J. Farrar (22p.), R. Ballagh (26p.), B. Donegan (44p.). Litho Irish Security Stamp Ptg Ltd)

1985 (20 June). Anniversaries. T **219** and similar multicoloured designs. Chalk-surfaced paper. P 15×14 (22p.) or 14×15 (others).

618	22p. Type **219**	70	80
619	26p. Thomas Ashe (patriot) (Birth cent) (*vert*)	70	60
620	44p. "Bishop George Berkeley" (James Lathan) (philosopher) (300th birth anniv) (*vert*)	1·00	3·00
618/20 *Set of 3*		2·25	4·00

220 Group of Young People

(Des J. Farrar and N. Mooney. Litho Irish Security Stamp Ptg Ltd)

1985 (1 Aug). International Youth Year. T **220** and similar multicoloured design. Chalk-surfaced paper. P 15×14 (22p.) or 14×15 (26p).

621	22p. Type **220**	55	50
622	26p. Students and young workers (*vert*)	55	50

221 Visual Display Unit

(Des B. Donegan (44p.), C. Rycraft (others). Litho Irish Security Stamp Ptg Ltd)

1985 (3 Oct). Industrial Innovation. T **221** and similar horiz designs. Multicoloured. Chalk-surfaced paper. P 15×14.

623	22p. Type **221**	50	75
624	26p. Turf cutting with hand tool and with modern machinery	50	55
625	44p. "The Key Man" (Sean Keating) (150th anniv of Institution of Engineers of Ireland)	1·00	2·50
623/5 *Set of 3*		1·75	3·50

222 Lighted Candle and Holly

223 "Virgin and Child in a Landscape" (Adrian van Ijsenbrandt)

(Des R. Mahon (No. 626). Litho Irish Security Stamp Ptg Ltd)

1985 (26 Nov). Christmas. T **222** and designs as T **223** showing paintings. Multicoloured. Chalk-surfaced paper. P 15×14 (26p.) or 14×15 (others).

626	22p. Type **222**	50	50
	a. Sheetlet. No. 626×16	7·00	
627	22p. Type **223**	90	2·00
	a. Pair. Nos. 627/8	1·75	4·00
628	22p. "The Holy Family" (Murillo)	90	2·00
629	26p. "The Adoration of the Shepherds" (Louis le Nain) (*horiz*)	90	25
626/9 *Set of 4*		2·75	4·25

No. 626 was only issued in sheetlets of 16 sold at £3, providing a discount of 52p. off the face value of the stamps.

Nos. 627/8 were printed together, *se-tenant*, in horizontal and vertical pairs throughout the sheet.

224 Stylised Love Bird with Letter

225 Hart's Tongue Fern

(Des R. Hoek (22p.) T. Monaghan (26p.). Litho Irish Security Stamp Ptg Ltd)

1986 (30 Jan). Greetings Stamps. T **224** and similar vert design. Multicoloured. Chalk-surfaced paper. P 14×15.

630	22p. Type **224**	75	90
631	26p. Heart-shaped pillar-box	75	90

(Des I. Loe. Litho Irish Security Stamp Ptg Ltd)

1986 (20 Mar). Ferns. T **225** and similar vert designs. Multicoloured. Chalk-surfaced paper. P 14×15.

632	24p. Type **225**	70	70
633	28p. Rusty-back Fern	80	70
634	46p. Killarney Fern	1·25	2·10
632/4 *Set of 3*		2·50	3·25

226 "Harmony between Industry and Nature"

227 Boeing 747-200 over Globe showing Aer Lingus Routes

(Des G. van Gelderen. Litho Irish Security Stamp Ptg Ltd)

1986 (1 May). Europa. Protection of the Environment. T **226** and similar multicoloured design. Chalk-surfaced paper. P 14×15 (28p.) or 15×14 (39p.).

635	28p. Type **226**	6·00	50
636	39p. *Vanessa atalanta* (butterfly) and tractor in field ("Preserve hedgerows") (*horiz*)	18·00	6·00

(Des R. Ballagh. Litho Irish Security Stamp Ptg Ltd)

1986 (27 May). 50th Anniv of Aer Lingus (airline). T **227** and similar horiz design. Multicoloured. Chalk-surfaced paper. P 15×14.

637	28p. Type **227**	1·50	75
638	46p. de Havilland D.H.84 Dragon Mk 2 *Iolar* (first aircraft)	2·25	3·25

228 Grand Canal at Robertstown

229 *Severn* (19th-century paddle-steamer)

(Des B. Matthews. Litho Irish Security Stamp Ptg Ltd)

1986 (27 May). Irish Waterways. T **228** and similar multicoloured designs. Chalk-surfaced paper. P 14×15 (28p.) or 15×14 (others).

639	24p. Type **228**	1·25	1·00
640	28p. Fishing in County Mayo (*vert*)	1·40	1·00
641	30p. Motor cruiser on Lough Derg	1·50	2·50
639/41 *Set of 3*		3·75	4·00

(Des C. Rycraft. Litho Irish Security Stamp Ptg Ltd)

1986 (10 July). 150th Anniv of British and Irish Steam Packet Company. T **229** and similar horiz design. Multicoloured. P 15×14.

642	24p. Type **229**	1·00	1·00
643	28p. M.V. *Leinster* (modern ferry)	1·10	60

230 Kish Lighthouse and Bell 206B Jet Ranger III Helicopter

231 J. P. Nannetti (first president) and Linotype Operator (Dublin Council of Trade Unions Centenary)

(Des R. Ballagh. Litho Irish Security Stamp Printing Ltd)

1986 (10 July). Irish Lighthouses. T **230** and similar vert design. Multicoloured. P 14×15.

644	24p. Type **230**	1·50	75
645	30p. Fastnet Lighthouse	2·50	2·75

(Des R. Ballagh (Nos. 646/7), M. Cameron (No. 648), A. Mazer (Nos. 649/50). Litho Irish Security Stamp Ptg Ltd)

1986 (21 Aug). Anniversaries and Commemorations. T **231** and similar designs. Ordinary paper (24p.) or chalk-surfaced paper (others). P 14×15 (Nos. 646/7, 649) or 15×14 (others).

646	24p. multicoloured	50	90
647	28p. black and brownish grey	60	80
648	28p. multicoloured	60	80
649	30p. multicoloured	70	1·00
650	46p. multicoloured	80	1·75
646/50 Set of 5		3·00	4·75

Designs: Vert—No. 647, Arthur Griffith (statesman); No. 649, Clasped hands (International Peace Year). Horiz—No. 648, Woman surveyor (Women in Society); No. 650, Peace dove (International Peace Year).

232 William Mulready and his Design for 1840 Envelope

233 "The Adoration of the Shepherds" (Francesco Pascucci)

(Des C. Harrison (24p.), A. Mazer from aquatints by M. A. Hayes (others). Litho Irish Security Stamp Ptg Ltd)

1986 (2 Oct). Birth Bicentenaries of William Mulready (artist) (24p.) and Charles Bianconi (originator of Irish mail coach service) (others). T **232** and similar multicoloured designs. Chalk-surfaced paper. P 14×15 (28p.) or 15×14 (others).

651	24p. Type **232**	70	70
652	28p. Bianconi car outside Hearns Hotel, Clonmel (*vert*)	85	55
653	39p. Bianconi car on the road	1·40	1·75
651/3 Set of 3		2·75	2·75

(Des C. O'Neill (21p.) Litho Irish Security Stamp Ptg Ltd)

1986 (20 Nov). Christmas. T **233** and similar multicoloured design. Chalk-surfaced paper. P 15×14 (21p.) or 14×15 (28p.).

654	21p. Type **233**	1·10	1·40
	a. Sheetlet. No. 654×12	12·00	
655	28p. "The Adoration of the Magi" (Frans Francken III) (*vert*)	65	60

No. 654 was only issued in sheetlets of 12 sold at £2.50 providing a discount of 2p. off the face value of the stamps.

234 "Butterfly and Flowers" (Tara Collins)

(Litho Irish Security Stamp Ptg Ltd)

1987 (27 Jan). Greetings Stamps. Children's Paintings. T **234** and similar multicoloured design. Chalk-surfaced paper. P 15×14 (24p.) or 14×15 (28p.).

656	24p. Type **234**	75	1·25
657	28p. "Postman on Bicycle delivering Hearts" (Brigid Teehan) (*vert*)	1·25	1·25

235 Cork Electric Tram

(Des C. Rycraft. Litho Irish Security Stamp Ptg Ltd)

1987 (4 Mar). Irish Trams. T **235** and similar horiz designs. Multicoloured. Chalk-surfaced paper. P 15×14.

658	24p. Type **235**	75	65
659	28p. Dublin standard tram No. 291	80	85
660	30p. Howth (Great Northern Railway) tram	1·00	2·00
661	46p. Galway horse tram	1·40	2·25
658/61 Set of 4		3·50	5·25
MS662 131×85 mm. Nos. 658/61		3·75	5·25

No. **MS**662 exists with the sheet margins overprinted in red for "HAFNIA 87" and in black for "STAMPA 87".

236 Ships from Crest (Bicentenary of Waterford Chamber of Commerce)

237 Bord na Mona Headquarters and "The Turf Cutter" sculpture (John Behan), Dublin

(Des K. Uhlemann (24p.), J Farrer (28p.), A. Mazer and Wendy Walsh (30p.), M. Cameron (39p.). Litho Irish Security Stamp Ptg Ltd)

1987 (9 Apr). Anniversaries. T **236** and similar designs. Chalk-surfaced paper. P 14×15 (30p.) or 15×14 (others).

663	24p black, ultramarine and deep grey-green	70	60
664	28p. multicoloured	70	60
665	30p. multicoloured	70	2·00
666	39p. multicoloured	75	1·75
663/6 Set of 4		2·50	4·50

Designs: Horiz—28p. Canon John Hayes and symbols of agriculture and development (Birth centenary and 50th anniv of Muintir na Tire Programme); 39p. Mother Mary Martin and International Missionary Training Hospital, Drogheda (50th anniv of Medical Missionaries of Mary). Vert—30p. *Calceolaria burbidgei* and College crest (300th anniv of Trinity College Botanic Gardens, Dublin).

(Des M. Lunt. Litho Harrison)

1987 (14 May). Europa. Modern Architecture. T **237** and similar horiz design. Multicoloured. P 15×14.

667	28p. Type **237**	3·50	60
668	39p. St. Mary's Church, Cong	6·50	6·50

238 Kerry Cow

239 Fleadh Nua, Ennis

(Des B. Driscoll. Litho Irish Security Stamp Ptg Ltd)

1987 (2 July). Irish Cattle. T **238** and similar horiz designs. Multicoloured. Chalk-surfaced paper. P 15×14.

669	24p. Type **238**	80	75
670	28p. Friesian cow and calf	95	60
671	30p. Hereford bullock	1·00	2·25
672	39p. Shorthorn bull	1·10	2·25
669/72 Set of 4		3·50	5·25

(Des R. Ballagh. Litho Irish Security Stamp Ptg Ltd)

1987 (27 Aug). Festivals. T **239** and similar multicoloured designs. Chalk-surfaced paper. P 14×15 (vert) or 15×14 (horiz).

673	24p. Type **239**	75	70
674	28p. Rose of Tralee International Festival	80	60
675	30p. Wexford Opera Festival (*horiz*)	1·50	2·00
676	46p. Ballinasloe Horse Fair (*horiz*)	1·50	2·00
673/6 Set of 4		4·00	4·75

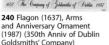

240 Flagon (1637), Arms and Anniversary Ornament (1987) (350th Anniv of Dublin Goldsmiths' Company)

241 Scenes from "The Twelve Days of Christmas" (carol)

(Des B. Donegan (No. 677), R. Ballagh (No. 678), A. Mazer and Breda Mathews (No. 679), Libby Carton (No. 680). Litho Harrison (46p.) or Irish Security Stamp Ptg Ltd (others))

1987 (1 Oct). Anniversaries and Commemorations. T **240** and similar designs. Ordinary paper (46p.) or chalk-surfaced paper (others). P 15×14 (horiz) or 14×15 (vert).

677	**240**	24p. multicoloured	80	80
		a. Yellow omitted	£3500	
678		24p. grey and black	80	80
679		28p. multicoloured	1·00	60
680		46p. multicoloured	1·40	1·10
677/80	*Set of 4*		3·50	3·00

Designs: Vert—24p. (No. 678) Cathal Brugha (statesman); 46p. Woman chairing board meeting (Women in Society). Horiz—28p. Arms of Ireland and inscription (50th anniv of Constitution).

(Des M. Cameron (21p.), A. Mazer (others). Litho Irish Security Stamp Ptg Ltd)

1987 (17 Nov). Christmas. T **241** and similar multicoloured designs. Chalk-surfaced paper. P 15×14 (21p.) or 14×15 (others).

681		21p. Type **241**	60	1·00
		a. Sheetlet. No. 681×14	7·50	
		b. Gold omitted	£1200	
682		24p. The Nativity (detail, late 15th-cent Waterford Vestments) (*vert*)	75	1·00
683		28p. Figures from Neapolitan crib, *c* 1850 (*vert*)	75	80
681/3	*Set of 3*		1·90	2·50

No. 681 represents a special rate for greetings cards within Ireland and to all E.E.C. countries. It was only issued in sheetlets of 14 stamps and 1 label sold at £2.90, providing an additional discount of 4p. off the face value of the stamps.

242 Acrobatic Clowns spelling "LOVE"

243 "Robert Burke" (Sidney Nolan) and Map of Burke and Wills Expedition Route

(Des M. Cameron (24p.), Aislinn Adams (28p.). Litho Irish Security Stamp Ptg Ltd)

1988 (27 Jan). Greetings Stamps. T **242** and similar multicoloured design. Chalk-surfaced paper. P 15×14 (24p.) or 14×15 (28p.).

684		24p. Type **242**	75	60
685		28p. Pillar box and hearts (*vert*)	75	65

(Des A. Mazer. Litho Irish Security Stamp Ptg Ltd)

1988 (1 Mar). Bicentenary of Australian Settlement. T **243** and similar horiz design. Multicoloured. Chalk-surfaced paper. P 15×14.

686		24p. Type **243**	1·00	60
687		46p. "Eureka Stockade" (mural detail, Sidney Nolan)	1·25	1·75

244 Past and Present Buildings of Dublin

245 Showjumping

(Des S. Conlin. Litho Irish Security Stamp Ptg Ltd)

1988 (1 Mar). Dublin Millennium. Chalk-surfaced paper. P 15×14.

688	**244**	28p. multicoloured	55	55
		a. Booklet pane. No. 688×4	2·00	

No. 688a was printed with either Irish or English inscriptions in the centre of the pane and came from £2.24 stamp booklets, No. SB30. Loose panes could also be purchased from the Philatelic Bureau, Dublin and its agents. They exist overprinted for "STAMPA 88" (in blue on Irish version and red on English) and "Sydpex 88" (both green on gold).

One imperforate example of No. 688a was discovered. It has since been divided up into four single stamps.

(Des Ann Flynn Litho Irish Security Stamp Ptg Ltd)

1988 (7 Apr). Olympic Games, Seoul. T **245** and similar horiz design. Multicoloured. Chalk-surfaced paper. P 15×14.

689		28p. Type **245**	1·00	1·40
		a. Sheetlet. Nos. 689/90, each×5	9·00	
690		28p. Cycling	1·00	1·40

Nos. 689/90 were printed together, *se-tenant*, in a sheetlet containing five of each design and two stamp-size labels.

246 William T. Cosgrave (statesman)

(Des R. Ballagh (24p.), J. Farrer (30p.), K. Uhlemann (50p.). Litho Irish Security Stamp Ptg Ltd)

1988 (7 Apr). Anniversaries and Events. T **246** and similar designs. Chalk-surfaced paper. P 14×15 (vert) or 15×14 (horiz).

691		24p. brownish grey and black	45	45
692		30p. multicoloured	80	1·00
693		50p. multicoloured	1·00	1·90
691/3	*Set of 3*		2·00	3·00

Designs: Horiz—30p. Members with casualty and ambulance (50th anniv of Order of Malta Ambulance Corps). Vert—50p. Barry Fitzgerald (actor) (Birth centenary).

247 Air Traffic Controllers and Airbus Industrie A320

(Des C. Rycraft (28p.), M. Cameron (39p.). Litho Irish Security Stamp Ptg Ltd)

1988 (12 May). Europa. Transport and Communications. T **247** and similar horiz design. Multicoloured. Chalk-surfaced paper. P 15×14.

694		28p. Type **247**	2·25	55
695		39p. Globe with stream of letters from Ireland to Europe	3·25	3·50

248 *Sirius* (paddle-steamer) (150th anniv of regular transatlantic steamship services)

249 Cottonweed

(Des C. Rycraft. Litho Irish Security Stamp Ptg Ltd)

1988 (12 May). Transatlantic Transport Anniversaries. T **248** and similar horiz design. Multicoloured. Chalk-surfaced paper. P 15×14.

696		24p. Type **248**	1·25	50
697		46p. Short S20 seaplane *Mercury* and Short S.21 flying boat *Maia* (Short-Mayo composite aircraft) in Foynes Harbour (50th anniv of first commercial transatlantic flight)	2·00	3·00

(Des Frances Poskitt. Litho Irish Security Stamp Ptg Ltd)

1988 (21 June). Endangered Flora of Ireland. T **249** and similar vert designs. Multicoloured. Chalk-surfaced paper. P 14×15.

698	24p. Type **249**	70	55
699	28p. Hart's Saxifrage	80	55
700	46p. Purple Milk-Vetch	1·00	2·75
698/700 *Set of 3*		2·25	3·50

250 Garda on Duty   **251** Computer and Abacus (Institute of Chartered Accountants in Ireland Centenary)

(Des D. Teskey. Litho Irish Security Stamp Ptg Ltd)

1988 (23 Aug). Irish Security Forces. T **250** and similar horiz designs. Multicoloured. Chalk-surfaced paper. P 15×14.

701	28p. Type **250**	80	1·10
	a. Strip of 4. Nos. 701/4	3·00	4·00
702	28p. Army unit with personnel carrier	80	1·10
703	28p. Navy and Air Corps members with *Eithne* (helicopter patrol vessel)	80	1·10
704	28p. Army and navy reservists	80	1·10
701/4 *Set of 4*		3·00	4·00

Nos. 701/4 were printed together, both horizontally and vertically *se-tenant*, throughout the sheet of 20 (4×5).

(Des C. Rycraft (24p.), K. King and A. Mazer (46p.). Litho Irish Security Stamp Ptg Ltd)

1988 (6 Oct). Anniversaries. T **251** and similar multicoloured design. Chalk-surfaced paper. P 14×15 (24p.) or 15×14 (46p.).

705	24p. Type **251**	50	40
706	46p. *Duquesa Santa Ana* off Donegal (*horiz*) (400th anniv of Spanish Armada)	1·75	1·50

252 "President Kennedy" (James Wyeth)

(Des A. Mazer. Litho Irish Security Stamp Ptg Ltd)

1988 (24 Nov). *25th Death Anniv of John F. Kennedy* (American statesman). Chalk-surfaced paper. P 15×14.

707	**252**	28p. multicoloured	1·00	80

253 St. Kevin's Church, Glendalough

(Des Ann Flynn (21p.), B. Donegan (others). Litho Irish Security Stamp Ptg Ltd)

1988 (24 Nov). Christmas. T **253** and similar vert designs. Multicoloured. Chalk-surfaced paper. P 14×15.

708	21p. Type **253**	80	1·00
	a. Sheetlet. No. 708×14	10·00	
709	24p. The Adoration of the Magi	50	60
710	28p. The Flight into Egypt	60	45
711	46p. The Holy Family	1·00	3·00
708/11 *Set of 4*		2·50	4·50

No. 708 represents a special rate for greetings cards within Ireland and to all E.E.C. countries. It was only issued in sheetlets of 14 stamps and 1 label sold at £2.90, providing an additional discount of 4p. off the face value of the stamps.

The designs of Nos. 709/11 are from a 15th-century French Book of Hours.

254 Spring Flowers spelling "Love" in Gaelic

(Des Susan Dubsky (24p.), A. Mazer (28p.). Litho Irish Security Stamp Ptg Ltd)

1989 (24 Jan). Greetings Stamps. T **254** and similar multicoloured design. Chalk-surfaced paper. P 15×14 (24p.) or 14×15 (28p.).

712	24p. Type **254**	75	55
713	28p. "The Sonnet" (William Mulready) (*vert*).	75	55

255 Italian Garden, Garinish Island

(Des Frances Poskitt. Litho Irish Security Stamp Ptg Ltd)

1989 (11 Apr). National Parks and Gardens. T **255** and similar horiz designs. Multicoloured. Chalk-surfaced paper. P 15×14.

714	24p. Type **255**	70	55
715	28p. Lough Veagh, Glenveagh National Park	80	55
716	32p. Barnaderg Bay, Connemara National Park	90	1·25
717	50p. St. Stephen's Green, Dublin	1·40	1·75
714/17 *Set of 4*		3·50	3·75

256 "Silver Stream", 1908

(Des C. Rycraft. Litho Irish Security Stamp Ptg Ltd)

1989 (11 Apr). Classic Irish Cars. T **256** and similar horiz designs. Multicoloured. Chalk-surfaced paper. P 15×14.

718	24p. Type **256**	50	55
	a. Booklet pane. Nos. 718/19, each ×2	2·00	
	b. Booklet pane. Nos. 718/21	3·25	
719	28p. Benz "Comfortable", 1898	50	55
720	39p. "Thomond" 1929	1·25	1·50
721	46p. Chambers' 8 h.p. model, 1905	1·50	1·50
718/21 *Set of 4*		3·25	3·75

Booklet panes Nos. 718a/b come from £2.41 stamp booklets, No. SB32, and stamps from them have one or two adjacent sides imperforate. Such panes were also available loose from the Philatelic Bureau, Dublin, and its agents.

257 Ring-a-ring-a-roses   **258** Irish Red Cross Flag (50th anniv)

(Des C. Harrison. Litho Irish Security Stamp Ptg Ltd)

1989 (11 May). Europa. Children's Games. T **257** and similar horiz design. Multicoloured. Chalk-surfaced paper. P 15×14.

722	28p. Type **257**		75	75
723	39p. Hopscotch		1·00	2·25

Nos. 722/3 were each issued in sheets of 10 showing additional illustrations in the left-hand sheet margin.

(Des Q Design (24p.), R. Hoek (28p.). Litho Irish Security Stamp Ptg Ltd)

1989 (11 May). Anniversaries and Events. T **258** and similar vert design. Chalk-surfaced paper. P 14×15.

724	24p. vermilion and black		55	60
725	28p. new blue, black and lemon		1·25	1·10

Design:—28p. Circle of twelve stars (Third direct elections to European Parliament).

259 Saints Kilian, Totnan and Colman (from 12th-century German manuscript)

(Des P. Effert. Litho Irish Security Stamp Ptg Ltd)

1989 (15 June). 1300th Death Anniv of Saints Kilian, Totnan and Colman. Chalk-surfaced paper. P 13½.

726	**259**	28p. multicoloured	45	1·10
		a. Booklet pane. No. 726a×4 with margins all round	1·75	

A stamp in a similar design was issued by West Germany.

No. 726a exists with text in Irish, English, German or Latin on the pane margin.

260 19th-century Mail Coach passing Cashel

261 Crest and 19th-century Dividers (150th anniv of Royal Institute of Architects of Ireland)

(Des Katie O'Sullivan and B. Donegan. Litho Irish Security Stamp Ptg Ltd)

1989 (27 July). Bicentenary of Irish Mail Coach Service. Chalk-surfaced paper. P 15×14.

727	**260**	28p. multicoloured	1·50	75

(Des R. Ballagh (24p.), A. Mazer (28p.), K. Uhlemann (30p.), Carey Clarke (46p.). Litho Irish Security Stamp Ptg Ltd)

1989 (27 July). Anniversaries and Commemorations. T **261** and similar designs. Chalk-surfaced paper. P 15×14 (30p.) or 14×15 (others).

728	24p. grey and black		65	55
729	28p. multicoloured		65	55
730	30p. multicoloured		1·75	2·25
731	46p. orange-brown		3·00	3·25
728/31	*Set of 4*		5·50	6·00

Designs:—Vert—24p. Sean T. O'Kelly (statesman) (drawing by Sean O'Sullivan); 46p. Jawaharlal Nehru (Birth centenary) Horiz—30p. Margaret Burke-Sheridan (soprano) (portrait by De Gennaro) and scene from *La Boheme* (Birth centenary).

262 "*NCB Ireland* rounding Cape Horn" (Des Fallon)

(Des I. Caulder. Litho Irish Security Stamp Ptg Ltd)

1989 (31 Aug). First Irish Entry in Whitbread Round the World Yacht Race. Chalk-surfaced paper. P 15×14.

732	**262**	28p. multicoloured	1·50	1·25

263 Willow/Red Grouse

264 "The Annunciation"

(Des R. Ward. Litho Irish Security Stamp Ptg Ltd)

1989 (5 Oct). Game Birds. T **263** and similar square designs. Multicoloured. Chalk-surfaced paper. P 13½.

733	24p. Type **263**		1·25	70
734	28p. Lapwing		1·25	70
735	39p. Woodcock		1·50	3·00
736	46p. Ring-necked Pheasant		1·50	3·00
733/6	*Set of 4*		5·00	6·75
MS737	128×92 mm. Nos. 733/6		5·00	7·00

No. **MS**737 exists overprinted on the margins to commemorate "STAMPA 89" the Irish National Stamp Exhibition.

(Des Jacinta Fitzgerald (21p.), J. McEvoy from 13th-century Flemish Psalter (others). Litho Irish Security Stamp Ptg Ltd)

1989 (14 Nov). Christmas. T **264** and similar vert designs. Multicoloured. Chalk-surfaced paper. P 14×15.

738	21p. Children decorating crib		75	75
	a. Sheetlet. No. 738×14		9·50	
739	24p. Type **264**		75	60
740	28p. "The Nativity"		75	55
741	46p. "The Adoration of the Magi"		1·10	2·50
738/41	*Set of 4*		3·00	4·00

No. 738 represents a special rate for greetings cards within Ireland and to all E.E.C. countries. It was only issued in sheetlets of 14 stamps and 1 label sold at £2.90, providing an additional discount of 4p. off the face value of the stamps.

265 Logo (Ireland's Presidency of the European Communities)

(Des B. Donegan (30p.), Q. Design (50p.). Litho Irish Security Stamp Ptg Ltd)

1990 (9 Jan). European Events. T **265** and similar horiz design. Multicoloured. Chalk-surfaced paper. P 15×14.

742	30p. Type **265**		1·00	60
743	50p. Logo and outline map of Ireland (European Tourism Year)		2·25	3·00

266 Dropping Messages from Balloon

267 Silver Kite Brooch

(Des Aislinn Adams (26p.), Patricia Sleeman and R. Vogel (30p.). Litho Irish Security Stamp Ptg Ltd)

1990 (30 Jan). Greetings Stamps. T **266** and similar vert design. Chalk-surfaced paper. P 14×15.

744	26p. multicoloured		1·50	1·25
745	30p. rosine, pale buff and reddish brown		1·50	1·25

Design:—30p. Heart and "Love" drawn in lipstick.

Two Types of 20, 28, 52p.:

A. Irish Security Stamp Ptg Ltd printing (coarse background screen. Less distinct centre detail)

B. Enschedé printing (fine background screen. Clear centre detail)

Two Types of £1, £2, £3

C. Irish Security Stamp Ptg Ltd printing

D. Enschedé printing

(Des M. Craig and Q. Design. Litho Walsall (Nos. 748c, 755b), Enschedé (Nos. 751b, 753b, 762b, 763b, 764b, 765b) or Irish Security Stamp Ptg Ltd (others))

1990 (8 Mar)–**97**. Irish Heritage and Treasures. T **267** and similar designs. Chalk-surfaced paper (5, 20, 26, 28, 30, 32, 37, 38, 41, 44, 50, 52p., £1, £5) or ordinary paper (others). P 14×15 (10, 20, 30, 32p., £5) or 15×14 (others).

746	1p. black and new blue (26.7.90)	10	10
	a. Chalk-surfaced paper (10.91)	1·75	1·75
747	2p. black and bright red-orange (26.7.90)	10	10
	a. Chalk-surfaced paper (15.11.90)	1·00	1·50
	ab. Booklet pane. Nos. 747a, 748b×3, 752 and 754×2 plus label	5·00	
	ac. Booklet pane Nos. 747a×2, 755×2 and 820 (17.10.91)	5·00	
748	4p. black and bluish violet (26.7.90)	15	30
	a. Booklet pane. Nos. 748 and 755a×3 (16.11.95)	8·00	
	b. Chalk-surfaced paper (15.11.90)	1·00	1·50
	ba. Booklet pane. Nos. 748b×3, 753×4 plus label (17.10.91)	5·00	
	bb. Booklet pane. Nos. 748b and 1084×3 (6.3.97)	6·00	
	c. Perf 13×13½. Chalk-surfaced paper (24.9.93)	1·50	1·75
	ca. Booklet pane. Nos. 748c and 755b×3 (4p. at bottom right)	6·00	
	cb. Ditto, but 4p. at top left (2.3.94)	6·50	
749	5p. black and bright green (29.1.91)	20	10
	a. Ordinary paper (5.92)	7·00	2·50
750	10p. black and bright red-orange (26.7.90)	30	25
	a. Chalk-surfaced paper (9.93)	25·00	3·00
751	20p. black and lemon (A) (29.1.91)	50	40
	a. Ordinary paper (3.92)	10·00	6·00
	b. Type B (Enschedé ptg) (16.11.95)	1·75	1·25
752	26p. black and bluish violet	1·50	65
	a. Ordinary paper (5.90)	7·00	1·50
	ab. Perf 13½ (3.5.90)	1·75	4·00
753	28p. black and bright red-orange (A) (3.4.91)	70	1·50
	a. Ordinary paper (5.91)	6·50	6·50
	b. Type B (Enschedé ptg) (16.11.95)	1·75	1·50
754	30p. black and new blue	1·25	1·50
	a. Ordinary paper (5.90)	2·50	2·50
	ab. Perf 13½ (3.5.90)	2·00	4·00
755	32p. black and bright green	1·50	1·50
	a. Ordinary paper (5.90)	3·50	3·50
	b. Perf 13½×13. Chalk-surfaced paper (24.9.93)	2·00	2·75
756	34p. black and lemon (26.7.90)	1·50	1·50
757	37p. brownish black and brt green (3.4.91)	1·75	1·50
	a. Ordinary paper (11.91)	30·00	25·00
758	38p. black and bluish violet (3.4.91)	1·75	2·75
	a. Ordinary paper (5.95)	25·00	20·00

758b	40p. black and new blue (14.5.92)	3·00	3·00
	ba. Chalk-surfaced paper (9.93)	6·00	6·00
759	41p. black and bright red-orange (10.90)	1·75	2·50
	a. Ordinary paper (10.90)	8·00	8·00
760	44p. agate and lemon (3.4.91)	2·50	3·00
760a	45p. black and bluish violet (14.5.92)	3·75	2·75
761	50p. black and lemon	1·75	2·25
	a. Ordinary paper (5.90)	6·50	6·50
762	52p. black and new blue (A) (3.4.91)	3·50	3·50
	a. Ordinary paper (2.96)	20·00	20·00
	b. Type B (Enschedé ptg) (16.11.95)	2·50	2·50
763	£1 black and lemon (C)	3·25	2·25
	a. Ordinary paper (5.90)	22·00	6·50
	b. Type D (Enschedé ptg) (16.11.95)	4·25	3·25
764	£2 black and bright green (C) (26.7.90)	4·50	3·25
	a. Chalk-surfaced paper (9.93)	35·00	20·00
	b. Type D (Enschedé ptg) (chalk surfaced paper) (16.11.95)	8·25	8·50
765	£5 black and new blue (C) (29.1.91)	10·00	9·00
	a. Ordinary paper (10.97)	32·00	38·00
	b. Type D (Enschedé ptg) (16.11.95)	22·00	20·00
746/65 Set of 22		40·00	40·00

Designs: Vert (as T **267**)—1p., 2p. Type **267**; 4p., 5p. Dunamase Food Vessel; 26p., 28p. Lismore Crozier; 34p., 37p., 38p., 40p. Gleensheen Collar; 41p., 44p., 45p. Silver thistle brooch; 50p., 52p. Broighter Boat. (24×40 mm)—£5 St. Patrick's Bell Shrine. Horiz (as T **267**)—10p. Derrinboy Armlets; 20p. Gold dress fastener; 30p. Enamelled latchet brooch; 32p. Broighter Collar. (40×24 mm)—£1 Ardagh Chalice; £2 Tara Brooch.

Nos. 747a and 748b were initially only available from booklet pane No. 747ab, but were subsequently issued in sheet form during March (4p.) and October (2p.) 1991. Nos 748c and 755b only occur from booklet panes Nos. 748ca/cb.

With the exception of Nos. 747ac and 748ba each of the listed booklet panes shows either the upper and lower edges (Nos. 748a, 748bb) or the three outer edges of the pane imperforate. Booklet panes Nos. 535ca and 547bb, which include Nos. 752ab and 754ab, and also Nos. 747ac and 748ba each show stamps from the right-hand vertical row imperforate at top, right or at foot depending on the format of the design. The following variations exist:

2p. Imperf at left (booklet pane No. 747ab)
4p. Imperf at left or right (booklet pane No. 747ab)
26p. Imperf at top (p 13½) (booklet pane No. 535ca)
28p. Imperf at foot (booklet pane No. 748ba)
30p. Imperf at right (p 13½) (booklet pane No. 547bb)
32p. Imperf at right (booklet pane No. 747ac)

For 4, 28 and 32p. stamps in same designs as Nos. 748, 753 and 755, but printed in photogravure, see Nos. 808/10.

For 32p. value as No. 755, but 29×24 mm and self-adhesive see No. 823.

Imperf at foot (booklet pane No. 747ac)
Imperf at left (booklet panes Nos. 748a, 748bb)
Imperf at foot (booklet pane No. 748ba)
Imperf at foot and left (p 13×13½) (booklet pane No. 748ca)
Imperf at right (p 13½) (booklet pane No. 748cb)
Imperf at foot and left (booklet pane No. 747ac)
Imperf at top or top and right (booklet pane No. 747ab)
Imperf at top or foot (booklet pane No. 748a)
Imperf at top, top and right or foot (p 13½×13) (booklet pane No. 748ca)
Imperf at top and right, foot and right or foot (p 13½×13) (booklet pane No. 748cb)

268 Posy of Flowers

269 Player heading Ball

(Des M. Cameron. Litho Irish Security Stamp Ptg Ltd)

1990 (22 Mar). Greetings Stamps. T **268** and similar vert designs. Multicoloured. P 14×15.

766	26p. Type **268**	1·60	2·50
	a. Booklet pane. Nos. 766/9	5·75	
767	26p. Birthday presents	1·60	2·50
768	30p. Flowers, ribbon and horseshoe	1·60	2·50
769	30p. Balloons	1·60	2·50
766/9 Set of 4		5·75	9·00

Nos. 766/9 come from £1.98 discount stamp booklets, No. SB34.

Booklet pane No. 766a exists with the 26p. values at left or right and the right-hand stamp (either No. 767 or 769) imperforate at right. The booklet pane also contains 8 small greetings labels.

(Des C. Harrison. Litho Irish Security Stamp Ptg Ltd)

1990 (5 Apr). World Cup Football Championship, Italy. T **269** and similar vert design. Multicoloured. Chalk-surfaced paper. P 14×15.

770	30p. Type **269**	1·50	2·00
	a. Sheetlet. Nos. 770/1, each×4	11·00	
771	30p. Tackling	1·50	2·00

Nos. 770/1 were printed together, *se-tenant*, in a sheetlet of 8 stamps and 1 central stamp-size label.

270 Battle of the Boyne, 1690

(Des S. Conlin. Litho Irish Security Stamp Ptg Ltd)

1990 (5 Apr). 300th Anniv of the Williamite Wars (1st issue). T **270** and similar horiz designs. Multicoloured. Chalk-surfaced paper. P 13½.

772	30p. Type **270**	1·75	2·00
	a. Pair. Nos. 772/3	3·50	4·00
773	30p. Siege of Limerick, 1690	1·75	2·00

Nos. 772/3 were printed together, *se-tenant*, in horizontal and vertical pairs throughout the sheet.

See also Nos. 806/7.

271 1990 Irish Heritage 30p. Stamp and 1840 Postmark

(Des Q. Design. Litho Irish Security Stamp Ptg Ltd)

1990 (3 May). 150th Anniv of the Penny Black. T **271** and similar horiz design. Multicoloured. Chalk-surfaced paper. P 15×14.

774	30p. Type **271**	90	1·00
	a. Ordinary paper	1·50	3·00
	ab. Booklet pane. Nos. 774a/5a, each×2	6·00	
775	50p. Definitive stamps of 1922, 1969, 1982 and 1990	1·25	2·50
	a. Ordinary paper	1·50	3·00

Nos. 774a and 775a were only issued in £6 booklets, No. SB35.

In booklet pane No. 774ab one example of each value is imperforate at right.

Booklet pane No. 774ab exists with the margins overprinted in red in connection with "STAMPA 90", the Irish National Stamp Exhibition.

For other booklet panes containing Nos. 774a/5a see Nos. 547ba/bb.

272 General Post Office, Dublin

273 Medical Missionary giving Injection

(Des P. Keogh. Litho Irish Security Stamp Ptg Ltd)

1990 (3 May). Europa. Post Office Buildings. T **272** and similar vert design. Multicoloured. P 14×15.

776	30p. Type **272**	1·00	60
777	41p. Westport Post Office, County Mayo	1·75	3·25

Nos. 776/7 were each printed in sheets of 10 stamps and 2 stamp-size labels.

(Des I. Calder (26, 50p.), R. Ballagh (30p.). Litho Irish Security Stamp Ptg Ltd)

1990 (21 June). Anniversaries and Events. T **273** and similar designs. P 15×14 (horiz) or 14×15 (vert).

778	26p. multicoloured	80	40
779	30p. black	1·00	2·75
780	50p. multicoloured	1·00	1·75
778/80	*Set of 3*	2·50	4·50

Designs: Vert—30p. Michael Collins (statesman) (Birth centenary). Horiz—50p. Missionaries working at water pump (Irish missionary service).

274 Narcissus "Foundling" and Japanese Gardens, Tully

(Des I. Loe. Litho Irish Security Stamp Ptg Ltd)

1990 (30 Aug). Garden Flowers. T **274** and similar vert designs. Multicoloured. P 14×15.

781	26p. Type **274**	60	55
	a. Booklet pane. Nos. 781/2, each×2	3·50	
	b. Booklet pane. Nos. 781/4	3·50	
782	30p. *Rosa x hibernica* and Malahide Castle Gardens	70	80
783	41p. *Primula* "Rowallane Rose" and Rowallane Garden	1·25	2·50
784	50p. *Erica erigena* "Irish Dusk" and Palm House, National Botanical Gardens	1·50	2·75
781/4	*Set of 4*	3·50	6·00

Both booklet panes show the stamps as horizontal rows of four imperforate at top and at right. Stamps from the right of the pane, 30p. on No. 781a, 50p. on No. 781b, are imperforate at top and right with the other values imperforate at top only.

No. 781a exists overprinted in blue for Collectors' Road Shows at Waterford and Galway.

275 *Playboy of the Western World* (John Synge)

(Des R. Ballagh. Litho Irish Security Stamp Ptg Ltd)

1990 (18 Oct). Irish Theatre. T **275** and similar horiz designs. Multicoloured. P 13½.

785	30p. Type **275**	1·25	1·75
	a. Horiz strip of 4. Nos. 785/8	4·50	6·25
786	30p. *Juno and the Paycock* (Sean O'Casey)	1·25	1·75
787	30p. *The Field* (John Keane)	1·25	1·75
788	30p. *Waiting for Godot* (Samuel Beckett)	1·25	1·75
785/8	*Set of 4*	4·50	6·25

Nos. 785/8 were printed together in sheets of 20 (4×5), producing horizontal *se-tenant* strips of 4 and vertical *se-tenant* pairs of Nos. 785 and 788 or 786/7.

276 Nativity

(Des Pamela Leonard (No. 789), B. Cronin (others). Litho Irish Security Stamp Ptg Ltd)

1990 (15 Nov). Christmas. T **276** and similar vert designs. Multicoloured. Chalk-surfaced paper (50p.) or ordinary paper (others). P 14×15.

789	26p. Child praying by bed	75	80
	a. Sheetlet. No. 789×12	8·50	
790	26p. Type **276**	60	60
791	30p. Madonna and Child	90	90
792	50p. Adoration of the Magi	1·75	3·50
789/92	*Set of 4*	3·50	5·25

No. 789 was only issued in sheetlets of 12 sold at £2.86, providing a discount of 26p. off the face value of the stamps.

277 Hearts in Mail Sack and Postman's Cap

278 Starley "Rover" Bicycle, 1886

(Des Liz Manning (26p.), Louise Mullally (30p.). Litho Irish Security Stamp Ptg Ltd)

1991 (29 Jan). Greetings Stamps. T **277** and similar vert design. Multicoloured. Chalk-surfaced paper. P 14×15.

793	26p. Type **277**	85	1·00
794	30p. Boy and girl kissing	90	1·00

(Des E. Patton. Litho Irish Security Stamp Ptg Ltd)

1991 (5 Mar). Early Bicycles. T **278** and similar vert designs. Multicoloured. Chalk-surfaced paper. P 14×15.

795	26p. Type **278**	90	60
796	30p. Child's horse tricycle, 1875	1·00	1·00
797	50p. "Penny Farthing", 1871	1·75	2·50
795/7 Set of 3		3·25	3·75
MS798 113×72 mm. Nos. 795/7		3·25	4·00

No. **MS**798 exists with privately-applied marginal overprints for the "Collectorex 91" Exhibition, Dublin, the I.P.T.A. Collectors' Road Show, Birr (both in black) and "STAMPA 91" Exhibition, Dublin (in red or blue).

279 Cuchulainn (statue by Oliver Sheppard) and Proclamation

(Des I. Calder. Litho Irish Security Stamp Ptg Ltd)

1991 (3 Apr). 75th Anniv of Easter Rising. Chalk-surfaced paper. P 15×14.

799	**279**	32p. multicoloured	1·50	1·75

280 Scene from *La Traviata* (50th anniv of Dublin Grand Opera Society)

(Des K. Uhlemann (28p.), M. Craig and I. Calder (32p.), M. Craig (44p.), M. Craig and Q. Design (52p.). Litho Irish Security Stamp Ptg Ltd)

1991 (11 Apr). "Dublin 1991 European City of Culture". T **280** and similar horiz designs. Multicoloured. Chalk-surfaced paper. P 13½ (52p.) or 15×14 (others).

800	28p. Type **280**	1·00	1·00
	a. Booklet pane. Nos. 800/2	3·75	
	b. Booklet pane. Nos. 800/3	3·75	
801	32p. City Hall and European Community emblem	1·10	1·60
802	44p. St. Patrick's Cathedral (800th anniv)	90	1·60
803	52p. Custom House (bicent) (44×27 mm)	1·00	1·60
800/3 Set of 4		3·50	5·25

281 *Giotto* Spacecraft approaching Halley's Comet

(Des C. Rycraft. Litho Irish Security Stamp Ptg Ltd)

1991 (14 May). Europa. Europe in Space. T **281** and similar horiz design. Multicoloured. P 15×14.

804	32p. Type **281**	1·00	1·00
805	44p. Hubble Telescope orbiting Earth	1·25	3·00

Nos. 804/5 were each issued in sheetlets of 10 (2×5) with illustrations of space launches on enlarged left hand margins.

282 Siege of Athlone

283 John A. Costello (statesman)

(Des S. Conlin. Litho Irish Security Stamp Ptg Ltd)

1991 (14 May). 300th Anniv of the Williamite Wars (2nd issue). T **282** and similar horiz design. Multicoloured. Chalk-surfaced paper. P 15×14.

806	28p. Type **282**	1·40	1·75
	a. Pair. Nos. 806/7	2·75	3·50
807	28p. Generals Ginkel and Sarsfield (signatories of Treaty of Limerick)	1·40	1·75

Nos. 806/7 were printed together, *se-tenant*, in horizontal and vertical pairs throughout the sheet.

1991 (14 May). As Nos. 748, 753 and 755, but printed in photogravure by Enschedé. Chalk-surfaced paper. P 14×15 (32p.) or 15×14 (others).

808	4p. black and bluish violet	70	1·00
	a. Booklet pane. Nos. 808×2, 809 and 810×2 plus label	4·25	
809	28p. black and reddish orange	2·00	4·00
810	32p. black and bright green	70	80
808/10 Set of 3		3·00	5·25

Nos. 808/10 were only available in £1 stamp booklets, Nos. SB39/40. Booklet pane No. 808a has imperforate outer edges giving stamps imperforate at left or right (4p.), at left and foot (28p.) and at top and right (32p.).

(Des R. Ballagh (28p.), Q. Design (others). Litho Irish Security Stamp Ptg Ltd)

1991 (2 July). Anniversaries. T **283** and similar designs. Chalk-surfaced paper (28p.). P 15×14 (52p.) or 14×15 (others).

811	28p. black	1·00	70
812	32p. multicoloured	1·25	1·00
813	52p. multicoloured	1·50	2·50
811/13 Set of 3		3·25	3·75

Designs: Vert—28p. Type **283** (Birth centenary) (drawing by Sean O'Sullivan); 32p "Charles Stewart Parnell (Sydney (Hall) (Death centenary). Horiz—52p. Meeting of United Irishmen (Bicentenary).

284 Player on 15th Green, Portmarnock (Walker Cup)

285 Wicklow Cheviot

(Des E. Patton. Litho Irish Security Stamp Ptg Ltd)

1991 (3 Sept). Golf Commemorations. T **284** and similar multicoloured design. Chalk-surfaced paper (32p.). P 15×14 (28p.) or 14×15 (32p.).

814	28p. Type **284**	1·00	75
815	32p. Logo and golfer of 1900 (Centenary of Golfing Union of Ireland) (*vert*)	1·25	1·00

(Des Pamela Leonard. Litho Irish Security Stamp Ptg Ltd)

1991 (3 Sept). Irish Sheep. T **285** and similar multicoloured designs. Chalk-surfaced paper. P 15×14 (52p.) or 14×15 (others).

816	32p. Type **285**	1·00	80
817	38p. Donegal Blackface	1·10	1·75
818	52p. Galway (*horiz*)	1·60	3·25
816/18 Set of 3		3·25	5·00

286 Boatyard

(Des C. Rycraft. Litho Irish Security Stamp Ptg Ltd)

1991 (17 Oct). Fishing Fleet. T **286** and similar horiz designs. Multicoloured. Chalk-surfaced paper. P 15×14.

819	28p. Type **286**	70	65
	a. Booklet pane. Nos. 819/22	4·50	
	b. Booklet pane. Nos. 819/20 each×2	4·50	
820	32p. Traditional inshore trawlers	80	80
821	44p. Inshore lobster pot boat	1·60	2·50
822	52p. *Veronica* (fish factory ship)	1·90	2·75
819/22 *Set of 4*		4·50	6·00

In pane No. 819a, from booklet No. SB41, the 32p. and 52p. values are imperforate at right.

Booklet pane No. 819a exists with the gutter margin overprinted in connection with the "PHILANIPPON '91" International Stamp Exhibition, Tokyo.

For a further booklet pane including No. 820 see No. 747ac.

(Litho Printset-Cambec Pty Ltd, Australia or Sprintpak SNP, Australia (No. 823) or Irish Security Stamp Ptg Ltd (No. 823a))

1991 (31 Oct)–**95**. As No. 755, but larger, 27×21 mm, and self-adhesive. P 11½.

823	32p. black and bright green	1·75	1·00
	a. Perf 9½×9 (8.6.95)	1·75	1·50

Examples of No. 823 have rounded perforations at each corner of the stamp and pointed die-cut "teeth". No. 823a shows a perforation at each corner and has rounded teeth. The background screen on 823a is also coarser than the original and the value is further away from the collar. Initially both printers showed the stamps separate on the backing paper, but from September 1996 printings of No. 823a retained the surplus self-adhesive paper around each stamp. Printings from July 1992 contained "reminder" labels inserted 20 stamps and 10 stamps from the end of the coil.

Nos. 823/a were only available in coils of 100, or as strips of 3 from the Philatelic Bureau.

287 The Annunciation

(Des Q. Design (No. 827) T. Gayer (others). Litho Irish Security Stamp Ptg Ltd)

1991 (14 Nov). Christmas. T **287** and similar vert designs. Chalk-surfaced paper. P 14×15.

827	28p. multicoloured	1·00	1·00
	a. Sheetlet. No. 827×13	11·50	
828	28p. dull ultramarine, sage-green and black	1·00	65
829	32p. scarlet and black	1·10	75
830	52p. multicoloured	2·00	3·25
827/30 *Set of 4*		4·50	5·00

Designs:—No. 827 Three Kings; No. 828, Type **287**; No. 829, The Nativity; No. 830, Adoration of the Kings.

No. 827 was only issued in sheetlets of 13 stamps and two labels (at the centre of rows 1 and 2) sold at £3.36 providing a discount of 28p. off the face value of the stamps.

288 Multicoloured Heart

(Des T. Monaghan (28p.), R. Ballagh (32p.). Litho Irish Security Stamp Ptg Ltd)

1992 (28 Jan). Greetings Stamps. T **288** and similar multicoloured design. P 15×14 (28p.) or 14×15 (32p.).

831	28p. Type **288**	1·00	95
832	32p. "LOVE" at end of rainbow (*vert*)	1·10	1·10

289 Healthy Family on Apple

(Des Pamela Leonard. Litho Irish Security Stamp Ptg Ltd)

1992 (25 Feb). "Healthy Living" Campaign. P 14×15.

833	**289**	28p. multicoloured	1·25	1·00

290 Boxing

(Des C. Harrison. Litho Irish Security Stamp Ptg Ltd)

1992 (25 Feb). Olympic Games, Barcelona. T **290** and similar horiz design. P 15×14.

834	32p. Type **290**	75	90
835	44p. Sailing	1·00	2·25
MS836	130×85 mm. Nos. 834/5×2	4·25	6·00
	a. On chalk-surfaced paper	£180	

No. **MS**836 exists overprinted in black on the margin in connection with the "World Colombian Stamp Expo '92", Chicago. The chalk-surfaced paper variety is only known with this marginal overprint.

291 *Mari* (cog) and 14th-century Map

(Des C. Rycraft. Litho Irish Security Stamp Ptg Ltd)

1992 (2 Apr). Irish Maritime Heritage. T **291** and similar multicoloured design. Chalk-surfaced paper. P 15×14 (32p.) or 14×15 (52p.).

837	32p. Type **291**	1·00	90
838	52p. *Ovoca* (trawler) and chart (*vert*)	1·50	2·75

292 Chamber Logo and Commercial Symbols   **293** Cliffs and Cove

(Des E. Patton. Litho Irish Security Stamp Ptg Ltd)

1992 (2 Apr). Bicentenary of Galway Chamber of Commerce and Industry. Chalk-surfaced paper. P 15×14.

839	**292**	28p. multicoloured	1·00	1·00

(Des Pamela Leonard. Litho Irish Security Stamp Ptg Ltd)

1992 (2 Apr). Greetings Stamps. T **293** and similar vert designs. Multicoloured. Chalk-surfaced paper. P 14×15.

840	28p. Type **293**	1·10	1·10
	a. Booklet pane. Nos. 840/3	4·00	
841	28p. Meadow	1·10	1·10
842	32p. Fuchsia and Honeysuckle	1·10	1·10
843	32p. Lily pond and dragonfly	1·10	1·10
840/3 *Set of 4*		4·00	4·00

Nos. 840/3 come from £2.40 stamp booklets, No. SB42.

Booklet pane No. 840a exists with the 28p. values at left or right and has the right-hand stamp (either No. 841 or 843) imperforate at right. The booklet pane also contains 8 small greetings labels.

Booklet pane No. 840a exists overprinted on the margin for Regional Stamp Shows at Sligo and Waterford.

294 Fleet of Columbus

(Des S. Conlin. Litho Irish Security Stamp Ptg Ltd)

1992 (14 May). Europa. 500th Anniv of Discovery of America by Columbus. T **294** and similar horiz design. Multicoloured. P 15×14.

844	32p. Type **294**	1·25	90
845	44p. Columbus landing in the New World	2·00	3·00

Nos. 844/5 were each issued in sheetlets of 10 (2×5) with illustrated left or right margins.

295 Irish Immigrants

(Des Pamela Leonard. Litho Irish Security Stamp Ptg Ltd)

1992 (14 May). Irish Immigrants in the Americas. T **295** and similar horiz design. Multicoloured. P 13½.

846	52p. Type **295**	1·75	1·75
	a. Pair. Nos. 846/7	3·50	3·50
847	52p. Irish soldiers, entertainers and politicians	1·75	1·75

Nos. 846/7 were printed together, *se-tenant*, in horizontal and vertical pairs throughout the sheet.

296 Pair of Pine Martens

(Des R. Ward. Litho Irish Security Stamp Ptg Ltd)

1992 (9 July). Endangered Species. Pine Marten. T **296** and similar horiz designs. Multicoloured. P 15×14.

848	28p. Type **296**	1·00	70
849	32p. Marten on branch	1·00	80
	a. Imperf between (vert pair)	£500	
850	44p. Female with kittens	1·60	1·50
851	52p. Marten catching Great Tit	2·00	2·50
848/51	Set of 4	5·00	5·00

297 "The Rotunda and New Rooms" (James Malton)

(Des J. McEvoy (28, 44p.), E. Patton (32, 52p.). Litho Irish Security Stamp Ptg Ltd)

1992 (2 Sept). Dublin Anniversaries. T **297** and similar multicoloured designs. Chalk-surfaced paper (32p.). P 15×14 (28, 44p.) or 13½ (32, 52p.).

852	28p. Type **297**	1·00	65
853	32p. Trinity College Library (27×44 mm)	1·00	1·00
854	44p. "Charlemont House"	1·25	2·00
855	52p. Trinity College main gate (27×44 mm)	1·40	2·25
852/5	Set of 4	4·25	5·50

Anniversaries—28, 44p. Bicentenary of publication of Melton's *Views of Dublin*; 32, 52p. 400th anniv of founding of Trinity College.

298 European Star and Megalithic Dolmen

(Des R. Ballagh. Litho Irish Security Stamp Ptg Ltd)

1992 (15 Oct). Single European Market. P 15×14.

856	**298**	32p. multicoloured	55	80
		a. Booklet pane. No. 856×4	2·00	
		b. Booklet pane. No. 856×3	2·50	

Three versions of booklet pane No. 856a exist showing the stamps arranged as a block of 4, as singles or in two vertical pairs. The first two versions exist overprinted for "STAMPA '92" (in blue on the block of four pane and in red on the other).

The booklet panes also exist overprinted for Regional Stamp Shows at Galway, Dundalk, Kilkenny and Limerick.

299 Farm Produce

(Des Frances Poskitt. Litho Irish Security Stamp Ptg Ltd)

1992 (15 Oct). Irish Agriculture. T **299** and similar vert designs. Multicoloured. P 14×15.

857	32p. Type **299**	1·25	1·25
	a. Horiz strip of 4. Nos. 857/60	4·50	4·50
858	32p. Dairy and beef herds	1·25	1·25
859	32p. Harvesting cereals	1·25	1·25
860	32p. Market gardening	1·25	1·25
857/60	Set of 4	4·50	4·50

Nos. 857/60 were printed together, *se-tenant*, in horizontal strips of 4 throughout the sheet with each strip forming a composite design.

300 "The Annunciation" (from illuminated manuscript)   **301** Queen of Hearts

(Des Frances Poskitt (No. 861), J. McEvoy (others). Litho Irish Security Stamp Ptg Ltd)

1992 (19 Nov). Christmas. T **300** and similar vert designs. Multicoloured. Chalk-surfaced paper. P 14×15.

861	28p. Congregation entering church	80	65
	a. Sheetlet. No. 861×13	9·25	
862	28p. Type **300**	80	65
863	32p. "Adoration of the Shepherds" (Da Empoli)	1·10	1·00
864	52p. "Adoration of the Magi" (Rotten-hammer)	1·40	1·50
861/4	Set of 4	3·75	3·50

No. 861 was only issued in sheetlets of 13 stamps and two labels (at the centre of rows 1 and 2) sold at £3.36 providing a discount of 28p. off the face value of the stamps.

(Des C. Harrison (28p.), Q. Design (32p.) Litho Irish Security Stamp Ptg Ltd)

1993 (26 Jan). Greetings Stamps. T **301** and similar multicoloured design. Chalk-surfaced paper. P 14×15 (28p.) or 15×14 (32p.).

865	28p. Type **301**	90	75
866	32p. Hot air balloon trailing hearts (*horiz*)	1·00	85

302 "Evening at Tangier" (Sir John Lavery)

(Des E. Patton. Litho Irish Security Stamp Ptg Ltd)

1993 (4 Mar). Irish Impressionist Painters. T **302** and similar multicoloured designs. Chalk-surfaced paper. P 13.

867	28p. Type **302**	90	65
	a. Booklet pane. Nos. 867/70 with margins all round	3·00	
	b. Booklet pane. Nos. 867/8 with margins all round	3·00	
868	32p. "The Goose Girl" (William Leech)	95	70
869	44p. "La Jeune Bretonne" (Roderic O'Conor) (vert)	1·10	2·00
	a. Booklet pane. Nos. 869/70 with margins all round	3·00	
870	52p. "Lustre Jug" (Walter Osborne) (vert)	1·25	2·75
867/70 Set of 4		3·75	5·50

Booklet pane No. 867a exists in two slightly different versions, one containing two se-tenant pairs and the other the stamps perforated individually.

The booklet panes exist overprinted in the margin in connection with Regional Stamp Shows at Mullingar, Tralee (overprint reads "Summer Regional Show"), Cork and Letterkenny. No. 867b also comes with a blue marginal overprint for "STAMPA 93".

303 Bee Orchid

(Des I. Loe. Litho Irish Security Stamp Ptg Ltd)

1993 (20 Apr). Irish Orchids. T **303** and similar vert designs. Multicoloured. P 14×15.

871	28p. Type **303**	90	60
872	32p. O'Kelly's Orchid	1·10	80
873	38p. Dark Red Helleborine	1·60	2·25
874	52p. Irish Lady's Tresses	1·90	2·75
871/4 Set of 4		5·00	5·75
MS875	130×71 mm. Nos. 871/4	5·00	6·00

No. **MS**875 exists overprinted in red on the margin in connection with "STAMPA 93". This miniature sheet was also re-issued with a wider upper margin, showing the Irish and Thai flags, for the "Bangkok '93" International Stamp Exhibition. Such sheets were only available from the Philatelic Bureau and the An Post stand at the exhibition.

304 "Pears in a Copper Pan" (Hilda van Stockum)

(Des E. Patton. Litho Irish Security Stamp Ptg Ltd)

1993 (18 May). Europa. Contemporary Art. T **304** and similar vert design. Multicoloured. Chalk-surfaced paper. P 13.

876	32p. Type **304**	75	75
877	44p. "Arrieta Orzola" (Tony O'Malley)	1·10	1·10

Nos. 876/7 were each issued in sheetlets of 10 stamps and two labels (in positions 1 and 4 of the top row).

305 Cultural Activities

(Des K. Uhlemann and B. Donegan. Litho Irish Security Stamp Ptg Ltd)

1993 (8 July). Centenary of Conradh Na Gaelige (cultural organization). T **305** and similar multicoloured design. Chalk-surfaced paper. P 15×14 (32p.) or 14×15 (52p.).

878	32p. Type **305**	85	75
879	52p. Illuminated manuscript cover (vert)	1·25	1·50

306 Diving

(Des C. Harrison. Litho Irish Security Stamp Ptg Ltd)

1993 (8 July). Centenary of Irish Amateur Swimming Association. T **306** and similar horiz design. Multicoloured. Chalk-surfaced paper. P 15×14.

880	32p. Type **306**	75	1·50
	a. Horiz pair. Nos. 880/1	1·50	3·00
881	32p. Swimming	75	1·50

Nos. 880/1 were printed together, se-tenant, in horizontal pairs throughout the sheet.

307 Nurse with Patient and Hospital Buildings (250th anniv of Royal Hospital, Donnybrook)

(Des K. Uhlemann (28p.), Q. Design (32p.), C. Rycraft (44p.), P. Monahan (52p.). Litho Irish Security Stamp Ptg Ltd)

1993 (2 Sept). Anniversaries and Events. T **307** and similar multicoloured designs. Chalk-surfaced paper. P 15×14 (28p., 44p.), 14×15 (32p.) or 13½ (52p.).

882	28p. Type **307**	1·25	60
883	32p. College building and crest (Bicent of St. Patrick's College, Carlow) (vert)	80	60
884	44p. Map of Neolithic field system, Céide (Opening of interpretative centre)	1·50	1·60
885	52p. Edward Bunting (musicologist) (150th death anniv) (28×44 mm)	1·50	2·00
882/5 Set of 4		4·50	4·25

308 Great Northern Railways Gardner at Drogheda

(Des C. Rycraft. Litho Irish Security Stamp Ptg Ltd)

1993 (12 Oct). Irish Buses. T **308** and similar horiz designs. Multicoloured. Chalk-surfaced paper. P 15×14.

886	28p. Type **308**	85	70
	a. Booklet pane. Nos. 886/7, each×2	2·50	
	b. Booklet pane. Nos. 886/9	3·50	
887	32p. C.I.E. Leyland Titan at College Green, Dublin	1·00	70
888	52p. Horse-drawn omnibus at Old Baal's Bridge, Limerick	1·75	2·50
	a. Horiz pair. Nos. 888/9	3·50	5·00
889	52p. Char-a-banc at Lady's View, Killarney	1·75	2·50
886/9 Set of 4		4·75	5·75

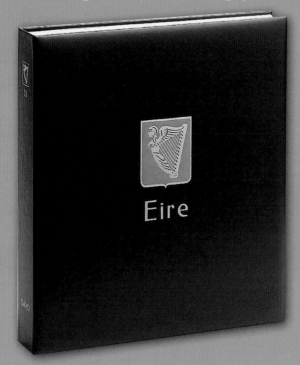

Nos. 888/9 were printed together, *se-tenant*, in horizontal pairs throughout the sheet.

Booklet panes Nos. 886a/b come from £2.84 stamp booklets, No. SB47, and have the outer edges of the pane imperforate.

309 The Annunciation

(Des Pamela Leonard (No. 890), C. Harrison (others). Litho Irish Security Stamp Ptg Ltd)

1993 (16 Nov). Christmas. T **309** and similar multicoloured designs. Chalk-surfaced paper. P 14×15 (No. 890) or 15×14 (others).

890	28p. The Flight into Egypt (*vert*)	80	80
	a. Sheetlet. No. 890×13	8·50	
891	28p. Type **309**	80	55
892	32p. Holy Family	90	70
893	52p. Adoration of the shepherds	1·40	2·50
890/3	Set of 4	3·50	4·00

No. 890 was only issued in sheetlets of 13 stamps and two labels (at the centre of rows 1 and 2) sold at £3.36 providing a discount of 28p. off the face value of the stamps.

310 Aeroplane skywriting "Love"

311 Smiling Sun

(Des Jean Colton (28p.). E. Rainsberry (32p.) Litho Questa)

1994 (27 Jan). Greetings Stamps. T **310** and similar multicoloured design. Chalk-surfaced paper. P 15×14 (28p.) or 14×15 (32p.).

894	28p. Type **310**	90	75
895	32p. Couple within heart (*vert*)	1·00	85

(Des S. Young. Litho Irish Security Stamp Ptg Ltd)

1994 (27 Jan). Greetings Booklet Stamps. T **311** and similar vert designs. Multicoloured. P 14×15.

896	32p. Type **311**	1·00	1·50
	a. Booklet pane. No. 896/9	3·50	
897	32p. Smiling daisy	1·00	1·50
898	32p. Smiling heart	1·00	1·50
899	32p. Smiling rose	1·00	1·50
896/9	Set of 4	3·50	5·50

Nos. 896/9 come from £2.56 stamp booklets, No. SB48.

Booklet pane No. 896a exists with the right-hand stamp (either No. 897 or 899) imperforate at right. Each booklet pane also contains 8 small greeting labels.

The booklet pane also exists overprinted for Regional Stamp Shows at Cork and Letterkenny and from the Dublin International Stamp and Card Show.

(Des S. Young. Litho Irish Security Stamp Ptg Ltd)

1994 (18 Feb). Hong Kong '94 International Stamp Exhibition. Chinese New Year ("Year of the Dog"). P 14×15.

MS900	137×34 mm. Nos. 896/8	6·50	8·50

The example of No. 898 in the above miniature sheet is imperforate at right.

312 Stylised Logo of Macra na Feirme
(50th anniv)

(Des K. and R. Uhlemann (28p.), Creative Inputs (32p.), E. Patton (38, 52p.). Litho Irish Security Stamp Ptg Ltd)

1994 (2 Mar). Anniversaries and Events. T **312** and similar horiz designs. Chalk-surfaced paper. P 15×14.

901	28p. gold and deep ultramarine	75	65
902	32p. multicoloured	1·00	75
903	38p. multicoloured	2·50	2·25
904	52p. black, cobalt and bright blue	1·25	2·00
901/4	Set of 4	5·00	5·50

Designs: (40×36 *mm*)—32p. "The Taking of Christ" (Caravaggio) (Loan of painting to National Gallery). (40×29 *mm*)—38p. Sir Horace Plunkett with 19th-century milk carts and modern tankers (Centenary of Irish Co-operative Organisation Society); 52p. Congress emblem (Centenary of Irish Congress of Trade Unions).

313 St. Brendan visiting Iceland

(Des C. Harrison. Litho Irish Security Stamp Ptg Ltd)

1994 (18 Apr). Europa. St. Brendan's Voyages. T **313** and similar horiz design. Multicoloured. Chalk-surfaced paper. P 15×14.

905	32p. Type **313**	75	70
906	44p. St. Brendan discovering Faroe Islands	1·50	2·00
MS907	82×76 mm. Nos. 905/6	2·75	4·50

Nos. 905/6 were each issued in sheetlets of 10 (2×5) with enlarged illustrated left margins.

No. **MS**907 also exists overprinted in blue on the margins in connection with "Stampa' 94".

314 First Meeting of Dail, 1919

315 Irish and Argentine Footballers

(Des R. Hoek. Litho Irish Security Stamp Ptg Ltd)

1994 (27 Apr). Parliamentary Anniversaries. T **314** and similar horiz design. Multicoloured. Chalk-surfaced paper. P 15×14.

908	32p. Type **314** (75th anniv)	90	1·00
	a. Booklet pane. Nos. 908/9, each×2	2·50	
	b. Booklet pane. Nos. 908/9	1·50	
909	32p. European Parliament (fourth direct elections)	90	1·00

Booklet panes Nos. 908a/b come from £1.92 stamp booklets, No. SB49, and have the outer edges of the panes imperforate. Booklet pane No. 908a contains examples of No. 908 either imperforate at top or at right, and No. 909 imperforate at foot or at top and right. In booklet pane No. 908b No. 908 is imperforate at right and No. 909 fully perforated.

(Des J. Donohoe (Nos. 910/11), E. Patton (others). Litho Irish Security Stamp Ptg Ltd (Nos. 910/11) or Enschedé (others))

1994 (31 May). Sporting Anniversaries and Events. T **315** and similar multicoloured designs. Chalk-surfaced paper (Nos. 910/11). P 14×15 (Nos. 910/11) or 13×13½ (others).

910	32p. Type **315**	80	1·25
	a. Sheetlet. Nos. 910/11, each×4	6·00	
911	32p. Irish and German footballers	80	1·25
912	32p. Irish and Dutch women's hockey match (*horiz*)	2·00	1·25
913	52p. Irish and English women's hockey match (*horiz*)	2·25	2·50
910/13	Set of 4	5·25	5·50

Anniversaries and Events:—Nos. 910/11, World Cup Football Championship, U.S.A.; No. 912, Women's Hockey World Cup, Dublin; No. 913, Centenary of Irish Ladies' Hockey Union.

Nos. 910/11 were printed together, *se-tenant*, in sheetlets of 8 stamps and one central label.

316 *Arctia caja*

(Des I. Loe)

1994 (12 July). Moths. T **316** and similar horiz designs. Multicoloured.

(a) Litho Irish Security Stamp Ptg Ltd. Chalk-surfaced paper. P 15×14

914	28p. Type **316**	65	60
915	32p. *Calamia tridens*	75	70
916	38p. *Saturnia pavonia*	90	1·10
917	52p. *Deilephila elpenor*	1·50	2·00
914/17 *Set of 4*		3·50	4·00
MS918 120×71 mm. Nos. 914/17		3·50	4·00

(b) Litho Printset-Cambec Pty Ltd, Australia. Self-adhesive. Chalk-surfaced paper. P 11½

919	32p. *Calamia tridens*	1·25	1·75
920	32p. Type **316**	1·25	1·75
921	32p. *Deilephila elpenor*	1·25	1·75
922	32p. *Saturnia pavonia*	1·25	1·75
919/22 *Set of 4*		4·50	6·25

No. **MS**918 also exists with the "Philakorea' 94" International Stamp Exhibition, Seoul, logo added at bottom right and also comes overprinted in black for Collectors' Road Show, Sligo, or in red for "Stampa '94".

Nos. 919/22 are smaller, 37×25 mm, and occur, *se-tenant*, in strips of 4 or rolls of 100 with the surplus self-ahesive paper around each stamp removed.

317 Statue of Edmund Rice and Class

(Des S. Conlin (No. 923), Design Factory (Nos. 926, 927), E. Patton (Nos. 924, 925). Litho Walsall (Nos. 925, 927), Irish Security Stamp Ptg Ltd (others))

1994 (6 Sept). Anniversaries and Events. T **317** and similar multicoloured designs. Chalk-surfaced paper. P 13½ (No. 923), 14 (Nos. 925, 927), 14×15 (No. 924) or 15×14 (No. 926).

923	28p. St. Lawrence Gate, Drogheda (44×27 *mm*)	1·50	1·25
924	32p. Type **317**	1·00	1·25
925	32p. Edmund Burke (politician)	1·00	1·25
926	52p. Vickers FB-27 Vimy and map (*horiz*)	1·50	1·75
927	52p. Eamonn Andrews (broadcaster)	1·25	1·75
923/7 *Set of 5*		5·50	6·75

Anniversaries and Events:—No. 923, 800th anniv of Drogheda; No. 924, 150th death anniv of Edmund Rice (founder of Irish Christian Brothers); Nos. 925, 927, The Irish abroad; No. 926, 75th anniv of Alcock and Brown's first Transatlantic flight.

318 George Bernard Shaw (author) and *Pygmalion* Poster

(Des R. Ballagh. Litho Irish Security Stamp Ptg Ltd)

1994 (18 Oct). Irish Nobel Prizewinners. T **318** and similar horiz designs. Multicoloured. Chalk-surfaced paper. P 15×14.

928	28p. Type **318**	60	90
	a. Pair. Nos. 928/9	1·10	1·75
	b. Booklet pane. Nos. 928/9 and 930×2 with margins all round	2·25	
	c. Booklet pane. Nos. 928/31 with margins all round	2·25	
	d. Booklet pane. Nos. 928/30 with margins all round	2·25	
929	28p. Samuel Beckett (author) and pair of boots	60	90
930	32p. Sean MacBride (human rights campaigner) and peace doves	70	90
	a. Booklet pane. Nos. 930 and 931×2 with margins all round	2·25	
931	52p. William Butler Yeats (poet) and poem	1·10	2·00
928/31 *Set of 4*		2·75	4·25

Nos. 928/9 were printed together, *se-tenant*, in horizontal and vertical pairs throughout the sheet.

The booklet panes also exist overprinted for Regional Stamp Shows at Waterford, Galway, Athlone and Kilkenny.

319 The Annunciation (ivory plaque)   **320** Tree of Hearts

(Des Pamela Leonard (No. 932), Q. Design (others). Litho Irish Security Stamp Ptg Ltd)

1994 (17 Nov). Christmas. T **319** and similar vert designs. Chalk-surfaced paper. P 14×15.

932	28p. Nativity	70	60
	a. Sheetlet. No. 932×13	8·00	
933	28p. Type **319**	80	60
934	32p. Flight into Egypt (wood carving)	90	70
935	52p. Nativity (ivory plaque)	1·40	2·00
932/5 *Set of 4*		3·50	3·50

No. 932 was only issued in sheetlets of 13 stamps and two labels (at the centre of rows 1 and 2) sold at £3.36 providing a discount of 28p. off the face value of the stamps.

(Des Bridget Flinn. Litho Irish Security Stamp Ptg Ltd)

1995 (24 Jan). Greetings Stamps. T **320** and similar vert designs. Multicoloured. Chalk-surfaced paper. P 14×15.

936	32p. Type **320**	1·25	1·25
	a. Booklet pane. Nos. 936/9	4·50	
937	32p. Teddy bear holding balloon	1·25	1·25
938	32p. Clown juggling hearts	1·25	1·25
939	32p. Bouquet of flowers	1·25	1·25
936/9 *Set of 4*		4·50	4·50

Nos. 936/9 were only available from £2.56 stamp booklets (No. SB51) containing two examples of No. 936a. This pane, which also includes 8 small greetings labels, exists in two different forms with either No. 936 at left and No. 938 at right or No. 937 at left and No. 939 at right. In each instance the righthand stamp is imperforate at right.

(Des Bridget Flynn. Litho Irish Security Stamp Ptg Ltd)

1995 (24 Jan). Chinese New Year ("Year of the Pig"). P 14×15.

MS940 137×74 mm. Nos. 936, 938/9		4·50	4·50

The example of No. 939 in the above miniature sheet is imperforate at right.

321 West Clare Railway Steam Locomotive No. 1 *Kilkee* at Kilrush Station

(Des C. Rycraft. Litho Irish Security Stamp Ptg Ltd)

1995 (28 Feb). Transport. Narrow Gauge Railways. T **321** and similar horiz designs. Multicoloured. Chalk-surfaced paper. P 15×14.

941	28p. Type **321**	85	60
942	32p. County Donegal Railway tank locomotive No. 2 *Blanche* at Donegal Station	1·10	90
943	38p. Cork and Muskerry Railway tank locomotive No. 1 *City of Cork* on Western Road, Cork	1·40	1·75
944	52p. Cavan and Leitrim tank locomotive No. 3 *Lady Edith* on Arigna Tramway	1·90	2·50
941/4 *Set of 4*		4·75	5·25
MS945 127×83 mm. Nos. 941/4		4·75	5·50

No. **MS**945 also exists with the "Singapore '95" International Stamp Exhibition logo added.

322 English and Irish Rugby Players

(Des C. Harrison. Litho Walsall)

1995 (6 Apr). World Cup Rugby Championship, South Africa. T **322** and similar horiz design. Multicoloured. Chalk-surfaced paper. P 14.

946	32p. Type **322**	1·00	75
947	52p. Australian and Irish players	1·40	1·75
MS948	108×77 mm. £1 Type **322**	3·00	3·50

No. **MS**948 also exists overprinted for Regional Stamp Shows at Limerick and Letterkenny.

323 Peace Dove and Skyscrapers

(Des R. Ballagh)

1995 (6 Apr). Europa. Peace and Freedom. T **323** and similar horiz design. Multicoloured. Chalk-surfaced paper.

(a) Litho Irish Security Stamp Ptg Ltd. P 15×14

949	32p. Type **323**	75	75
950	44p. Peace dove and map of Europe and North Africa	1·25	2·00

(b) Litho Printset Cambec Pty Ltd, Melbourne. Self-adhesive. P 11½

951	32p. Type **323**	90	90
952	32p. As No. 950	90	90

Nos. 949/50 were issued in sheetlets of 10 (2×5) with illustrated left margins.

Nos. 951/2 are smaller, 34½×23 mm, and occur, *se-tenant*, in pairs or rolls of 100 with the surplus self-adhesive paper around each stamp removed.

324 Soldiers of the Irish Brigade and Memorial Cross

325 Irish Brigade, French Army, 1745

(Des E. Daniels. Photo Belgian Post Office Ptg Wks, Malines)

1995 (15 May). 250th Anniv of Battle of Fontenoy. Chalk-surfaced paper. P 11½.

953	**324** 32p. multicoloured	1·25	80

A similar stamp was issued by Belgium.

(Des D. McAllister. Litho Irish Security Stamp Ptg Ltd)

1995 (15 May). Military Uniforms. T **325** and similar vert designs. Multicoloured. Chalk-surfaced paper. P 14×15.

954	28p. Type **325**	70	60
	a. Booklet pane. Nos. 954/5, each×2	2·50	
	b. Booklet pane. Nos. 954/5 and 957/8	2·50	
	c. Booklet pane. Nos. 954/5 and 957	2·50	
	d. Booklet pane. Nos. 954/5 and 958	2·50	
955	32p. Tercio Irlanda, Spanish army in Flanders, 1605	80	75
956	32p. Royal Dublin Fusiliers, 1914	80	75
957	38p. St. Patrick's Battalion, Papal Army, 1860	80	1·25
958	52p. 69th Regiment, New York State Militia, 1861	1·25	1·75
954/8 *Set of 5*		4·00	4·50

Booklet panes Nos. 954a/b come with the two right-hand stamps (Nos. 954/5 or 955 and 958) imperforate at right.

The booklet panes also exist overprinted for Regional Stamp Shows at Sligo, Waterford and Galway and for "Stampa '95" (two panes).

326 Guglielmo Marconi and Original Radio Transmitter

(Des E. Junger (No. 959), S. Young (No. 960). Litho Irish Security Stamp Ptg Ltd)

1995 (8 June). Centenary of Radio. T **326** and similar horiz design. Multicoloured. Chalk-surfaced paper. P 13½.

959	32p. Type **326**	7·50	8·50
	a. Pair. Nos. 959/60	15·00	17·00
960	32p. Traditional radio dial	7·50	8·50

Nos. 959/60 were printed together, *se-tenant*, in horizontal and vertical pairs throughout the sheet.

327 Bartholomew Mosse (founder) and Hospital Building

(Des A. May (No. 961), S. Woulfe Flanagan (No. 962), Q. Design (No. 963), Creative Inputs (No. 964). Litho Questa (Nos. 961/2) or Irish Security Stamp Ptg Ltd (others))

1995 (27 July). Anniversaries. T **327** and similar multicoloured designs. Chalk-surfaced paper. P 15×14 (Nos. 961), 14½ (No. 962), 14½×14 (No. 963) or 13½ (No. 964).

961	28p. Type **327** (250th anniv of Rotunda Hospital)	1·40	70
962	32p. St. Patrick's House, Maynooth College (Bicent) (27×44 *mm*)	80	80
963	32p. Laurel wreath and map of Europe (50th anniv of end of Second World War)	80	80
964	52p. Geological map of Ireland (150th anniv of Geological Survey of Ireland) (36×36 *mm*)	1·25	1·50
961/4 *Set of 4*		3·75	3·50

328 Natterjack Toad

329 *Crinum moorei*

(Des I. Loe. Litho Irish Security Stamp Ptg Ltd)

1995 (1 Sept). Reptiles and Amphibians. T **328** and similar horiz designs. Chalk-surfaced paper.

(a) P 15×14

965	32p. Type **328**	1·00	1·25
	a. Horiz strip. Nos. 965/8	3·50	4·50
966	32p. Common Lizards	1·00	1·25
967	32p. Smooth Newts	1·00	1·25
968	32p. Common Frog	1·00	1·25
965/8 *Set of 4*		3·50	4·50

(b) Self-adhesive. P 9½

969	32p. Type **328**	1·25	1·75
970	32p. Common Lizard	1·25	1·75
971	32p. Smooth Newt	1·25	1·75
972	32p. Common Frog	1·25	1·75
969/72 *Set of 4*		4·50	6·25

Nos. 965/8 were printed together, *se-tenant*, in horizontal strips of 4 with the backgrounds forming a composite design.

Nos. 969/72 are smaller, 37×25 mm, and occur, *se-tenant*, in strips of 4 or rolls of 100 with the surplus self-adhesive paper around each stamp removed.

(Des Frances Poskitt. Litho Irish Security Stamp Ptg Ltd)

1995 (9 Oct). Bicentenary of National Botanic Gardens, Glasnevin. Flowers. T **329** and similar vert designs. Multicoloured. Chalk-surfaced paper. P 14×15.

973	32p. Type **329**	1·50	70
	a. Booklet pane. Nos. 973×2 and 974/5	3·00	
	b. Booklet pane. Nos. 973/5	3·00	
974	38p. *Sarracenia × moorei*	1·00	2·00
975	44p. *Solanum crispum* "Glasnevin"	2·00	2·50
973/5 *Set of 3*		3·25	4·75

Booklet panes Nos. 973a/b come from £2·60 stamp booklets, No. SB53, and have the outer edges of the pane imperforate so that examples of each value exist imperforate on one or two sides.

330 Anniversary Logo and Irish
United Nations Soldier

(Des Jarlath Hayes. Litho Enschedé)

1995 (19 Oct). 50th Anniv of United Nations. T **330** and similar horiz
design. Multicoloured. Chalk-surfaced paper. P 13×13½.

976	32p. Type **330**	80	70
977	52p. Emblem and "UN"	1·25	1·40

Nos. 976/7 were each issued in sheets of 10 (2×5) with enlarged
illustrated left margins.

331 "Adoration of the Shepherds"
(illuminated manuscript)
(Benedetto Bardone)

(Des Q. Design. Litho Irish Security Stamp Ptg Ltd)

1995 (16 Nov). Christmas. T **331** and similar horiz designs.
Multicoloured. Chalk-surfaced paper. P 15×14.

978	28p. Adoration of the Magi	80	55
	a. Sheetlet. No. 978×13	9·50	
979	28p. Type **331**	70	55
980	32p. "Adoration of the Magi" (illuminated manuscript) (Bardone)	85	60
981	52p. "The Holy Family" (illuminated manuscript) (Bardone)	1·40	2·50
978/81 *Set of 4*		3·25	3·75

No. 978 was only issued in sheetlets of 13 stamps and two labels
(at centre of rows 2 and 3) sold at £3.36 providing a discount of 28p.
off the face value of the stamps.

332 Zig and Zag on   **333** Wheelchair Athlete
Heart

(Des Double Z Enterprises. Litho Irish Security Stamp Ptg Ltd)

1996 (23 Jan). Greetings Stamps. T **332** and similar vert designs.
Multicoloured. Chalk-surfaced paper. P 14×15.

982	32p. Type **332**	1·25	75
	a. Booklet pane. Nos. 982/5	8·00	
983	32p. Zig and Zag waving	2·50	2·50
984	32p. Zig and Zag in space suits	2·50	2·50
985	32p. Zig and Zag wearing hats	2·50	2·50
982/5 *Set of 4*		8·00	7·50

Nos. 983/5 were only issued in £2.56 stamp booklets, No. SB54.
No. 982 was available from sheets and booklets.
Booklet pane No. 982a, which also includes eight small
greetings labels, exists in two different forms with either
No. 982 or 984 at right. In each instance the right-hand stamp is
imperforate at right.

(Des Double Z Enterprises. Litho Irish Security Stamp Ptg Ltd)

1996 (23 Jan). Chinese New Year ("Year of the Rat"). Chalk-surfaced
paper. P 14×15.

MS986	130×74 mm. Nos. 982, 984/5	4·00	4·00

The example of No. 982 in No. **MS**986 is imperforate at right.
No. **MS**986 also exists overprinted for the Collectors' Road Show at
Kilkenny.

(Des C. Harrison. Litho Irish Security Stamp Ptg Ltd)

1996 (1 Feb). Olympic and Paralympic Games, Atlanta. T **333** and
similar vert. designs. Multicoloured. Chalk-surfaced paper.
P 14×15.

987	28p. Type **333**	70	65
988	32p. Running	80	80
	a. Strip of 3. Nos. 988/90	2·25	2·25
989	32p. Throwing the discus	80	80
990	32p. Single kayak	80	80
987/90 *Set of 4*		2·75	2·75

Nos. 988/90 were printed together, *se-tenant*, as horizontal and
vertical strips of 3 in sheets of 9.

334 Before the Start, Fairyhouse   **335** Irish and French Coloured
Race Course   Ribbons Merging

(Des P. Curling and Q. Design. Litho Irish Security Stamp Ptg Ltd)

1996 (12 Mar). Irish Horse Racing. T **334** and similar horiz designs.
Multicoloured. Chalk-surfaced paper. P 15×14.

991	28p. Type **334**	70	65
	a. Booklet pane. Nos. 991×2 and 992/3	3·75	
992	32p. Steeplechase, Punchestown	80	80
	a. Pair. Nos. 992/3	1·60	1·60
	b. Booklet pane. Nos. 992/5	3·75	
	c. Booklet pane. Nos. 992×2 and 994	3·75	
993	32p. On the Flat, The Curragh	80	80
	a. Booklet pane. Nos. 993×2 and 995	3·75	
994	38p. Steeplechase, Galway	1·25	1·25
995	52p. After the race, Leopardstown	1·50	1·50
991/5 *Set of 5*		4·50	4·50

Nos. 992/3 were printed together, *se-tenant*, in horizontal and
vertical pairs throughout the sheet.
Booklet pane Nos. 991a, 992b/c and 993a come from £4.92
stamp booklets, No. SB55, with the right-hand edge of the panes
imperforate. The complete booklet contains two examples of No. 992
and one each of Nos. 991, 993 and 995 imperforate at right.
The booklet panes also exist overprinted for Collectors' Road Shows
at Cork (No. 992c), Limerick (No. 991a) or Sligo (No. 993a) and for
"Stampa '96" (No. 992c).
For designs as Nos. 992/3 in miniature sheet see No. **MS**1003.

(Des R. Ballagh. Litho Irish Security Stamp Ptg Ltd)

1996 (12 Mar). "L'Imaginaire Irlandais" Festival Of Contemporary Irish
Arts, France. Chalk-surfaced paper. P 15×14.

996	**335** 32p. multicoloured	1·00	1·00

336 Louie Bennett (suffragette)   **337** Newgrange Passage Tomb
(Boyne Valley World Heritage
Site)

(Des S. Young)

1996 (2 Apr). Europa. Famous Women. T **336** and similar horiz design.
Chalk-surfaced paper.

(a) Litho Questa. P 15×14

997	**336** 32p. deep reddish violet	80	70
998	– 44p. myrtle-green	1·10	1·25

(b) Litho Irish Security Stamp Ptg Ltd. Self-adhesive. P 9½

999	**336** 32p. deep reddish violet	1·10	1·25
1000	– 32p. dull green	1·10	1·25

Design:—Nos. 998, 1000, Lady Augusta Gregory (playwright).
Nos. 997/8 were each issued in sheetlets of 10 (2×5) with enlarged
illustrated left margins.
Nos. 999/1000 are smaller, 37×25 mm, and occur, *se-tenant*, in
rolls of 100 with the surplus self-adhesive paper around each stamp
removed.

(Des L. Belton (28p.), Q. Design (32p.). Litho Walsall)

1996 (2 Apr). Anniversaries and Events. T **337** and similar horiz
design. Chalk-surfaced paper. P 14.

1001	28p. grey-brown and black	1·00	60
1002	32p. multicoloured	1·10	90

Designs:—32p. Children playing (50th anniv of U.N.I.C.E.F.).

(Litho Irish Security Stamp Printing Ltd)

1996 (18 May). "CHINA '96" 9th Asian International Stamp Exhibition, Peking. Sheet 120×95 mm containing Nos. 992/3. Chalk-surfaced paper. P 15×14.

MS1003	Steeplechase, Punchestown; 32p. On the Flat, The Curragh	11·00	11·00

338 Stanley Woods

(Des J. Dunne. Litho Questa)

1996 (30 May). Isle of Man Tourist Trophy Motorcycle Races. Irish Winners. T **338** and similar horiz designs. Multicoloured. Chalk-surfaced paper. P 14.

1004	32p. Type **338**	80	50
1005	44p. Artie Bell	1·00	1·50
1006	50p. Alec Bennett	1·10	1·50
1007	52p. Joey and Robert Dunlop	1·10	1·50
1004/7 *Set of 4*		3·50	4·50
MS1008 100×70 mm. 50p. As 52p.		2·50	2·75

No. **MS**1008 also exists overprinted for "Stampa '96" and for the Collectors' Road Show at Dundalk.

339 Michael Davitt (founder of The Land League)

(Des R. Ballagh (28p.), J. Tobin (32p.), C. Harrison (38p.), L. Belton (52p.). Litho Enschedé)

1996 (4 July). Anniversaries and Events. T **339** and similar multicoloured designs. Chalk-surfaced paper. P 13½×13 (28p.) or 13×13½ (others).

1009	28p. Type **339** (150th birth anniv)	65	60
1010	32p. Presidency logo (Ireland's Presidency of European Union) (*horiz*)	65	70
1011	38p. Thomas McLaughlin (hydro-electric engineer) and Árdnacrusha Power Station (Birth centenary) (*horiz*)	1·00	1·10
1012	52p. Mechanical peat harvester (50th anniv of Bord na Móna) (*horiz*)	1·25	1·75
1009/12 *Set of 4*		3·25	3·75

340 *Ciara* (coastal patrol vessel)

(Des G. Fallon. Litho Irish Security Stamp Ptg Ltd)

1996 (18 July). 50th Anniv of Irish Naval Service. T **340** and similar multicoloured designs. Chalk-surfaced paper. P 14×15 (52p.) or 15×14 (others).

1013	32p. Type **340**	80	70
	a. Booklet pane. No. 1013×3	2·75	
	b. Booklet pane. Nos. 1013/15	2·75	
1014	44p. *Cliona* (corvette)	1·40	1·50
1015	52p. *M–1* (motor torpedo boat) (*vert*)	1·50	1·60
1013/15 *Set of 3*		3·25	3·50

Booklet panes Nos. 1013a/b come from £2.24 stamp booklets, No. SB56. Stamps from No. 1013a have either one or two adjacent sides imperforate and those from No. 1013b are imperforate at foot (32, 44p.) or at right and foot (52p.).

The booklet panes also exist overprinted for "Stampa '96" (No. 1013b) or for the Collectors' Road Shows at Galway (No. 1013b) and Waterford (No. 1013a).

341 Blind Woman with Child

(Des E. Patton. Litho Irish Security Stamp Ptg Ltd)

1996 (3 Sept). People with Disabilities. T **341** and similar vert design. Multicoloured. Chalk-surfaced paper. P 14×15.

1016	28p. Type **341**	1·25	1·25
	a. Pair. Nos. 1016/17	2·50	2·50
1017	28p. Man in wheelchair playing bowls	1·25	1·25

Nos. 1016/17 were printed together, *se-tenant*, in horizontal and vertical pairs throughout the sheet.

342 Green-winged Teal

(Des R. Ward. Litho Irish Security Stamp Ptg Ltd)

1996 (24 Sept). Freshwater Ducks. T **342** and similar horiz designs. Multicoloured. Chalk-surfaced paper. P 15×14.

1018	32p. Type **342**	1·00	70
1019	38p. Common Shoveler	1·10	1·25
1020	44p. European Wigeon	1·25	1·75
1021	52p. Mallard	1·60	2·00
1018/21 *Set of 4*		4·50	5·00
MS1022 127×85 mm. Nos. 1018/21		4·50	5·50

343 Scene from *Man of Aran*　　**344** Visit of the Magi

(Des J. Reddy. Litho Irish Security Stamp Ptg Ltd)

1996 (17 Oct). Centenary of Irish Cinema. T **343** and similar horiz designs. Multicoloured. Chalk-surfaced paper. P 13½.

1023	32p. Type **343**	85	1·10
	a. Strip of 4. Nos. 1023/6	3·00	4·00
1024	32p. *My Left Foot*	85	1·10
1025	32p. *The Commitments*	85	1·10
1026	32p. *The Field*	85	1·10
1023/6 *Set of 4*		3·00	4·00

Nos. 1023/6 were printed together, *se-tenant*, in vertical and horizontal strips of 4 throughout the sheet.

(Des T. Monaghan (No. 1027), E. Patton (others). Litho Irish Security Stamp Ptg Ltd)

1996 (19 Nov). Christmas. T **344** and similar vert designs from 16th-century "Book of Hours" (Nos. 1028/30). Multicoloured. Chalk-surfaced paper (Nos. 1028/30). P 14×15.

1027	28p. The Holy Family	75	60
	a. Sheetlet. No. 1027×15	10·00	
1028	28p. Type **344**	60	40
1029	32p. The Annunciation	65	50
1030	52p. The Shepherds receiving news of Christ's birth	1·10	1·60
1027/30 *Set of 4*		2·75	2·75

No. 1027 was only issued in sheetlets of 15 stamps sold at £3.92 providing a discount of 28p. off the face value of the stamps.

345 Magpie

(Des K. Mullarney)

1997 (16 Jan)–**2000**. Birds. T **345** and similar multicoloured designs.

(a) Litho Walsall (Nos. 1038ac, 1053ac, 1054ac, 1055ac, 1057ac, 1058ac), Questa (Nos. 1038as, 1039s) or Irish Security Stamp Ptg Ltd (others). Chalk-surfaced paper (1p., 2p., 4p., 10p., 20p., 30p. (Nos. 1039/52), £5) or ordinary paper (others). P 15×14 (5p., 28p., 40p., 50p., £1, £5) or 14×15 (others)

(i) Size 23×26 mm (vert) or 26×23 mm (horiz)

1031	1p. Type **345** (27.8.97)	10	75
	a. Ordinary paper (11.00)	2·50	2·75
1032	2p. Gannet (27.8.97)	15	75
1033	4p. Corncrake (27.8.97)	50	60
	a. Ordinary paper (3.98)	4·00	4·00
1034	5p. Wood Pigeon (*horiz*) (2.4.98)	20	1·00
	a. Chalk-surfaced paper (9.98)	1·75	2·00
1035	10p. Kingfisher (27.8.97)	40	1·25
	a. Ordinary paper (11.00)	1·50	2·00
1036	20p. Lapwing (27.8.97)	65	1·00
1037	28p. Blue Tit (*horiz*)	2·50	50
	a. Chalk-surfaced paper (10.97)	3·00	2·25
1038	30p. Blackbird (2.4.98)	85	1·00
	a. Chalk-surfaced paper (4.98)	2·00	2·50
	ab. Booklet pane. Nos. 1038a and 1039, each×5 (4.9.98)	17·00	
	ac. Perf 14 (*phosphor frame*) (17.11.98)	1·25	1·25
	ap. Phosphor frame (25.1.99)	2·10	2·50
	aq. Sheetlet. Nos. 1038ap, 1039p and 1040/52 (16.2.99)	17·00	
	ar. Booklet pane. Nos. 1038ap and 1039p, each×5 (25.1.99)	18·00	
	as. Perf 11×13 (*phosphor frame*) (4.01)	2·10	2·50
	at. Booklet pane. Nos. 1038as and 1039s, each ×5	19·00	
	p. Phosphor frame (*ordinary paper*) (6.12.99)	1·00	1·25
1039	30p. Goldcrest (4.9.98)	2·00	2·50
	p. Phosphor frame (25.1.99)	2·10	2·50
	s. Perf 11×13 (*phosphor frame*) (4.01)	2·10	2·50
1040	30p. Stonechat (*phosphor frame*) (16.2.99)	1·25	1·50
1041	30p. Lapwing (*phosphor frame*) (16.2.99)	1·25	1·50
1042	30p. Gannet (*phosphor frame*) (16.2.99)	1·25	1·50
1043	30p. Corncrake (*phosphor frame*) (16.2.99)	1·25	1·50
1044	30p. Type **345** (*phosphor frame*) (16.2.99)	1·25	1·50
1045	30p. Kingfisher (*phosphor frame*) (16.2.99)	1·25	1·50
1046	30p. Peregrine Falcon (*phosphor frame*) (16.2.99)	1·25	1·50
1047	30p. Barn Owl (*phosphor frame*) (16.2.99)	1·25	1·50
1048	30p. Robin (*phosphor frame*) (16.2.99)	1·25	1·50
1049	30p. Song Thrush (*phosphor frame*) (16.2.99)	1·25	1·50
1050	30p. Wren (*phosphor frame*) (16.2.99)	1·50	1·50
1051	30p. Pied Wagtail (*phosphor frame*) (16.2.99)	1·50	1·50
1052	30p. Puffin (*phosphor frame*) (16.2.99)	1·25	1·50
1053	32p. Robin	2·25	55
	a. Chalk-surfaced paper (10.97)	3·00	2·00
	ac. Perf 14 (*phosphor frame*) (17.11.98)	2·25	2·25
	p. Phosphor frame (30.6.99)	2·00	2·25
	pa. Booklet pane. No. 1053p×5, plus 5 airmail labels	9·00	
1054	35p. Stonechat (2.4.98)	1·25	2·00
	a. Chalk-surfaced paper (4.98)	3·50	2·75
	ac. Perf 14 (*phosphor frame*) (17.11.98)	2·00	2·00
	p. Phosphor frame (12.00)	2·50	2·00
1055	40p. Ringed Plover (*horiz*) (2.4.98)	1·50	2·50
	ac. Perf 14. Chalk-surfaced paper (*phosphor frame*) (17.11.98)	2·00	1·00
	p. Phosphor frame (6.01)	2·00	1·50
1056	44p. Puffin	3·75	3·00
1057	45p. Song Thrush (2.4.98)	2·25	3·50
	a. Chalk-surfaced paper (9.98)	4·00	4·00
	ac. Perf 14 (*phosphor frame*) (17.11.98)	1·50	2·00
	ap. Phosphor frame (30.6.99)	2·50	2·75
	apa. Booklet pane. No. 1057ap×4, plus 4 labels	9·00	
	p. Phosphor frame (*ordinary paper*) (18.5.99)	2·50	2·75
	pa. Booklet pane. No. 1057p×4, plus 4 labels (30.6.99)	9·00	
1058	50p. European Sparrow Hawk (*horiz*) (2.4.98)	2·00	2·25
	a. Chalk-surfaced paper (8.98)	7·00	7·00
	ac. Perf 14 (*phosphor frame*) (17.11.98)	2·50	1·25
	p. Phosphor frame (6.01)	2·75	1·50
1059	52p. Barn Owl	4·50	2·25

(ii) Size 26×47 mm (vert) or 47×26 mm (horiz)

1060	£1 Greenland White-fronted Goose	3·50	1·60
	a. Chalk-surfaced paper (11.98)	10·00	3·50
1061	£2 Pintail (*horiz*) (2.4.98)	4·00	4·25
	a. Chalk-surfaced paper (6.99)	7·50	7·50
1062	£5 Shelduck (27.8.97)	9·00	11·00
	a. Ordinary paper (9.98)	25·00	22·00
1031/62 Set of 32		50·00	48·00

(b) Booklet stamps. Litho Irish Security Stamp Ptg Ltd. Size 23×20 (5p.) or 20×23 (others). Chalk-surfaced paper (4p., 30p. (No. 1083), 32p.) or ordinary paper (others). P 14×15 (5p.) or 15×14 (others)

1080	4p. Corncrake (6.12.97)	1·75	2·50
	a. Booklet pane. Nos. 1080 and 1085×3	6·25	
1081	5p. Wood Pigeon (*horiz*) (2.4.98)	1·75	2·00
	a. Booklet pane. Nos. 1081×2 and 1082×3 plus label	6·75	
	b. Chalk-surfaced paper	2·00	2·50
	ba. Booklet pane. Nos. 1081b×2 and 1082a×3 plus label	35·00	
	bb. Booklet pane. Nos. 1081b×2 and 1083×3 plus label	7·50	
1082	30p. Blackbird (2.4.98)	2·00	2·25
	a. Chalk-surfaced paper	12·00	12·00
1083	30p. Goldcrest ("all-over" phosphor) (16.2.99)	1·50	2·00
1084	32p. Robin (6.3.97)	1·00	1·50
1085	32p. Peregrine Falcon (6.12.97)	1·75	1·50

(c) Self-adhesive. Size 24×29 mm

(i) Litho Irish Security Stamp Ptg Ltd. P 9×10

1086	30p. Goldcrest (2.4.98)	1·00	1·25
	a. Vert pair. Nos. 1086/7	2·00	2·50
	p. Phosphor frame (14.12.98)	1·50	1·75
	pa. Vert pair. Nos. 1086p/7p	3·00	3·50
	pb. Perf 9 (10.00)	1·50	2·00
	pba. Vert pair. Nos. 1086pb/7pb	3·00	4·00
1087	30p. Blackbird (2.4.98)	1·00	1·25
	p. Phosphor frame (14.12.98)	1·50	1·75
	pb. Perf 9 (10.00)	1·50	2·00
1088	32p. Peregrine Falcon (6.3.97)	2·50	4·00
	a. Vert pair. Nos. 1088/9	5·00	8·00
1089	32p. Robin (6.3.97)	2·50	4·00

(ii) Litho SNP Cambec, Melbourne. P 11½

1090	30p. Goldcrest (2.4.98)	2·00	2·00
	a. Vert pair. Nos. 1090/1	4·00	4·00
	p. Phosphor frame (17.11.98)	1·00	1·25
	pa. Vert pair. Nos. 1090p/1p	2·00	2·50
1091	30p. Blackbird (2.4.98)	2·00	2·00
	p. Phosphor frame (17.11.98)	1·00	1·25
1092	32p. Peregrine Falcon (4.97)	4·50	6·50
	a. Vert pair. Nos. 1092/3	9·00	13·00
1093	32p. Robin (4.97)	4·50	6·50

Nos. 1039/s were only issued in £3 stamp booklets, Nos. SB67/b, with upper and lower edges of the pane imperforate and a margin at either end.

The sheet stamps with phosphor frames (except No. 1054p), No. 1038ar and Nos. 1086pb/7pb show the actual designs slightly reduced to provide a clear 2 mm border on which the phosphor frame appears.

The sheetlet, No. 1038aq, repeats the vertical designs from other values in the set. The designs showing the Wren and Pied Wagtail only occur in the sheetlet. It also exists overprinted for the Collectors' Road Show at Limerick.

Nos. 748bb (containing No. 1084), 1080a, 1081a and 1081ab show the upper and lower edges of the panes imperforate. On booklet pane No. 1081ba the three 30p. have "all-over" phosphor, but this does not extend to the two 5p. stamps or the label.

Used examples of No 1038p are known with yellow omitted.

Booklet panes Nos. 1053pa, 1057apa and 1057pa show the stamps as a horizontal row with margins on three sides and the airmail labels attached at right.

Nos. 1086/7, 1088/9, 1090/1 and 1092/3 were produced in rolls of 100, each containing two designs. Nos. 1086/9 retain the surplus self-adhesive paper around each stamp, but this was removed for Nos. 1086pb/7pb and 1090/3.

The sheetlet of 30p. designs, No. 1038aq, also exists overprinted on the margins for Collectors Road Shows at Limerick (in black), Cork (in red), Killarney (in green), Sligo (in deep blue), and Galway (in maroon).

For £2 value in miniature sheet see No. **MS**1131.

346 Pair of Doves

(Des Double Z Enterprises. Litho Irish Security Stamp Ptg Ltd)

1997 (28 Jan). Greetings Stamps. T **346** and similar vert designs. Multicoloured. Chalk-surfaced paper. P 14×15.

1100	32p. Type **346**	85	50
	a. Booklet pane. No. 1100/3	3·75	
1101	32p. Cow jumping over moon	1·10	1·25
1102	32p. Pig going to market	1·10	1·25
1103	32p. Cockerel	1·10	1·25
1100/3	*Set of 4*	3·75	3·75

Nos. 1101/3 were only issued in £2.56 stamp booklets. No. 1100 was available from sheets and booklets.

Booklet pane No. 1100a, which also includes eight small greetings labels exists in two forms with No. 1101 either at left or right. In each instance the right-hand stamp, No. 1101 or No. 1103, is imperforate at right.

(Des Double Z Enterprises. Litho Irish Security Stamp Ptg Ltd)

1997 (28 Jan). "HONG KONG '97" International Stamp Exhibition. Chinese New Year ("Year of the Ox"). Chalk surfaced paper. P 14×15.

MS1104 124×74 mm. Nos. 1101/3		3·25	3·25

The example of No. 1103 in No. **MS**1104 is imperforate at right.

No. **MS**1104 also exists overprinted for the Collectors' Road Show at Limerick.

347 Troops on Parade

(Des Q. Design. Litho Irish Security Stamp Ptg Ltd)

1997 (18 Feb–6 Dec). 75th Anniv of Irish Free State. T **347** and similar horiz designs. Multicoloured. Chalk-surfaced paper. P 15×14.

1105	28p. Page from the "Annals of the Four Masters", quill and 1944 ½d. O'Clery stamp (27 Aug)	75	55
1106	32p. Type **347**	1·00	1·25
	a. Pair. Nos. 1106/7	2·00	2·50
1107	32p. The Dail, national flag and Constitution	1·00	1·25
1108	32p. Athlete, footballer and hurling players (3 Apr)	1·00	1·25
	a. Pair. Nos. 1108/9	2·00	2·50
1109	32p. Singer, violinist and bodhran player (3 Apr)	1·00	1·25
1110	32p. Stained glass window and 1929 9d. O'Connell stamp (27 Aug)	1·00	1·00
1111	32p. G.P.O., Dublin, and 1923 2d. map stamp (6 Dec)	1·00	1·00
1112	52p. Police personnel and Garda badge	1·75	2·00
	a. Pair. Nos. 1112/13	3·50	4·00
1113	52p. The Four Courts and Scales of Justice	1·75	2·00
1114	52p. Currency, blueprint and food processing plant (3 Apr)	1·75	2·00
	a. Pair. Nos. 1114/15	1·75	4·00
1115	52p. Books, palette and Seamus Heaney manuscript (3 Apr)	1·75	2·00
1116	52p. Air Lingus airliner and 1965 1s.5d air stamp (27 Aug)	1·75	1·50
1105/16	*Set of 12*	14·00	15·00
MS1117 174×209 mm. As Nos. 1105/16, but each with face value of 32p. (6 Dec)		12·00	15·00

Nos. 1106/7, 1108/9, 1112/13 and 1114/15 were each printed together, *se-tenant*, in horiz or vert pairs throughout the sheets.

348 Grey Seals   **349** Dublin Silver Penny of 997

(Des Rosemary Davis. Litho Irish Security Stamp Ptg Ltd)

1997 (6 Mar). Marine Mammals. T **348** and similar multicoloured designs. Chalk-surfaced paper. P 14×15 (28p., 32p.) or 15×14 (others).

1118	28p. Type **348**	75	60

1119	32p. Bottle-nosed Dolphins	85	80
1120	44p. Harbour Porpoises (*horiz*)	1·25	1·40
1121	52p. Killer Whale (*horiz*)	1·40	1·50
1118/21	*Set of 4*	3·75	3·75
MS1122 150×68 mm. As Nos. 1118/21. P 15		6·00	6·00

No. **MS**1122 also exists overprinted for the Collectors' Road Show at Dublin.

(Des Creative Inputs. Litho Irish Security Stamp Ptg Ltd)

1997 (3 Apr). Millenary of Irish Coinage. Chalk-surfaced paper. P 15×14.

1123	**349** 32p. multicoloured	65	65

350 "The Children of Lir"

(Des P. Lynch)

1997 (14 May). Europa. Tales and Legends. T **350** and similar horiz design. Multicoloured.

(a) Litho Walsall. Chalk-surfaced paper. P 14

1124	32p. Type **350**	75	60
1125	44p. Oisin and Niamh	1·10	2·00

(b) Litho Irish Security Stamp Ptg Ltd. Self-adhesive. P 9½

1126	32p. Type **350**	1·75	1·75
	a. Horiz pair. Nos. 1126/7	3·50	3·50
1127	32p. Oisin and Niamh	1·75	1·75
1124/7	*Set of 4*	4·75	5·00

Nos. 1124/5 were each issued in sheetlets of 10 (2×5) with enlarged illustrated left margins.

Nos. 1126/7, which are smaller 37×25 mm, occur in rolls of 100.

351 Emigrants waiting to board Ship

352 Kate O'Brien (novelist) (birth centenary)

(Des Q. Design. Litho Irish Security Stamp Ptg Ltd)

1997 (14 May). 150th Anniv of The Great Famine. T **351** and similar horiz designs. Chalk-surfaced paper. P 15×14.

1128	28p. deep dull blue, vermilion and pale yellow-ochre	1·00	70
1129	32p. reddish orange, deep dull blue and pale yellow-ochre	1·25	70
1130	52p. brown, dp dull blue and pale yell-ochre	1·75	3·00
1128/30	*Set of 3*	3·50	4·00

Designs—32p. Family and dying child; 52p. Irish Society of Friends soup kitchen.

(Des K. Mullarney. Litho Irish Security Stamp Ptg Ltd)

1997 (29 May). "Pacific '97" International Stamp Exhibition, San Francisco. Sheet, 100×70 mm, containing No. 1061. Multicoloured. Chalk-surfaced paper. P 14.

MS1131 Pintail (47×26 *mm*)		6·50	8·50

(Des Creative Inputs. Litho Irish Security Stamp Ptg Ltd (No. 1133) or Walsall (others)

1997 (1 July). Anniversaries. T **352** and similar vert designs. Multicoloured. Chalk-surfaced paper. P 14×15 (No. 1133), 14½ (No. 1134) or 14 (others).

1132	28p. Type **352**	75	1·00
1133	28p. St. Columba crossing to Iona (stained glass window) (1400th death anniv)	75	1·00
1134	32p. "Daniel O'Connell" (J. Haverty) (politician) (150th death anniv) (27×49 mm)	85	70
1135	52p. "John Wesley" (N. Hone) (founder of Methodism) (250th anniv of first visit to Ireland)	1·40	2·50
1132/5	*Set of 4*	3·25	4·75

353 The Baily Lighthouse

(Des Design Image. Litho Irish Security Stamp Ptg Ltd)

1997 (1 July). Lighthouses. T **353** and similar multicoloured designs. Chalk-surfaced paper. P 15×14 (32p.) or 14×15 (others).

1136	32p. Type **353**..	1·40	1·60
	a. Pair. Nos. 1136/7...............................	2·75	3·00
	b. Booklet pane. Nos. 1136×2 and 1137.....	3·50	
	c. Booklet pane. Nos. 1136/7, each×2.......	4·50	
	d. Perf 15..	1·40	2·00
	da. Booklet pane. Nos. 1136d/9d	4·50	
1137	32p. Tarbert..	1·40	1·60
	d. Perf 15..	1·40	2·00
1138	38p. Hookhead (vert).............................	1·40	1·50
	d. Perf 15..	1·40	2·00
	da. Booklet pane. Nos. 1138d/9d	2·75	
1139	50p. The Fastnet (vert)...........................	1·75	2·00
	d. Perf 15..	1·40	2·00
1136/9 *Set of 4*...		5·50	6·00

Nos. 1136/7 were printed together, *se-tenant*, in horizontal or vertical pairs throughout the sheet.

Nos. 1136d/9d only exist from booklet panes Nos. 1136da and 1138da.

The booklet panes also exist overprinted for Collectors' Road Shows at Sligo (No. 1136b), Tralee (No. 1138da), Galway (No. 1136c) or Limerick (No. 1136da) and also for "Stampa '97" (Nos. 1136b/c, 1136da and 1138da).

354 Commemorative Cross

355 Dracula and Bat

(Des L. Rafael. Litho Irish Security Stamp Ptg Ltd)

1997 (12 Sept). Ireland–Mexico Joint Issue. 150th Anniv of Mexican St. Patrick's Battalion. Ordinary paper. P 13½.

1140	**354** 32p. multicoloured................................	55	60

(Des Passmore Design. Litho Irish Security Stamp Ptg Ltd)

1997 (1 Oct). Centenary of Publication of Bram Stoker's *Dracula*. T **355** and similar multicoloured designs. Chalk-surfaced paper. P 14×15 (vert) or 15×14 (horiz).

1141	28p. Type **355**	60	55
1142	32p. Dracula and female victim.............	65	60
1143	38p. Dracula emerging from coffin (horiz).....	80	90
1144	52p. Dracula and wolf (horiz)................	1·10	1·75
1141/4 *Set of 4*		2·75	3·50
MS1145 150×90 mm. As Nos. 1141/4. P 15......		3·25	3·75

A second miniature sheet, 75×55 mm, containing No. 1142, was only available as a promotional item connected with the purchase of funsize bars of various Mars products or at face value from the Philatelic Bureau.

356 "The Nativity" (Kevin Kelly)

357 Christmas Tree

(Des Creative Inputs (Nos. 1146/8). Q. Design (No. 1149). Litho Irish Security Stamp Ptg Ltd)

1997 (18 Nov). Christmas.

*(a) Stained Glass Windows. T **356** and similar vert designs. Multicoloured. Chalk-surfaced paper. P 14×15*

1146	28p. Type **356**	70	55
1147	32p. "The Nativity" (Sarah Purser and A. E. Child)...	80	65
1148	52p. "The Nativity" (A. E. Child)............	1·50	2·25
1146/8 *Set of 3*...		2·75	3·00

(b) Self-adhesive booklet stamp. P 9×10

1149	28p. Type **357**	80	80
	a. Booklet pane. No. 1149×20................	14·50	

No. 1149 was only available from £5.32 stamp booklets.

358 Holding Heart

(Des B. Asprey. Litho Irish Security Stamp Ptg Ltd)

1998 (26 Jan). Greetings Stamps (1st series). T **358** and similar vert designs based on the "love is..." cartoon characters of Kim Casali. Multicoloured. Chalk-surfaced paper. P 14×15.

1150	32p. Type **358**	1·10	50
	a. Booklet pane. Nos. 1150/3.................	4·00	
1151	32p. Receiving letter..............................	1·10	1·25
1152	32p. Sitting on log.................................	1·10	1·25
1153	32p. With birthday presents...................	1·10	1·25
1150/3 *Set of 4*		4·00	3·75

Nos. 1151/3 were only available from £2.56 stamp booklets containing two examples of No. 1150a. This pane exists in two different forms with either No. 1150 at right and No. 1153 at left or No. 1152 at right and No. 1151 at left. In each instance the right-hand stamp is imperforate at right. No. 1150 is available from both sheets and booklets.

For 30p. values in these designs see Nos. 1173/6.

(Des B. Asprey. Litho Irish Security Stamp Ptg Ltd)

1998 (26 Jan). Chinese New Year ("Year of the Tiger"). Chalk surfaced paper. P 14×15.

MS1154 124×73 mm. Nos. 1151/3........................		4·50	5·50

The example of No. 1152 in No. **MS**1154 is imperforate at right.

359 Lady Mary Heath and Avro Avian over Pyramids

360 Show-jumping

(Des V. Killowry. Litho Irish Security Stamp Ptg Ltd)

1998 (24 Feb). Pioneers of Irish Aviation. T **359** and similar horiz designs. Multicoloured. Chalk-surfaced paper. P 15×14.

1155	28p. Type **359**	60	55
	a. Booklet pane. Nos. 1155/8.................	3·50	
	b. Booklet pane. Nos. 1155/6 each×2......	3·00	
1156	32p. Col. James Fitzmaurice and Junkers W.33 *Bremen* over Labrador.............	65	60
	a. Booklet pane. Nos. 1156×2 and 1157....	3·00	
	b. Booklet pane. Nos. 1156 and 1158×2...	3·00	
1157	44p. Captain J. P. Saul and Fokker FVIIa/3m *Southern Cross*	1·25	1·25
1158	52p. Captain Charles Blair and Sikorsky V-s 44 (flying boat)................................	1·50	1·50
1155/8 *Set of 4*...		3·50	3·50

Booklet panes Nos. 1155b and 1156a/b have margins all round. On No. 1155a there are margins on three sides, but the two right-hand stamps (Nos. 1156 and 1158) are each imperforate at right.

(Des P. Curling. Litho Irish Security Stamp Ptg Ltd)

1998 (2 Apr). Equestrian Sports. T **360** and similar multicoloured designs. Chalk-surfaced paper. P 14×15 (45p.) or 15×14 (others).

1159	30p. Type **360**	90	60
1160	32p. Three-day eventing........................	95	65
1161	40p. Gymkhana......................................	1·00	1·60
1162	45p. Dressage (vert)..............................	1·00	1·60

1159/62 Set of 4	3·50	4·00
MS1163 126×84 mm. Nos. 1159/62	3·50	4·00

361 Figure of "Liberty"

(Des R. Ballagh. Litho Irish Security Stamp Printing Ltd)

1998 (6 May). Bicentenary of United Irish Rebellion. T **361** and similar horiz designs. Multicoloured. Chalk-surfaced paper. P 15×14.

1164	30p. Type **361**	1·00	1·00
	a. Horiz strip of 3. Nos. 1164/6	2·75	2·75
1165	30p. United Irishman	1·00	1·00
1166	30p. French soldiers	1·00	1·00
1167	45p. Wolfe Tone	1·00	1·25
	a. Horiz pair. Nos. 1167/8	2·00	2·50
1168	45p. Henry Joy McCracken	1·00	1·25
1164/8 Set of 5		4·50	5·00

Nos. 1164/6 and 1167/8 were each printed together, horizontally se-tenant, in strips of 3 (30p.) or in pairs (45p.) throughout sheets of 12.

362 Gathering of the Boats, Kinvara

(Des J. Dunne. Litho Irish Security Stamp Ptg Ltd)

1998 (6 May). Europa. Festivals. T **362** and similar horiz design. Multicoloured.

(a) P 15×14

1169	30p. Type **362**	1·50	80
1170	40p. Puck Fair, Killorglin	1·50	95

(b) Self-adhesive. Chalk-surfaced paper. P 9½

1171	30p. Type **362**	2·00	1·50
1172	30p. Puck Fair, Killorglin	2·00	1·50

Nos. 1169/70 were each issued in sheetlets of 10 (2×5) with enlarged illustrated left margins.

Nos. 1171/2, which are smaller 37×26 mm, occur in rolls of 100 with the surplus self-adhesive paper retained.

1998 (6 May). Greetings Stamps (2nd series). Vert designs as Nos. 1150/3, but with changed face value. Multicoloured. Chalk-surfaced paper. P 14×15.

1173	30p. As No. 1153	95	95
	a. Booklet pane. Nos. 1173/6	3·50	
1174	30p. As No. 1152	95	95
1175	30p. As No. 1151	95	95
1176	30p. Type **358**	95	95
1173/6 Set of 4		3·50	3·50

Nos. 1173/6 were only available from £2.40 stamp booklets containing two examples of No. 1173a. This pane exists in two different forms with either No. 1176 at right and No. 1173 at left or No. 1174 at right and No. 1175 at left. In each instance the right-hand stamp is imperforate at right.

363 Cyclists rounding Bend

(Des C. Harrison. Litho Irish Security Stamp Ptg Ltd)

1998 (2 June). Visit of "Tour de France" Cycle Race to Ireland. T **363** and similar horiz designs. Multicoloured. Chalk-surfaced paper. P 15×14.

1177	30p. Type **363**	85	85
	a. Horiz strip of 4. Nos. 1177/80	3·00	3·00
1178	30p. Two cyclists ascending hill	85	85
1179	30p. "Green jersey" cyclist and other competitor	85	85
1180	30p. "Yellow jersey" (race leader)	85	85
1177/80 Set of 4		3·00	3·00

Nos. 1177/80 were printed together, se-tenant, in horizontal strips of 4 throughout the sheet.

364 Voter and Local Councillors of 1898

(Des J. Dunne. Litho Irish Security Stamp Ptg Ltd)

1998 (2 June). Democracy Anniversaries. T **364** and similar horiz designs. Multicoloured. Chalk-surfaced paper. P 15×14.

1181	30p. Type **364** (Cent of Local Government (Ireland) Act)	60	60
1182	32p. European Union flag and harp symbol (25th anniv of Ireland's entry into European Community)	65	65
1183	35p. Woman voter and suffragettes, 1898 (Cent of women's right to vote in local elections)	75	1·25
1184	45p. Irish Republic flag (50th anniv of Republic of Ireland Act)	1·00	1·40
1181/4 Set of 4		2·75	3·50

365 Asgard II (cadet brigantine)   **366** Ashworth Pillarbox (1856)

(Des FOR Design. Litho Irish Security Stamp Ptg Ltd)

1998 (20 July). Cutty Sark International Tall Ships Race, Dublin. T **365** and similar multicoloured designs. Chalk-surfaced paper.

(a) P 14×15 (30p.) or 15×14 (45p. £1)

1185	30p. Type **365**	1·00	1·00
	a. Pair. Nos. 1185/6	2·00	2·00
	b. Perf 15	1·10	1·25
	ba. Booklet pane. Nos. 1185bx2 and 1186b with margins all round	3·50	
1186	30p. U.S.C.G. Eagle (cadet barque)	1·00	1·00
	b. Perf 15	1·40	1·75
	ba. Booklet pane. Nos. 1186b/8b with margins all round	3·50	
1187	45p. Boa Esperanza (replica caravel) (horiz)	1·25	1·00
	b. Perf 15	1·75	2·50
1188	£1 Royalist (training brigantine) (horiz)	2·00	2·75
	b. Perf 15	2·00	2·75
1185/8 Set of 4		4·75	5·25

(b) Self-adhesive. P 9½

1189	30p. Boa Esperanza (horiz)	1·10	1·10
	a. Strip of 4. Nos. 1189/92	4·00	4·00
1190	30p. Type **365**	1·10	1·10
1191	30p. U.S.C.G. Eagle	1·10	1·10
1192	30p. Royalist (horiz)	1·10	1·10
1189/92 Set of 4		4·00	4·00

Nos. 1185b/8b were only available from £2.65 stamp booklets.

Nos. 1189/92 are smaller, 37×26 mm, and occur, se-tenant, in strips of 4 or rolls of 100 with the surplus self-adhesive paper around each stamp retained.

Nos. 1185ba and 1186ba also exist overprinted for "Stampa 98".

(Des M. Craig. Litho Irish Security Stamp Ptg Ltd)

1998 (3 Sept). Irish Postboxes. T **366** and similar vert designs. Multicoloured. Chalk-surfaced paper. P 15×14.

1193	30p. Type **366**	75	1·00
	a. Horiz strip of 4. Nos. 1193/6	2·75	3·50
1194	30p. Irish Free State wallbox (1922)	75	1·00
1195	30p. Double pillarbox (1899)	75	1·00
1196	30p. Penfold pillarbox (1866)	75	1·00
1193/6 Set of 4		2·75	3·50

Nos. 1193/6 were printed together, se-tenant, in horizontal strips of 4 throughout the sheet of 12.

367 Mary Immaculate College, Limerick   **368** Cheetah

(Des J. McPartlin (45p), E. Patton (others). Litho Irish Security Stamp Ptg Ltd)

1998 (3 Sept). Anniversaries. T **367** and similar multicoloured designs. Chalk-surfaced paper. P 14×15 (40p.) or 15×14 (others).
1197	30p. Type **367** (centenary)	75	60
1198	40p. Newtown School, Waterford (bicent) (vert)	1·00	1·50
1199	45p. Trumpeters (50th anniv of Universal Declaration of Human Rights)	1·10	1·75
1197/9 Set of 3		2·50	3·50

(Des FOR Design. Litho Irish Security Stamp Ptg Ltd)

1998 (4 Sept). "Portugal '98" International Stamp Exhibition, Lisbon. Sheet 101×71 mm, containing design as No. 1187. Chalk-surfaced paper. P 15×14.
MS1200 45p. *Boa Esperanza* (caravel) (*horiz*) .... 6·00 7·00

(Des F. O'Conner. Litho Walsall)

1998 (8 Oct). Endangered Animals. T **368** and similar multicoloured designs. P 14.
1201	30p. Type **368**	1·00	1·25
	a. Horiz pair. Nos. 1201/2	2·00	2·50
1202	30p. Scimitar-horned Oryx	1·00	1·25
1203	40p. Golden Lion Tamarin (*vert*)	1·10	1·25
1204	45p. Tiger (*vert*)	1·40	1·50
1201/4 Set of 4		4·00	4·75
MS1205 150×90 mm. As Nos. 1201/4. P 15		3·50	4·25

Nos. 1201/4 were printed together, *se-tenant*, in horizontal pairs throughout the sheet.
No. **MS**1205 also exists with an enlarged top margin overprinted for "Stampa 98" National Stamp Exhibition, Dublin.

369 The Holy Family   **370** Choir Boys

(Des P. Lynch (Nos. 1206/8), J. Laffan (No. 1209))

1998 (17 Nov). Christmas.

(a) Litho Irish Security Stamp Ptg Ltd. T **369** and similar vert designs. Multicoloured. Chalk-surfaced paper. P 14×15
1206	30p. Type **369**	70	60
1207	32p. Shepherds	75	65
1208	45p. Three Kings	1·00	1·75
1206/8 Set of 3		2·25	2·75

(b) Litho SNP Cambec, Australia. Self-adhesive. Phosphor frame. P 11½
1209	30p. Type **370**	70	70
	a. Booklet pane. No. 1209×20	12·00	

No. 1209, on which the phosphor frame appears greenish yellow under UV. light, was only available from £5.40 stamp booklets.

371 Puppy and Heart   **372** Micheál Mac Liammóir

(Des M. Connor. Litho Irish Security Stamp Ptg Ltd)

1999 (26 Jan). Greetings Stamps. Pets. T **371** and similar vert designs. Multicoloured. Chalk-surfaced paper. Phosphor frame. P 14×15.
1210	30p. Type **371**	80	50
	a. Booklet pane. Nos. 1210/13	3·50	
1211	30p. Kitten and ball of wool	1·00	1·50
1212	30p. Goldfish	1·00	1·50
1213	30p. Rabbit with lettuce leaf	1·00	1·50
1210/13 Set of 4		3·50	4·50

Nos. 1211/13, on which the phosphor appears green under U.V. light, were only available from £2.40 stamp booklets containing two examples of No. 1210a. This pane exists in two different forms with either No. 1210 at left and No. 1213 at right or No. 1213 at left and No. 1210 at right. In each instance the right-hand stamp is imperforate at right. No. 1210 is available from both sheets and booklets.

(Des M. Connor. Litho Irish Security Stamp Ptg Ltd)

1999 (26 Jan). Chinese New Year ("Year of the Rabbit"). Chalk-surfaced paper. Phosphor frame. P 14×15.
MS1214 124×74 mm. Nos. 1211/13 .... 3·75 4·00
The example of No. 1213 is imperforate at right.

(Des Creative Inputs. Litho Irish Security Stamp Ptg Ltd)

1999 (16 Feb). Irish Actors and Actresses. T **372** and similar vert designs. Chalk-surfaced paper. Phosphor frame. P 14×15.
1215	30p. black and yellow-brown	65	60
1216	45p. black and bright green	1·00	1·10
1217	50p. black and ultramarine	1·00	1·25
1215/17 Set of 3		2·40	2·75

Designs: 45p. Siobhan McKenna; 50p. Noel Purcell.

373 Irish Emigrant Ship

(Des H. Paine and T. Mann. Litho Irish Security Stamp Ptg Ltd)

1999 (26 Feb). Ireland–U.S.A. Joint Issue. Irish Emigration. Chalk-surfaced paper. Phosphor frame. P 15×14.
1218   **373**   45p. multicoloured .... 1·25 1·00
A stamp in a similar design was issued by the U.S.A.

374 *Polly Woodside* (barque)   **375** Sean Lemass

(Des V. Killowry. Litho Walsall)

1999 (19 Mar). Maritime Heritage. T **374** and similar multicoloured designs. Chalk-surfaced paper. Phosphor frame. P 14.
1219	30p. Type **374**	55	60
1220	35p. *Ilen* (schooner)	65	70
1221	45p. R.N.L.I. "Cromer" class life boat (*horiz*)	80	85
1222	£1 *Titanic* (liner) (*horiz*)	2·00	2·50
1219/22 Set of 4		3·50	4·25
MS1223 150×90 mm. No. 1222×2. No phosphor frame		3·50	4·00

On Nos. 1219/22, the phosphor shows green under U.V. light.
No. **MS**1223 also exists overprinted for "Australia '99" International Stamp Exhibition, Melbourne, in gold, "Stampania' 99", Dublin, in deep blue and "Stampa '99" National Stamp Exhibition, Dublin, in red.

(Litho SNP Ausprint)

1999 (19 Mar). Ireland–Australia Joint Issue. *Polly Woodside* (barque). Sheet 137×72 mm. Multicoloured. Phosphorised paper. P 14×14½.
MS1224 45c. Type **603** of Australia; 30p. Type **374** (*No. MS*1224 *was sold at 52p. in Ireland*) .... 1·40 1·75
No. **MS**1224 includes the "Australia 99" emblem on the sheet margin and was postally valid in Ireland to the value of 30p.
The same miniature sheet was also available in Australia.

(Des Creative Inputs. Litho Irish Security Stamp Ptg Ltd)

1999 (29 Apr). Birth Centenary of Sean Lemass (politician). Chalk-surfaced paper. Phosphor frame. P 14×15.

1225	**375**	30p. black and deep bluish green...........	1·40	1·00

376 European Currency Emblem

(Des Creative Inputs. Litho Irish Security Stamp Ptg Ltd)

1999 (29 Apr). Introduction of Single European Currency. Chalk-surfaced paper. Phosphor frame. P 15×14.

1226	**376**	30p. multicoloured..	75	65

The face value of No. 1226 is shown in both Irish and Euro currencies.

377 European Flags

(Des J. McPartlin. Litho Irish Security Stamp Ptg Ltd)

1999 (29 Apr). 50th Anniv of Council of Europe. Chalk-surfaced paper. Phosphor frame. P 14×15.

1227	**377**	45p. multicoloured..	1·00	1·00

378 Swans, Kilcolman Nature Reserve

(Des F. O'Connor. Litho Irish Security Stamp Ptg Ltd)

1999 (29 Apr). Europe. Parks and Gardens. T **378** and similar horiz design. Chalk-surfaced paper. Phosphor frame.

(a) P 15×14

1228	30p. Type **378**	90	50
1229	40p. Fallow Deer, Phoenix Park..........................	1·00	1·75

(b) Self-adhesive. P 9½

1230	30p. Type **378**	1·50	2·25
1231	30p. Fallow Deer, Phoenix Park..........................	1·50	2·25

Nos. 1228/9 were each issued in sheets of 10 (2×5) with enlarged illustrated left margins.

Nos. 1230/1, which are smaller, 37×26 mm, were only available in rolls of 100 on which the surplus self-adhesive paper was retained.

379 Father James Cullen and St. Francis Xavier Church, Dublin

380 Elderly Man and Child using Computer

(Des Creative Inputs. Litho Irish Security Stamp Ptg Ltd)

1999 (15 June). Centenary of Pioneer Total Abstinence Association. Chalk-surfaced paper. Phosphor frame. P 14×15.

1232	**379**	32p. olive-brown, bistre and black..........	75	65

(Des C. Harrison. Litho Irish Security Stamp Ptg Ltd)

1999 (15 June). International Year of Older Persons. Chalk-surfaced paper. Phosphor frame. P 15×14.

1233	**380**	30p. multicoloured..............................	70	65

381 Postal Van, 1922

382 Danno Keeffe

(Des Creative Inputs. Litho Irish Security Stamp Ptg Ltd)

1999 (15 June). 125th Anniv of Universal Postal Union. T **381** and similar horiz design. Chalk-surfaced paper. Phosphor frame. P 15×14.

1234	30p. grey-green and slate-green......................	1·40	1·25
	a. Pair. Nos. 1234/5.................................	2·75	2·50
1235	30p. multicoloured.................................	1·40	1·25

Designs:—No. 1234, Type **381**; No. 1235, Modern postal lorries.

Nos. 1234/5 were printed together, *se-tenant*, in horizontal or vertical pairs throughout sheets of 16.

(Des F. O'Connor)

1999 (17 Aug). Gaelic Athletic Association "Millennium Football Team". T **382** and similar horiz designs. Multicoloured. Phosphor frame. Chalk-surfaced paper.

(a) Litho Irish Security Stamp Ptg Ltd. P 15×14

1236	30p. Type **382**	65	70
	a. Sheetlet. Nos. 1236/50 plus label..........	9·00	
1237	30p. Enda Colleran	65	70
1238	30p. Joe Keohane	65	70
1239	30p. Sean Flanagan	65	70
1240	30p. Sean Murphy	65	70
1241	30p. John Joe Reilly	65	70
1242	30p. Martin O'Connell	65	70
1243	30p. Mick O'Connell	65	70
1244	30p. Tommy Murphy	65	70
1245	30p. Sean O'Neilll	65	70
1246	30p. Sean Purcell	65	70
1247	30p. Pat Spillane	65	70
1248	30p. Mikey Sheehy	65	70
1249	30p. Tom Langan	65	70
1250	30p. Kevin Heffernan	65	70
1236/50 *Set of 15*..		9·00	9·50

(b) Self-adhesive booklet stamps. Litho SNP Ausprint, Australia. P 11½

1251	30p. Danno Keeffe	3·00	4·50
	a. Booklet pane. Nos. 1251, 1253, 1255, 1258, 1263×2 and 1263×2..........	11·00	
1252	30p. Enda Colleran	70	1·00
	a. Booklet pane. Nos. 1252, 1254, 1261 and 1264, each×2....................	4·50	
1253	30p. Joe Keohane	3·00	4·50
1254	30p. Sean Flanagan	70	1·00
1255	30p. Sean Murphy	3·00	4·50
1256	30p. John Joe Reilly	45	60
	a. Booklet pane. Nos. 1256 and 1260, each×4..	3·25	
1257	30p. Martin O'Connell	45	60
	a. Booklet pane. Nos. 1257×3, 1259×2 and 1265×3...............................	3·50	
1258	30p. Mick O'Connell	3·00	4·50
1259	30p. Tommy Murphy	70	1·00
1260	30p. Sean O'Neill	45	60
1261	30p. Sean Purcell	70	1·00
1262	30p. Pat Spillane	70	1·00
1263	30p. Mikey Sheehy	70	1·00
1264	30p. Tom Langan	70	1·00
1265	30p. Kevin Heffernan	45	60
1251/65 *Set of 15*..		15·00	22·00

Nos. 1236/50 were issued together, *se-tenant*, in sheetlets of 15 stamps and a label. No. 1236a also exists imperforate from a framed limited edition sold at £30. Such imperforate sheetlets were overprinted "NOT VALID FOR POSTAGE" on the reverse and stamps from them should not, according to An Post, be postmarked.

No. 1236a also exists with the margins overprinted in black for "Stamps '99" National Stamp Exhibition, Dublin and for Collectors' Road Shows at Kilkenny, Limerick, Cork, Killarney and Galway in 2000.

Nos. 1251/65 are smaller, 37×25 mm, and were only issued in four different £2.40 stamp booklets in which the surplus self-adheaive paper around each stamp was retained.

383 Douglas DC3

(Des V. Killowry. Litho Irish Security Stamp Ptg Ltd)

1999 (9 Sept). Commercial Aviation. T **383** and similar horiz designs. Multicoloured. Chalk-surfaced paper. Phosphor frame. P 15×14.

1266	30p. Type **383**	65	50
	a. Booklet pane. No. 1266×4, with margins all round	2·50	
	b. Booklet pane. Nos. 1266×9, with margins all round	2·75	
	c. Booklet pane. Nos. 1266/7, each×2, with margins all round	2·75	
	d. Booklet pane. Nos. 1266×2 and 1268, with margins all round	2·50	
1267	32p. Britten Norman Islander	75	55
1268	40p. Boeing 707	80	1·40
1269	45p. Lockheed Constellation	90	1·50
1266/9	*Set of 4*	2·75	3·50

Booklet pane No. 1266d exists overprinted for "Stampa '99" National Stamp Exhibition, Dublin.
See also Nos. 1364/71.

384 Mammoth

(Des F. O'Connor. Litho Irish Security Stamp Ptg Ltd)

1999 (11 Oct). Extinct Irish Animals. T **384** and similar multicoloured designs. Chalk-surfaced paper. Phosphor frame.

(a) P 14×15 (30p.) or 15×14 (45p.)

1270	30p. Type **384**	70	70
	a. Pair. Nos. 1270/1	1·40	1·40
1271	30p. Giant Deer	70	70
1272	45p. Wolves (*horiz*)	90	1·25
	a. Pair. Nos. 1272/3	1·75	2·50
1273	45p. Brown Bear (*horiz*)	90	1·25
1270/3	*Set of 4*	2·75	3·50
MS1274	150×63 mm. Nos. 1270/3. Without phosphor frame. P 15	2·75	3·00

(b) Self-adhesive. P 9½

1275	30p. Brown Bear (*horiz*)	90	1·00
	a. Horiz strip of 4. Nos. 1275/8	3·25	3·50
1276	30p. Type **384**	90	1·00
1277	30p. Wolves (*horiz*)	90	1·00
1278	30p. Giant Deer	90	1·00
1275/8	*Set of 4*	3·25	3·50

Nos. 1270/1 and 1272/3 were each printed together, *se-tenant*, in horizontal or vertical pairs throughout sheets of 16.
Nos. 1275/8, which are smaller, 37×25 mm (*horiz*) or 25×37 mm (*vert*), occur, *se-tenant*, in strips of 4 or rolls of 100 with the surplus self-adhesive paper around each stamp retained.
No. **MS**1274 also exists overprinted in red for the Collectors' Road Show ("Stampania 2000"), Dublin.

385 Holy Family

(Des P. Lynch. Litho Irish Security Stamp Ptg Ltd)

1999 (4 Nov). Christmas. Children's Nativity Plays. T **385** and similar multicoloured designs. Chalk-surfaced paper. Phosphor frame.

(a) Horiz designs. P 15×14

1279	30p. Type **385**	60	50
1280	32p. Visit of the Shepherds	65	55
1281	45p. Adoration of the Magi	1·25	1·50
1279/81	*Set of 3*	2·25	2·25

(b) Self-adhesive. Vert design, 25×29 mm. P 9½

1282	30p. Angel	70	50
	a. Booklet pane. No. 1282×20	12·50	

386 Grace Kelly (American actress)

(Des FOR Design. Litho Irish Security Stamp Ptg Ltd)

1999 (31 Dec). New Millennium (1st issue). Famous People of the 20th Century. T **386** and similar vert designs. Multicoloured. Chalk-surfaced paper. Phosphor frame. P 14×15.

1283	30p. Type **386**	1·75	2·00
	a. Sheetlet. Nos. 1283/8×2	15·00	
1284	30p. Jesse Owens (American athlete)	1·75	2·00
1285	30p. John F. Kennedy (former American President)	1·75	2·00
1286	30p. Mother Teresa (missionary)	1·75	2·00
1287	30p. John McCormack (tenor)	1·75	2·00
1288	30p. Nelson Mandela (South African statesman)	1·75	2·00
1283/8	*Set of 6*	9·50	11·00

Nos. 1283/8 were printed together, *se-tenant*, as two separate blocks of 6 in sheetlets of 12 with enlarged illustrated margins.
No. 1283a exists overprinted in black for "Stampa 2000" National Stamp Exhibition, Dublin.
See also Nos. 1289/94, 1300/5, 1315/20, 1377/82 and 1383/8.

387 Ruined Castle (Norman Invasion, 1169)

(Des FOR Design. Litho Irish Security Stamp Ptg Ltd)

2000 (1 Jan). New Millennium (2nd issue). Irish Historic Events. T **387** and similar horiz designs. Multicoloured. Chalk-surfaced paper. Phosphor frame. P 15×14.

1289	30p. Type **387**	1·75	2·00
	a. Sheetlet. Nos. 1289/94×2	15·00	
1290	30p. Flight of the Earls, 1607	1·75	2·00
1291	30p. Opening of Irish Parliament, 1782	1·75	2·00
1292	30p. Eviction (formation of the Land League)	1·75	2·00
1293	30p. First four Irish Prime Ministers (Irish Independence)	1·75	2·00
1294	30p. Irish soldier and personnel carrier (U.N. Peace-keeping)	1·75	2·00
1289/94	*Set of 6*	9·50	11·00

Nos. 1289/94 were issued in the same format as Nos. 1283/8.

388 Frog Prince

389 Revd. Nicholas Callan (electrical scientist)

(Des B. Castle. Litho Irish Security Stamp Ptg Ltd)

2000 (26 Jan). Greetings Stamps. Mythical Creatures. T **388** and similar vert designs. Multicoloured. Chalk-surfaced paper. Phosphor frame. P 14×15.

1295	30p. Type **388**	1·00	60
	a. Booklet pane. Nos. 1295/8	3·50	
	b. Booklet pane. Nos. 1295 and 1298	3·50	
1296	30p. Pegasus	1·00	1·25
1297	30p. Unicorn	1·00	1·25
1298	30p. Dragon	1·00	1·25
1295/8	*Set of 4*	3·50	4·00

No. 1295 was available from both sheets and booklets, but Nos. 1296/8 come from £3 booklets only.

The examples of No. 1295 in the booklet panes are imperforate at right. Booklet pane No. 1295a includes 8 greetings labels in horizontal rows above and below the stamps and No. 1295b 14 similar labels in the same position and as a block of 10 at left.

(Des B. Castle. Litho Irish Security Stamp Ptg Ltd)

2000 (26 Jan). Chinese New Year ("Year of the Dragon"). Chalk-surfaced paper. Phosphor frame. P 14×15.

MS1299	124×74 mm. Nos. 1296/8	3·00	3·00

On No. **MS**1299 No. 1298 is imperforate at right.

No. **MS**1299 exists overprinted in black for "Stampa 2000" National Stamp Exhibition, Dublin.

(Des FOR Design. Litho Irish Security Stamp Ptg Ltd)

2000 (29 Feb). New Millennium (3rd issue). Discoveries. T **389** and similar vert designs. Multicoloured. Chalk-surfaced paper. Phosphor frame. P 14×15.

1300	30p. Type **389**	1·75	2·00
	a. Sheetlet. Nos. 1300/5×2	15·00	
1301	30p. Birr Telescope	1·75	2·00
1302	30p. Thomas Edison (inventor of light bulb)	1·75	2·00
1303	30p. Albert Einstein (mathematical physicist)	1·75	2·00
1304	30p. Marie Curie (physicist)	1·75	2·00
1305	30p. Galileo Galilei (astronomer and mathematician)	1·75	2·00
1300/5	Set of 6	9·50	11·00

Nos. 1300/5 were printed in a similar format as Nos. 1283/8.

390 *Jeanie Johnston* (emigrant ship)

(Des V. Killowry. Litho Irish Security Stamp Ptg Ltd)

2000 (9 Mar). Completion of *Jeanie Johnston* Replica. Chalk-surfaced paper. Phosphor frame. P 15×14.

1306	**390**	30p. multicoloured	70	50

391 "Building Europe"   **392** Oscar Wilde

(Des J.-P. Cousin. Litho Irish Security Stamp Ptg Ltd)

2000 (9 May). Europa. Chalk-surfaced paper. Phosphor frame.

(a) Size 29×40 mm. P 14×15

1307	**391**	32p. multicoloured	80	55

(b) Size 25×37 mm. Self-adhesive. P 9½

1308	**391**	30p. multicoloured	1·25	1·25

No. 1307 was printed in sheetlets of 10 with an illustrated top left margin showing previous Europa stamp designs.

No. 1308 was produced in rolls of 100 with the surplus self-adhesive paper around each stamp retained.

> **DENOMINATION.** From No. 1309 to No. 1465 some Irish stamps were denominated both in Irish pounds and euros. As no cash for the latter was in circulation at that time, the catalogue continued to use the pound value.

(Des Passmore Design. Litho Irish Security Stamp Ptg Ltd)

2000 (22 May). Death Centenary of Oscar Wilde (writer). T **392** and similar multicoloured designs. Chalk-surfaced paper. Phosphor frame. P 14×15.

1309	30p. Type **392**	1·00	1·25
	a. Block of 4. Nos. 1309/12	3·50	4·50
1310	30p. *The Happy Prince*	1·00	1·25
1311	30p. Lady Bracknell from *The Importance of being Earnest*	1·00	1·25
1312	30p. *The Picture of Dorian Gray*	1·00	1·25
1309/12	Set of 4	3·50	4·50

MS1313	150×90 mm. £2 Type **392**. No phosphor frame	3·25	4·00
	a. With "The Stamp Show 2000" logo added to the sheet margin	3·25	4·00

Nos. 1309/12 were printed together, *se-tenant*, as blocks of 4, in sheets of 16.

No. **MS**1313 also exists overprinted in black for "Stampa 2000" National Stamp Exhibition, Dublin.

A further 30p. exists in a design similar to Type **392**, but 29×29 mm. This was printed in lithography by SNP Ausprint, Australia, in sheets of 20, each stamp having a *se-tenant* half-stamp size label attached at right inscribed "Oscar". These sheets could be personalised by the addition of a photograph in place of the inscription on the labels. Such stamps are not listed as they were not available at face value, the sheets of 20 containing the "Oscar" labels being sold for £10.

393 Ludwig van Beethoven (German composer)   **394** Running

(Des FOR Design. Litho Irish Security Stamp Ptg Ltd)

2000 (16 June). New Millennium (4th issue). The Arts. T **393** and similar vert designs. Multicoloured. Chalk-surfaced paper. Phosphor frame. P 14×15.

1315	30p. Type **393**	2·00	2·00
	a. Sheetlet. Nos. 1315/20×2	18·00	
1316	30p. Dame Ninette de Valois (ballet director)	2·00	2·00
1317	30p. James Joyce (author)	2·00	2·00
1318	30p. "Mona Lisa" (Leonardo da Vinci)	2·00	2·00
1319	30p. "Lady Lavery" (Sir John Lavery)	2·00	2·00
1320	30p. William Shakespeare (playwright)	2·00	2·00
1315/20	Set of 6	11·00	11·00

Nos. 1315/20 were printed in a similar format as Nos. 1283/8.

(Des J. Dunne. Litho Irish Security Stamp Ptg Ltd)

2000 (7 July). Olympic Games, Sydney. T **394** and similar square designs. Multicoloured. Chalk-surfaced paper. Phosphor frame. P 13½.

1321	30p. Type **394**	70	70
	a. Pair. Nos. 1321/2	1·40	1·40
1322	30p. Javelin throwing	70	70
1323	50p. Long jumping	1·00	1·25
	a. Pair. Nos. 1323/4	2·00	2·50
1324	50p. High jumping	1·00	1·25
1321/4	Set of 4	3·00	3·50

Nos. 1321/2 and 1323/4 were each printed together, *se-tenant*, as horizontal or vertical pairs in sheets of 16.

395 "Space Rocket over Flowers" (Marguerite Nyhan)   **396** Tony Reddin

(Adapted Q. Design. Litho Irish Security Stamp Ptg Ltd)

2000 (7 July). "Stampin' the Future" (children's stamp design competition). T **395** and similar multicoloured designs. Chalk-surfaced paper. Phosphor frame. P 14×15 (30p.) or 15×14 (others).

1325	30p. Type **395**	60	50
1326	32p. "Tree, rocket and hands holding globe in '2000" (Kyle Staunton) (*horiz*)	70	55
1327	45p. "People holding hands on globe" (Jennifer Branagan) (*horiz*)	90	1·10
	a. Pair. Nos. 1327/8	1·75	2·10
1328	45p. "Colony on Moon" (Diarmuid O'Ceochain) (*horiz*)	90	1·10
1325/8	Set of 4	2·75	3·00

Nos. 1327/8 were printed together, *se-tenant*, as horizontal or vertical pairs in sheets of 16.

(Des F. O'Connor and FOR Design)

2000 (2 Aug). "Hurling Team of the Millennium". T **396** and similar horiz designs. Multicoloured. Chalk-surfaced paper. Phosphor frame.

(a) Litho Irish Security Stamp Ptg Ltd. P 15×14

1329	30p. Type **396**	60	70
	a. Sheetlet. Nos. 1329/43	8·00	9·50
1330	30p. Bobby Rackard	60	70
1331	30p. Nick O'Donnell	60	70
1332	30p. John Doyle	60	70
1333	30p. Brian Whelahan	60	70
1334	30p. John Keane	60	70
1335	30p. Paddy Phelan	60	70
1336	30p. Lary Meagher	60	70
1337	30p. Jack Lynch	60	70
1338	30p. Jim Langton	60	70
1339	30p. Mick Mackey	60	70
1340	30p. Christy Ring	60	70
1341	30p. Jimmy Doyle	60	70
1342	30p. Ray Cummins	60	70
1343	30p. Eddie Keher	60	70
1329/43	*Set of 15*	8·00	9·50

(b) Self-adhesive booklet stamps. Litho SNP Ausprint, Australia. P 11½

1344	30p. Type **396**	60	1·00
	a. Booklet pane. Nos. 1344/5, each×3, and 1346×4	5·50	
1345	30p. Jimmy Doyle	60	1·00
1346	30p. John Doyle	60	1·00
1347	30p. Paddy Phelan	1·50	2·50
	a. Booklet pane. Nos. 1347/8, each×2, and 1349/50, each×3	8·00	
1348	30p. Jim Langton	1·50	2·50
1349	30p. Lary Meagher	60	1·00
1350	30p. Eddie Keher	60	1·00
1351	30p. Mick Mackey	60	1·00
	a. Booklet pane. No. 1351×4 and 1352/3, each×3	5·50	
1352	30p. Brian Whelahan	60	1·00
1353	30p. John Keane	60	1·00
1354	30p. Bobby Rackard	60	1·00
	a. Booklet pane. Nos. 1354/5, each×5	5·50	
1355	30p. Nick O'Donnell	60	1·00
1356	30p. Jack Lynch	60	1·00
	a. Booklet pane. Nos. 1356/7, each×3, and 1358×4	5·50	
1357	30p. Ray Cummins	60	1·00
1358	30p. Christy Ring	60	1·00
1344/58	*Set of 15*	9·75	16·00

Nos. 1329/43 were printed together, *se-tenant*, in sheetlets of 15 including a central label and illustrated margins. Imperforate examples come from framed sheetlets sold for £30.

No. 1329a also exists overprinted in black for Collectors' Road Shows in Kilkenny and Limerick during 2001.

Nos. 1344/58 are smaller, 33×23 mm, and were only issued in five different £3 stamp booklets on which the surplus self-adhesive paper around each stamp was retained.

397 Peacock Butterfly   **398** Tractor ploughing Field

(Des I. Loe. Litho Walsall)

2000 (6 Sept). Butterflies. T **397** and similar horiz designs. Multicoloured. Chalk-surfaced paper. Phosphor frame. P 13½×12½.

1359	30p. Type **397**	80	50
1360	32p. Small Tortoiseshell	85	55
1361	45p. Silver-washed Fritillary	1·25	1·75
1362	50p. Orange-tip	1·40	2·50
1359/62	*Set of 4*	3·75	4·75
MS1363	150×90 mm. Nos. 1359/62	4·75	5·00

Stamps in No. **MS**1363 are without imprint dates.

(Des V. Killowry. Litho Irish Security Stamp Ptg Ltd)

2000 (9 Oct). Military Aviation. Horiz designs as T **383**. Multicoloured. Chalk-surfaced paper. Phosphor frame.

(a) P 15×14

1364	30p. Hawker Hurricane Mk IIc	1·50	1·75
	a. Pair. Nos. 1364/5	3·00	3·50

	b. Booklet pane. Nos. 1364/5, each×2, with margins all round	4·00	
	c. Booklet pane. Nos. 1364/7 with margins all round	5·00	
	d. Booklet pane. Nos. 1364/5 and 1367 with margins all round	3·50	
1365	30p. Bristol F.2b Mk II	1·50	1·75
1366	45p. de Havilland DH.115 Vampire T.55	2·00	2·25
	a. Pair. Nos. 1366/7	4·00	4·50
	b. Booklet pane. Nos. 1366/7, each×2, with margins all round	5·00	
1367	45p. Sud SE. 3160 Alouette III (helicopter)	2·00	2·25
1364/7	*Set of 4*	6·25	7·25

(b) Self-adhesive. Size 37×25 mm. P 9½

1368	30p. Bristol F.2b Mk II	1·50	1·50
1369	30p. Hawker Hurricane Mk 11c	1·50	1·50
1370	30p. de Havilland DH.115 Vampire T.55	1·50	1·50
1371	30p. SUD SE. 3160 Alouette III	1·50	1·50
1368/71	*Set of 4*	5·50	5·50

Nos. 1364/5 and 1366/7 were each printed together, *se-tenant*, in horizontal or vertical pairs throughout sheets of 16.

Nos. 1368/71 occur, *se-tenant*, in rolls of 100 with the surplus backing paper removed.

(Des D5 Design. Litho Irish Security Stamp Ptg Ltd)

2000 (14 Nov). Centenary of An Roinn Talmhaíochta (Department of Agriculture). Phosphor frame. P 13½.

1372	**398** 50p. multicoloured	1·25	1·40

399 The Nativity   **400** Storming the Bastille, Paris, 1789

(Des P. Lynch)

2000 (14 Nov). Christmas. T **399** and similar vert designs. Multicoloured. Phosphor frame.

(a) Litho Irish Security Stamp Ptg Ltd. P 14×15

1373	30p. Type **399**	65	25
1374	32p. Three Magi	75	55
1375	45p. Shepherds	1·00	1·50
1373/5	*Set of 3*	2·10	2·10

(b) Litho SNP Ausprint, Australia. Self-adhesive. P 11½

1376	30p. Flight into Egypt (24×29 mm)	90	50
	a. Booklet pane. No. 1376×24	20·00	

No. 1376 was only available in £6.60 booklets with the phospher covering much of the surplus self-adhesive paper which was retained.

(Des FOR Design. Litho Irish Security Stamp Ptg Ltd)

2000 (31 Dec). New Millennium (5th issue). World Events. T **400** and similar horiz designs. Multicoloured. Chalk-surfaced paper. Phosphor frame. P 15×14.

1377	30p. Type **400**	1·75	2·00
	a. Sheetlet. Nos. 1377/82×2	15·00	
1378	30p. Early railway	1·75	2·00
1379	30p. Returning troop ship, 1945	1·75	2·00
1380	30p. Suffragettes	1·75	2·00
1381	30p. Destruction of the Berlin Wall, 1989	1·75	2·00
1382	30p. Internet communications	1·75	2·00
1377/82	*Set of 6*	9·50	11·00

Nos. 1377/82 were printed in a similar format to Nos. 1283/8.

(Des FOR Design. Litho Irish Security Stamp Ptg Ltd)

2001 (1 Jan). New Millennium (6th issue). Epic Journeys. Horiz designs as T **400**. Multicoloured. Chalk-surfaced paper. Phosphor frame. P 15×14.

1383	30p. Marco Polo	2·00	2·00
	a. Sheetlet. Nos. 1383/8×2	17·00	
1384	30p. Captain James Cook	2·00	2·00
1385	30p. Burke and Wills expedition crossing Australia, 1860	2·00	2·00
1386	30p. Ernest Shackleton in Antarctica	2·00	2·00
1387	30p. Charles Lindbergh and *Spirit of St. Louis*	2·00	2·00
1388	30p. Astronaut on Moon	2·00	2·00
1383/8	*Set of 6*	11·00	11·00

Nos. 1383/8 were printed in a similar format to Nos. 1283/8.

401 Goldfish

(Des Passmore Design)

2001 (24 Jan). Greetings Stamps. Pets. T **401** and similar vert designs. Multicoloured. Phosphor frame.

(a) Litho Irish Security Stamp Ptg Ltd. Chalk-surfaced paper. P 14×14½
1389	30p. Type **401**	80	50

(b) Litho Questa. Designs smaller, 25×30 mm. Self-adhesive. P 12
1390	30p. Lizard	1·00	1·10
	a. Booklet pane. Nos. 1390/4, each×2	9·00	
1391	30p. Frog	1·00	1·10
1392	30p. Type **401**	1·00	1·10
1393	30p. Snake	1·00	1·10
1394	30p. Tortoise	1·00	1·10
1390/4	*Set of 5*	4·50	5·00

Nos. 1390/4 were only available in £3 stamp booklets, on which the surplus self-adhesive paper was retained.

(Des Passmore Design. Litho Irish Security Stamp Ptg Ltd)

2001 (24 Jan). Chinese New Year ("Year of the Snake"). Chalk-surfaced paper. Phosphor frame. P 14×14½.
MS1395	124×75 mm. As Nos. 1391 and 1393/4, but larger, 28×39 mm	3·00	3·50

402 Television Presenter and Audience

(Des Q. Design. Litho Irish Security Stamp Ptg Ltd)

2001 (27 Feb). Irish Broadcasting. T **402** and similar horiz designs. Chalk-surfaced paper. Phosphor frame. P 15×14.
1396	30p. multicoloured	70	50
1397	32p. black, ultramarine and brt greenish bl..	80	55
1398	45p. black, brownish black and orange	1·00	1·10
1399	50p. blackish brown, olive yellow and lt grn	1·00	1·25
1396/9	*Set of 4*	3·00	3·00

Designs:—32p. Radio sports commentators; 45p. Family around radio; 50p. Play on television set.

403 Archbishop Narcissus Marsh and Library Interior

404 Bagpipe Player

(Des Creative Input. Litho Irish Security Stamp Ptg Ltd)

2001 (14 Mar). Literary Anniversaries. T **403** and similar vert design. Multicoloured. Chalk-surfaced paper. Phosphor frame. P 14×14½.
1400	30p. Type **403** (300th anniv of Marsh's Library)	60	50
1401	32p. Book of Common Prayer, 1551 (450th anniv of first book printed in Ireland)...	65	1·00

(Des Anne Farrall. Litho Irish Security Stamp Ptg Ltd)

2001 (14 Mar). 50th Anniv of Comhaltas Ceoltoiri Eireann (cultural organization). T **404** and similar multicoloured designs. Chalk-surfaced paper. Phosphor frame. P 14×14½ (30p.) or 14½×14 (45p.).
1402	30p. Type **404**	70	1·00
	a. Pair. Nos. 1402/3	1·40	2·00

1403	30p. Bodhran player	70	1·00
1404	45p. Young fiddler and Irish dancer (*horiz*)...	1·00	1·50
	a. Pair. Nos. 1404/5	2·00	2·50
1405	45p. Flautist and singer (*horiz*)	1·00	1·50
1402/5	*Set of 4*	3·00	4·50

Nos. 1402/3 and 1404/5 were each printed together, *se-tenant*, both horizontally and vertically, in sheets of 16.

405 Jordan Formula 1 Racing Car

406 Peter Lalor (leader at Eureka Stockade) and Gold License

(Des V. Killowry)

2001 (26 Apr). Irish Motorsport. T **405** and similar horiz designs. Multicoloured. Phosphor frame (except No. **MS**1410).

(a) Litho Walsall. P 13½×14
1406	30p. Type **405**	75	50
1407	32p. Hillman Imp on Tulip Rally	80	55
1408	45p. Mini Cooper S on Monte Carlo Rally	1·25	80
1409	£1 Mercedes SSK, winner of 1930 Irish Grand Prix	2·00	2·50
1406/9	*Set of 4*	4·25	4·00
MS1410	150×90 mm. £2 Type **405**	4·00	4·25

(b) Litho SNP Ausprint. Designs smaller, 37×25 mm. Self-adhesive. P 12
1411	30p. Type **405**	90	1·00
	a. Booklet pane. No. 1411×4 and Nos. 1412/14, each ×2	11·00	
1412	30p. Hillman Imp on Tulip Rally	1·40	1·75
1413	30p. Mini Cooper S on Monte Carlo Rally	1·40	1·75
1414	30p. Mercedes SSK, winner of 1930 Irish Grand Prix	1·40	1·75
1411/14	*Set of 4*	4·50	5·50

Nos. 1411/14 come from £3 stamp booklets, No. SB88.

(Des Passmore Design. Litho Irish Security Stamp Ptg Ltd)

2001 (3 May). Irish Heritage in Australia. T **406** and similar horiz designs. Multicoloured. Phosphor frame (except for No. **MS**1419). P 14½×14.
1415	30p. Type **406**	60	60
	a. Pair. Nos. 1415/16	1·10	1·10
1416	30p. Ned Kelly (bush ranger) and "Wanted" poster	60	60
1417	45p. Family leaving for Australia and immigrant ship	1·25	1·25
	a. Pair. Nos. 1417/18	2·50	2·50
1418	45p. Irish settler and life in gold camp	1·25	1·25
1415/18	*Set of 4*	3·25	3·25
MS1419	150×90 mm. £1 As No. 1416	2·25	2·50

Nos. 1415/16 and 1417/18 were each printed together, *se-tenant*, in sheetlets of 10 with the two designs *se-tenant* both horizontally and vertically.

407 Children playing in River

408 Blackbird

(Des F. O'Connor. Litho Irish Security Stamp Ptg Ltd)

2001 (16 May). Europa. Water Resources. T **407** and similar horiz design. Multicoloured. Phosphor frame.

(a) Size 40×29 mm. P 14½×14
1420	30p. Type **407**	1·25	50
1421	32p. Man fishing	1·50	75

(b) Designs smaller, 37×25 mm. Self-adhesive. P 9½
1422	30p. Type **407**	1·25	1·25
	a. Horiz pair. Nos. 1422/3	2·50	2·50
1423	30p. As 32p	1·25	1·25

Nos. 1420/1 were each printed in sheets of 10 with an enlarged, illustrated left margin.

Nos. 1422/3 were produced in rolls of 100, the two designs alternating, with the surplus self-adhesive paper around each stamp removed.

(Des K. Mullarney)

2001 (11 June). Dual Currency Birds. Vert designs as Nos. 1038, 1050, 1053, 1056/7 and 1060 (some with different face values) showing both Irish currency and euros as in T **408**. Multicoloured. Chalk-surfaced paper. Phosphor frame (30p. to 45p.). P 15×14 (£1) or 14×15 (others).

(a) Litho Irish Security Stamp Ptg Ltd

1424	30p./38c. Type **408**		1·50	1·25
1425	32p./41c. Robin		1·60	1·25
1426	35p./44c. Atlantic Puffin		1·75	2·50
1427	40p./51c. Wren		2·00	3·00
1428	45p./57c. Song Thrush		2·25	3·00
1429	£1/€1.25 Greenland White-fronted Goose (23×44 mm)		5·50	7·00
1424/9	*Set of 5*		13·00	16·00

(b) Litho SNP Ausprint. Designs as Nos. 1038/9, but 24×39 mm. Multicoloured. Chalk-surfaced paper. Phosphor frame. Self-adhesive. P 11

1430	30p./38c. Type **408**		1·50	1·50
	a. Vert pair. Nos. 1430/1		3·00	3·00
1431	30p./38c. Goldcrest		1·50	1·50

Nos. 1430/1 were produced in rolls of 100, containing the two designs, with the surplus self-adhesive paper around the stamp removed.

409 Irish Pikeman   **410** Ruffian 23 Yachts

(Des F O'Connor. Litho Irish Security Stamp Ptg Ltd)

2001 (10 July). 400th Anniv of Battle of Kinsale. Nine Years War. T **409** and similar square designs. Multicoloured. Chalk-surfaced paper. Phosphor frame. P 13½.

1432	30p. Type **409**		90	1·00
	a. Pair. Nos. 1432/3		1·75	2·00
1433	30p. English cavalry		90	1·00
1434	32p. Spanish pikeman		1·00	80
1435	45p. Town of Kinsale		1·40	1·50
1432/5	*Set of 4*		3·75	3·75

Nos. 1432/3 were printed together, *se-tenant* both horizontally and vertically, in sheets of 16.

(Des Creative Inputs. Litho Irish Security Stamp Ptg Ltd)

2001 (5 Sept). Yachts. T **410** and similar vert designs. Multicoloured. Chalk-surfaced paper. Phosphor frame.

(a) PVA gum. Size 29×40 mm. P 14×15

1436	30p. Type **410**		70	60
1437	30p. Howth 17 yacht		75	65
1438	45p. 1720 Sportsboat yacht		1·10	1·25
	a. Pair. Nos. 1438/9		2·10	2·50
1439	45p. Glen class cruising yacht		1·10	1·25
1436/9	*Set of 4*		3·25	3·25

30p (margin note)

(b) Self-adhesive. Size 25×37 mm. P 9½

1440	30p. Type **410**		1·00	1·00
	a. Vert strip of 4. Nos 1440/3		3·50	3·50
1441	30p. Howth 17 yacht		1·00	1·00
1442	30p. Glen class cruising yacht		1·00	1·00
1443	30p. 1720 Sportsboat yacht		1·00	1·00
1440/3	*Set of 4*		3·50	3·50

Nos. 1438/9 were printed together, *se-tenant*, in horizontal and vertical pairs throughout sheets of 16.

Nos. 1440/3 occur, *se-tenant*, as strips of 4 or rolls of 100 with the surplus self-adhesive paper around each stamp removed.

411 Padraic Carney (footballer)

(Des F. O'Connor and FOR Design)

2001 (5 Sept). Gaelic Athletic Association Hall of Fame 2001. T **411** and similar horiz designs. Chalk-surfaced paper. Phosphor frame.

(a) Litho Irish Security Stamp Ptg Ltd. PVA gum. Size 40×29 mm. P 14×15

1444	30p. Type **411**		90	90
	a. Horiz strip of 4. Nos. 1444/7		3·25	3·25

1445	30p. Frank Cummins (hurler)		90	90
1446	30p. Jack O'Shea (footballer)		90	90
1447	30p. Nicky Rackard (hurler)		90	90
1444/7	*Set of 4*		3·25	3·25

(b) Litho SNP Ausprint, Australia. Self-adhesive. Size 36×26 mm. P 11½

1448	30p. Type **411**		70	70
	a. Booklet pane. Nos. 1448×2, 1449/50 each ×3, 1451×2		7·00	
1449	30p. Frank Cummins (hurler)		70	70
1450	30p. Jack O'Shea (footballer)		70	70
1451	30p. Nicky Rackard (hurler)		70	70
1448/51	*Set of 4*		2·50	2·50

Nos. 1444/7 were printed together, *se-tenant*, as horizontal strips of 4 in sheets of 16.

Nos. 1448/51 were only issued in £3 stamp booklets, No. SB89, in which the surplus self-adhesive paper around each stamp was retained.

2001 (9 June). "Belgica 2001" International Stamp Exhibition, Brussels. No. **MS**1410 with "Belgica 2001" added to the sheet margin.

MS1452	150×90 mm. £2 Type **405**		4·00	4·25

(Des K. Mullarney. Litho SNP Ausprint)

2001 (9 Oct). Birds. Vert designs as Nos. 1038/9, 1048 and 1049, but 24×29 mm, each showing a letter in place of face values. Multicoloured. Chalk-surfaced paper. Phosphor frame. Self-adhesive. P 11.

1453	(N) Type **408**		1·60	80
	a. Booklet pane. Nos. 1453/4, each ×5		14·00	
1454	(N) Goldcrest		1·60	80
1455	(E) Robin		1·75	70
	a. Booklet pane. No. 1455×10		16·00	
1456	(W) Song Thrush		2·00	1·50
	a. Booklet pane. No. 1456×10		18·00	
1453/6	*Set of 4*		6·25	3·50

Nos. 1453/6 were only available in stamp booklets, Nos. SB90/2, and were intended to cover the changeover period to euros. Nos. 1453/4 were sold for 30p, No. 1455 for 32p. and No. 1456 for 45p.

The booklet panes retain the surplus self-adhesive paper around each stamp.

Perch (Perca fluviatilis)

413 Perch

(Des Rosemary Croley and Creative Inputs. Litho Irish Security Stamp Ptg Ltd)

2001 (9 Oct). Freshwater Fish. T **413** and similar horiz designs. Multicoloured. Chalk-surfaced paper. Phosphor frame. P 15×14.

1457	30p. Type **413**		75	50
	b. Booklet pane. Nos. 1457/60 with margins all round		3·00	
	c. Booklet pane. Nos. 1457/8 and 1460 each ×2 with margins all round		5·00	
1458	32p. Arctic Charr		80	85
	a. Horiz pair. Nos. 1458/9		1·60	1·60
	b. Booklet pane. Nos. 1458/9 and 1460×2 with margins all round		3·50	
1459	32p. Pike		80	85
1460	45p. Common Bream		1·10	1·25
1457/60	*Set of 4*		3·00	3·00

Nos. 1458/9 were printed together, *se-tenant*, as horizontal pairs throughout the sheet.

Booklet pane No. 1457b exists showing the stamps in two different arrangements.

414 "Out of Bounds" (sculpture by Eilis O'Connell)   **415** "The Nativity" (Richard King)

(Des Q. Design. Litho Irish Security Stamp Ptg Ltd)

2001 (5 Nov). 50th Anniv of Government Support for Arts. Chalk-surfaced paper. Phosphor frame. P 14×15.

1461	**414**	50p. multicoloured	1·25	1·40

(Des Q. Design)

2001 (5 Nov). Christmas. Paintings by Richard King. T **415** and similar vert designs. Multicoloured. Chalk-surfaced paper. Phosphor frame.

(a) Litho Irish Security Stamp Ptg Ltd. Designs 29×40 mm. P 14×15

1462	30p. Type **415**	70	50
1463	32p. "The Annunciation"	75	55
1464	45p. "Presentation in the Temple"	1·10	1·25
1462/4	Set of 3	2·25	2·10

(b) Litho SNP Ausprint. Design 24×29 mm. Self-adhesive. P 11½

1465	30p. "Madonna and Child"	1·10	50
	a. Booklet pane. No. 1465×24	25·00	

No. 1465 was only issued in £6.60 stamp booklets, No. SB94, in which the surplus self-adhesive paper around each stamp was retained.

416 Magpie

(Des K. Mullarney)

2002 (1 Jan)–04. New Currency. Birds as Nos. 1031/62, and new designs, with face values in cents and euros as T **416**. The 48c. peid wagtail stamps come with two different Gaelic inscriptions: I "Glasóg shráide". II GlasÚg shr·ide.

(a) Litho Irish Security Stamp Ptg Ltd. Chalk-surfaced paper Phosphor frame (38c. to 95c.). PVA gum. P 15×14 (3, 5, 47, 50, 51, 55, 60 (No. 1482), 75, 95c., €2, €10) or 14×15 (others)

(i) Size 23×26 mm or 26×23 mm

1466	1c. Type **416**	40	60
	a. Ordinary paper	10	50
1467	2c. Gannet	40	60
	a. Ordinary paper	10	50
1468	3c. Blue Tit (horiz)	15	60
1469	4c. Corncrake	20	60
1470	5c. Wood Pigeon (horiz)	20	60
1470a	7c. Common Stonechat (25.8.03)	1·50	75
1471	10c. Kingfisher	30	60
1472	20c. Lapwing	55	1·00
1473	38c. Blackbird	1·00	75
1474	41c. Chaffinch	70	60
	a. Booklet pane. Nos. 1474/5, each ×5 (6.8.02)	13·00	
1475	41c. Goldcrest (6.8.02)	2·50	3·50
1476	44c. Robin	1·00	65
1477	47c. Kestrel (17.6.02)	1·25	70
1477a	48c. Peregrine Falcon (25.8.03)	1·00	70
	ab. Booklet pane. Nos. 1477a/b, each ×5 (30.9.03)	18·00	
1477b	48c. Pied Wagtail (I) (30.9.03)	3·00	3·50
1478	50c. Grey Heron (horiz)	1·25	90
1479	51c. Roseate Tern (horiz)	1·25	75
1480	55c. Oystercatcher (horiz) (17.6.02)	1·25	2·00
1481	57c. Curlew	1·25	80
1482	60c. Jay (horiz) (17.6.02)	1·25	1·25
1482a	60c. Atlantic Puffin (5.1.04)	2·00	1·00
1482b	65c. Song Thrush (5.1.04)	2·00	1·00
1482c	75c. Ringed Plover (horiz) (6.1.03)	4·00	1·10
1482d	95c. Sparrowhawk (horiz) (6.1.03)	4·00	1·40

(ii) Size 47×26 mm or 26×47 mm

1483	€1 Barnacle Goose (horiz)	2·00	1·40
1484	€2 Greenland White-fronted Goose	3·25	3·00
1485	€5 Pintail (horiz)	7·50	7·00
1486	€10 Shelduck	16·00	18·00
1466/86	Set of 28	55·00	50·00

(b) Booklet stamps. Litho Irish Security Stamp Ptg Ltd. Size 20×23 mm. Chalk-surfaced paper. Phosphor frame (4, 38, 41, 48c.). PVA gum. P 15×14

1486a	4c. Corncrake (30.9.03)	1·00	1·75
	ab. Booklet pane. No. 1486a×2 and No. 1490a×4	5·50	
1487	10c. Kingfisher	4·00	4·75
	a. Booklet pane. Nos. 1487 and 1489×5	6·75	
1488	36c. Wren (6.8.02)	4·00	4·75
	a. Booklet pane. Nos. 1488 and 1490×4 plus label	6·00	
1489	38c. Blackbird	70	1·00
1490	41c. Chaffinch (6.8.02)	70	80
1490a	48c. Peregrine Falcon (30.9.03)	1·00	1·25

(c) Litho SNP Ausprint. Self-adhesive. Size 24×29 mm. Chalk-surfaced paper. Phosphor frame. P 11

1491	38c. Blackbird	1·00	1·00
	a. Vert pair. Nos. 1491/2	2·00	2·00
1492	38c. Goldcrest	1·00	1·00
1493	41c. Chaffinch (2.4.02)	1·00	1·00
	a. Vert pair. Nos. 1493/4	2·00	2·00
	b. Booklet pane. Nos. 1493/4, each ×5	8·50	

1494	41c. Goldcrest (2.4.02)	1·00	1·00
1495	44c. Robin (2.4.02)	1·25	1·00
	a. Booklet pane. No. 1495×10	11·00	
1495b	(N) Peregrine Falcon (25.8.03)	2·00	1·75
	ba. Booklet pane. No. 1495b/c	4·00	3·50
	bb. Booklet pane. Nos. 1495b/c, each ×5	18·00	
1495c	(N) Pied Wagtail (II) (25.8.03)	2·00	1·75
1495d	48c. Peregrine Falcon (30.9.03)	1·25	1·25
	da. Vert pair. Nos. 1495d/e	2·50	2·50
	db. Booklet pane. Nos. 1495d/e, each ×5	11·00	
1495e	48c. Pied Wagtail (II) (30.9.03)	1·25	1·25
1496	50c. Atlantic Puffin (6.1.03)	1·75	1·75
	a. Booklet pane. No. 1496×10	16·00	
1497	57c. Song Thrush (2.4.02)	1·50	1·50
	a. Booklet pane. No. 1497×10	13·00	
1497b	60c. Atlantic Puffin (5.1.04)	1·75	1·75
	ba. Booklet pane. No. 1497b×10	15·00	
1497c	65c. Song Thrush (5.1.04)	1·75	1·75
	ca. Booklet pane. No. 1497c×10	16·00	

(d) Photo Enschedé. Self-adhesive. Size 24×29 mm. Chalk-surfaced paper. Phosphor frame. P 11

1498	41c. Chaffinch (17.10.02)	1·00	1·00
	a. Vert pair. Nos. 1498/9	2·00	2·00
1499	41c. Goldcrest (17.10.02)	1·00	1·00
1500	48c. Peregrine Falcon (12.5.04)	1·25	1·25
	a. Vert pair. Nos. 1500/1	2·50	2·50
1501	48c. Pied Wagtail (I) (12.5.04)	1·25	1·25

No. 1475 was only issued in €4.10 stamp booklets, No. SB101, containing pane No. 1474a which has margins at either end and horizontal edges, and shows the stamps in the upper row (No. 1474) imperforate at top and those in the lower row (No. 1475) imperforate at foot.

No. 1477b was only issued in €4.80 stamp booklets, No. SB113, containing pane No. 1477ab which has margins at either end and the horizontal edges of the pane imperforate, giving stamps imperforate at either top or bottom.

Booklet pane No. 1486ab (from No. SB112) has the vertical edges of the pane imperforate so that Nos. 1486a and 1490a only exist imperforate at either left or right.

Booklet panes Nos. 1487a (from SB95) and 1488a (from SB102) have the vertical edges of the panes imperforate so that the 10c. only exist imperforate at left and the 38c. and 41c. imperforate at left or right.

Nos. 1491/2, 1493/4, 1495b/c, 1495d/e, 1498/9 and 1500/1 were each produced in rolls of 100 containing the two designs, with the surplus self-adhesive paper around each stamp removed. Nos. 1498/9 have every fifth stamp numbered on the backing paper.

Nos. 1493/4, 1495b/c and 1495d/e also come from booklets of 10, Nos. SB97, SB110 and SB114, with the surplus self-adhesive paper around each stamp retained.

Nos. 1495 and 1496/7c were only issued in separate stamp booklets, Nos. SB98/9 and SB116/17, with the surplus paper retained.

417 Reverse of Irish €1 Coin, 2002   **418** Teddy Bear

(Des Q. Design. Litho Irish Security Stamp Ptg Ltd)

2002 (1 Jan). Introduction of Euro Currency. Irish Coins. T **417** and similar horiz designs. Chalk-surfaced paper. Phosphor frame. P 15×14.

1506	38c. Type **417**	75	50
1507	41c. Reverse of 50p. coin, 1971–2001	80	60
1508	57c. Reverse of 1d. coin, 1928–1971	1·10	1·25
1506/8	Set of 3	2·40	2·10

(Des Passmore Design)

2002 (22 Jan). Greetings Stamps. Toys. T **418** and similar vert designs. Multicoloured. Chalk-surfaced paper. Phosphor frame.

(a) Litho Irish Security Stamp Ptg Ltd. Design 29×40 mm. PVA gum. P 14×15

1509	38c. Type **418**	70	50

(b) Litho SNP Ausprint. Designs 24×29 mm. Self-adhesive. P 11

1510	38c. Type **418**	80	80
	a. Booklet pane. Nos. 1510/14, each ×2	7·00	
1511	38c. Rag doll	80	80
1512	38c. Rocking horse	80	80
1513	38c. Train	80	80
1514	38c. Wooden blocks	80	80
1510/14	Set of 5	3·50	3·50

Nos. 1510/14 were only available in €3.80 stamp booklets, No. SB96, in which the surplus self-adhesive paper around each stamp was retained.

(Des Passmore Design. Litho Irish Security Stamp Ptg Ltd)

2002 (22 Jan). Chinese New Year ("Year of the Horse"). Chalk-surfaced paper. Phosphor frame. P 14×15.

MS1515	124×74 mm. As Nos. 1511/13, but 25×37 mm	4·00	4·50

419 Around the Camp Fire

(Des F. O'Connor. Litho Irish Security Stamp Ptg Ltd)

2002 (12 Mar). 75th Anniv of Scouting Ireland CSI. T **419** and similar horiz designs. Multicoloured. Chalk-surfaced paper. Phosphor frame. P 15×14.

1516	41c. Type **419**	75	75
	a. Pair. Nos. 1516/17	1·50	1·50
1517	41c. Setting up camp	75	75
1518	57c. Scouts canoeing	1·10	1·25
	a. Pair. Nos. 1518/19	2·00	2·50
1519	57c. Scouts on hill walk	1·10	1·25
1516/19	Set of 4	3·25	3·50

Nos. 1516/17 and 1518/19 were each printed together, *se-tenant*, as horizontal or vertical pairs in sheets of 16.

420 "Arkle"

(Des FOR Design. Litho Irish Security Stamp Ptg Ltd)

2002 (12 Mar). 250th Anniv of Steeplechasing in Ireland. Irish Steeplechasers. T **420** and similar horiz designs. Multicoloured. Chalk-surfaced paper. Phosphor frame. P 15×14.

1520	38c. Type **420**	1·00	1·00
	a. Horiz strip of 4. Nos. 1520/3	3·50	3·50
1521	38c. "L'Escargot"	1·00	1·00
1522	38c. "Dawn Run"	1·00	1·00
1523	38c. "Istabraq"	1·00	1·00
1520/3	Set of 4	3·50	3·50

Nos. 1520/3 were printed together, *se-tenant*, in horizontal rows of 4 throughout the sheet of 16.

421 Badger   **422** Roy Keane

(Des F. O'Connor. Litho Irish Security Stamp Ptg Ltd)

2002 (23 Apr). Irish Mammals. T **421** and similar multicoloured designs. Chalk-surfaced paper. Phosphor frame. P 15×14 (horiz) or 14×15 (vert).

1524	41c. Type **421**	75	60
1525	50c. Otter	90	70
1526	57c. Red Squirrel (*vert*)	1·10	80
1527	€1 Hedgehog (*vert*)	1·75	2·50
1524/7	Set of 4	4·00	4·25
MS1528	150×67 mm. €5 As 50c. Ordinary paper	15·00	18·00

(Des D5 Design)

2002 (14 May). World Cup Football Championship, Japan and South Korea (2002). Irish Footballers. T **422** and similar multicoloured designs. Phosphor frame. Chalk-surfaced paper.

(a) Litho Irish Security Stamp Ptg Ltd. Size 29×40 or 40×29 mm. PVA gum. P 14×15 (vert) or 15×14 (horiz)

1529	41c. Packie Bonner (*horiz*)	75	75
	a. Sheetlet. Nos. 1529/32, each ×4	9·00	
1530	41c. Type **422**	75	75
1531	41c. Paul McGrath	75	75

1532	41c. David O'Leary	75	75
1529/32	Set of 4	2·75	2·75

(b) Litho SNP Ausprint. Size 25×37 or 37×25 mm. Self-adhesive. P 11½

1533	41c. Packie Bonner (*horiz*)	1·00	1·00
	a. Booklet pane. Nos. 1533 and 1536, each ×2, and 1534/5, each ×3	9·00	
1534	41c. Type **422**	1·00	1·00
1535	41c. Paul McGrath	1·00	1·00
1536	41c. David O'Leary	1·00	1·00
1533/6	Set of 4	3·50	3·50

Nos. 1529/32 were printed together, *se-tenant*, in sheetlets of 16, with the four examples of No. 1529 as a horizontal strip, and the vertical designs as two blocks of 6 (2×3).

Nos. 1533/6 were only available from €4.10 stamp booklets, No. SB100, in which the surplus self-adhesive paper around the stamps was retained.

423 Clown

(Des Anne Farrall. Litho Irish Security Stamp Ptg Ltd)

2002 (14 May). Europa. Circus. T **423** and similar horiz design. Multicoloured. Phosphor frame. Chalk-surfaced paper.

(a) Size 40×29 mm. PVA gum. P 15×14

1537	41c. Type **423**	70	70
1538	44c. Girl on horse	70	70

(b) Self-adhesive. Size 37×25 mm. P 9

1539	41c. Type **423**	70	70
	a. Horiz pair. Nos. 1539/40	1·40	1·40
1540	41c. As No. 1538	70	70

Nos. 1537/8 were each printed in sheetlets of 10 with enlarged illustrated left margins.

Nos. 1539/40 were produced in rolls of 100, containing the two designs, with the surplus self-adhesive paper around each stamp removed.

424 Padre Pio   **425** Brian Ború leading Army

(Des FOR Design. Litho Irish Security Stamp Ptg Ltd)

2002 (17 June). Canonisation of St. Pio de Pietrelcina (Padre Pio). Phosphor frame. Chalk-surfaced paper. P 14×15.

1541	**424**	41c. multicoloured	75	70

(Des F. O'Connor. Litho Irish Security Stamp Ptg Ltd)

2002 (9 July). 1000th Anniv of Declaration of Brian Ború as High King of Ireland. T **425** and similar horiz designs. Multicoloured. Chalk-surfaced paper. Phosphor frame. P 15×14.

1542	41c. Type **425**	75	60
1543	44c. Leading fleet	75	70
1544	57c. Receiving surrender of the O'Neills	90	85
1545	€1 Decreeing primacy of bishopric of Armagh in the Irish Church	1·75	2·25
1542/5	Set of 4	3·75	4·00

426 "Before the Start" (J. B. Yeats)   **427** Archbishop Thomas Croke

(Des Q. Design. Litho Irish Security Stamp Ptg Ltd)

2002 (29 Aug). 140th Anniv of National Gallery of Ireland (2004) (1st series). Paintings. T **426** and similar horiz designs. Multicoloured. Chalk-surfaced paper. Phosphor frame. P 14½×14.

1546	41c. Type **426**	70	1·00
	a. Horiz strip of 4. Nos. 1546/9	2·50	3·50
	b. Booklet pane. No. 1546×4, with margins all round	2·50	
1547	41c. "The Conjuror" (Nathaniel Hone)	70	1·00
	b. Booklet pane. No. 1547×4, with margins all round	2·50	
1548	41c. "The Colosseum and Arch of Constantine, Rome" (Giovanni Panini)	70	1·00
	b. Booklet pane. No. 1548×4, with margins all round	2·50	
1549	41c. "The Gleaners" (Jules Breton)	70	1·00
	b. Booklet pane. No. 1549×4, with margins all round	2·50	
1546/9	Set of 4	2·50	3·50

Nos. 1546/9 were printed together, *se-tenant*, as horizontal strips of 4 in sheets of 16.
See also Nos. 1606/9 and 1700/3.

(Des F. O'Connor and FOR Design. Litho Irish Security Stamp Ptg Ltd)

2002 (17 Sept). Gaelic Athletic Association Hall of Fame 2002 (2nd series). Horiz designs as T **411**. Chalk-surfaced paper. Phosphor frame. P 15×14.

1550	41c. Peter McDermott (footballer)	75	1·00
	a. Horiz strip of 4. Nos. 1550/3	2·75	3·50
1551	41c. Jimmy Smyth (hurler)	75	1·00
1552	41c. Matt Connor (footballer)	75	1·00
1553	41c. Seanie Duggan (hurler)	75	1·00
1550/3	Set of 4	2·75	3·50

Nos. 1550/3 were printed together, *se-tenant*, as horizontal strips of 4 in sheets of 16.

(Des Creative Inputs. Litho Irish Security Stamp Ptg Ltd)

2002 (17 Sept). Death Centenary of Archbishop Croke (first patron of Gaelic Athletic Association). Chalk-surfaced paper. Phosphor frame. P 14×15.

1554	**427** 44c. multicoloured	80	70

428 U2   **429** "Adoration of the Magi"

(Des D5 Design. Litho Walsall)

2002 (17 Oct). Irish Rock Legends. T **428** and similar square designs. Multicoloured. Chalk-surfaced paper. Phosphor background. P 13½×13.

1555	41c. Type **428**	1·25	1·25
	a. Horiz pair. Nos. 1555/6	2·50	2·50
1556	41c. Phil Lynott	1·25	1·25
1557	57c. Van Morrison	1·40	2·00
	a. Horiz pair. Nos. 1557/8	2·75	4·00
1558	57c. Rory Gallagher	1·40	2·00
1555/8	Set of 4	4·75	6·00

MS1559 Four sheets, each 150×90 mm. (a) €2 Type **428**; (b) €2 No. 1556; (c) €2 No. 1557; (d) €2 No. 1558. P 13×13½ .... 11·00   16·00

Nos. 1555/6 and 1557/8 were each printed together, *se-tenant*, as horizontal pairs in sheets of 16.

(Des Red Star (No. 1563), Q. Design (others))

2002 (7 Nov). Christmas. Illustrations from *Les Très Riches Heures du Duc de Berry* (mediaeval book of hours). T **429** and similar vert designs. Multicoloured. Chalk-surfaced paper. Phosphor frame.

(a) Litho Irish Security Stamp Ptg Ltd. PVA gum. Size 29×40 mm. P 14×15

1560	41c. Type **429**	70	60
1561	44c. "The Annunciation to the Virgin Mary"	75	60
1562	57c. "The Annunciation to the Shepherds"	1·00	1·10
1560/2	Set of 3	2·25	2·10

(b) Litho SNP Ausprint. Self-adhesive. Size 24×29 mm. P 11

1563	41c. "The Nativity"	1·00	60
	a. Booklet pane. No. 1563×24	22·00	

No. 1563 was only available from €9.43 stamp booklets, No. SB104, in which the self-adhesive backing paper around each stamp was retained.

430 Labrador Puppies

(Des Passmore Design)

2003 (28 Jan). Greetings Stamps. Baby Animals. T **430** and similar vert designs. Multicoloured. Chalk-surfaced paper. Phosphor frame.

(a) Litho Irish Security Stamp Ptg Ltd. Design 29×40 mm. PVA gum. P 14×15

1564	41c. Type **430**	80	65

(b) Litho SNP Ausprint. Designs 24×29 mm. Self-adhesive. P 11

1565	41c. Type **430**	80	80
	a. Booklet pane. Nos. 1565/9, each ×2	7·00	
1566	41c. Chicks	80	80
1567	41c. Kids	80	80
1568	41c. Kittens	80	80
1569	41c. Baby rabbits	80	80
1565/9	Set of 5	3·50	3·50

Nos. 1565/9 were only available in €4.10 stamp booklets, No. SB106, in which the surplus self-adhesive paper around each stamp was retained.

(Des Passmore Design. Litho Irish Security Stamp Ptg Ltd)

2003 (28 Jan). Chinese New Year ("Year of the Goat"). Designs as Nos. 1566/8, but 29×40 mm. Chalk-surfaced paper. Phosphor frame. P 14×15.

MS1570 124×74 mm. 50c. Chicks; 50c. Kids; 50c. Kittens .... 3·75   4·50

On No. **MS**1570 the kittens design is imperforate at right.

431 St. Patrick   **432** Seven-spotted Ladybird

(Des F. O'Connor)

2003 (28 Feb). St. Patrick's Day. T **431** and similar vert designs. Multicoloured. Chalk-surfaced paper. Phosphor frame.

(a) Litho Irish Security Stamp Ptg Ltd. PVA gum. Size 29×40 mm. P 14×15

1571	41c. Type **431**	80	60
1572	50c. St. Patrick's Day Parade passing St. Patrick's Cathedral, Dublin	95	1·00
1573	57c. St. Patrick's Day Parade, New York	1·10	1·25
1571/3	Set of 3	2·50	2·50

(b) Litho SNP Ausprint. Self-adhesive. Size 25×36 mm. P 11

1574	41c. St. Patrick	85	90
	a. Booklet pane. No. 1574×10	8·50	
1575	50c. St. Patrick's Day Parade passing St. Patrick's Cathedral, Dublin	85	1·00
	a. Booklet pane. No. 1575×10	8·50	
1576	57c. St. Patrick's Day Parade, New York	95	1·25
	a. Booklet pane. No. 1576×10	9·50	
1574/6	Set of 3	2·40	2·75

Nos. 1571/3 also exist as separate panes of four or as a *se-tenant* pane of three from a premium stamp booklet, No. SP1, containing stamps with a face value of €7.40, which was only available through philatelic outlets at €8.

Nos. 1574/6 were only available from separate stamp booklets, Nos. SB107/9, in which the self-adhesive backing paper around each stamp was retained.

(Des I. Loe. Litho Walsall)

2003 (1 Apr). Irish Beetles. T **432** and similar horiz designs. Multicoloured. Chalk-surfaced paper. Phosphor background. P 13½×14.

1577	41c. Type **432**	90	60
1578	50c. Great Diving Beetle	1·00	70
1579	57c. Leaf Beetle	1·25	80
1580	€1 Green Tiger Beetle	2·25	2·50
1577/80	Set of 4	4·75	4·25
MS1581	150×68 mm. €2 Type **432**	4·25	5·00

433 Dingle Peninsula ("IRELAND for HOLIDAYS")   **434** "2003" and EYPD Logo

(Des J. Laffan. Litho Irish Security Stamp Ptg Ltd)

2003 (9 May). Europa. Poster Art. T **433** and similar vert design showing posters by Paul Henry. Multicoloured. Chalk-surfaced paper. Phosphor frame. P 14×15.

| 1582 | 41c. Type **433** | 80 | 65 |
| 1583 | 57c. Connemara ("IRELAND THIS YEAR") | 95 | 1·10 |

(Des P. Raftery. Litho Irish Security Stamp Ptg Ltd)

2003 (9 May). European Year of People with Disabilities. Chalk-surfaced paper. Phosphor frame. P 15×14.

| 1584 | **434** | 41c. multicoloured | 80 | 65 |

435 Athletes waving to Crowd   **436** Napier

(Des Irish International. Litho Walsall)

2003 (20 May). 11th Special Olympics World Summer Games, Dublin. T **435** and similar horiz designs. Multicoloured. Phosphor frame. P 14.

1585	41c. Type **435**	75	45
1586	50c. Swimmer	80	60
1587	57c. Athlete on starting block	95	65
1588	€1 Athlete running	2·25	3·25
1585/8	Set of 4	4·25	4·50

(Des V. Killowry)

2003 (30 June). Centenary of Gordon Bennett Race in Ireland. T **436** and similar horiz designs showing racing cars of 1903. Multicoloured. Chalk-surfaced paper.

(a) Litho Walsall. PVA gum. Size 39×29 mm. Phosphor background. P 14½×14

1589	41c. Type **436**	80	1·00
	a. Horiz strip of 4. Nos. 1589/92	3·00	3·50
1590	41c. Mercedes	80	1·00
1591	41c. Mors	80	1·00
1592	41c. Winton	80	1·00
1589/92	Set of 4	3·00	3·50

(b) Litho SNP Ausprint. Self-adhesive. Size 36×25 mm. Phosphor frame. P 11×11½

1593	41c. As No. 1592	80	90
	a. Horiz strip of 4. Nos. 1593/6	3·00	3·25
1594	41c. As No. 1591	80	90
1595	41c. As No. 1590	80	90
1596	41c. Type **436**	80	90
1593/6	Set of 4	3·00	3·25

Nos. 1589/92 were printed together, *se-tenant*, as horizontal strips of 4 in sheets of 16.

Nos. 1593/6 occur, *se-tenant*, as strips of 4 and rolls of 100 with the surplus self-adhesive paper around each stamp removed.

437 Henry Ford and Model T Ford, 1908–28   **438** Harry Ferguson flying first Irish Monoplane, 1909

(Des P. Raftery. Litho Walsall)

2003 (30 June). Centenary of the Ford Motor Company. Phosphor frame. P 14½×14.

| 1597 | **437** | 41c. multicoloured | 80 | 65 |

(Des V. Killowry. Litho Irish Security Stamp Ptg Ltd)

2003 (29 July). Centenary of Powered Flight. T **438** and similar horiz designs. Multicoloured. Chalk-surfaced paper. Phosphor frame. P 15×14.

1598	41c. Type **438**	80	60
1599	50c. Alcock and Brown's Vickers FB-27 Vimy over Galway after first transatlantic flight, 1919	1·10	80
1600	57c. *Wright Flyer I*, 1903	1·25	1·50
	a. Pair. Nos. 1600/1	2·50	3·00
1601	57c. Lillian Bland's biplane, 1910	1·25	1·50
1598/1601	Set of 4	4·00	4·00
MS1602	150×90 mm. €5 As No. 1600. No phosphor frame	8·50	10·00

Nos. 1600/1 were printed together, *se-tenant*, in horizontal and vertical pairs in sheets of 16.

439 Robert Emmet

(Des R. Ballagh. Litho Irish Security Stamp Ptg Ltd)

2003 (29 July). Bicentenary of Rebellion of 1803. T **439** and similar horiz designs. Multicoloured. Chalk-surfaced paper. Phosphor frame. P 15×14.

1603	41c. Type **439**	80	60
1604	50c. Thomas Russell	1·10	1·10
1605	57c. Anne Devlin	1·40	1·60
1603/5	Set of 3	3·00	3·00

(Litho Irish Security Stamp Ptg Ltd)

2003 (9 Sept). 140th Anniv of National Gallery of Ireland (2004) (2nd issue). Paintings. Multicoloured designs as T **426** but vert. Chalk-surfaced paper. Phosphor frame. P 14×15.

1606	48c. "Self-portrait as Timanthes" (James Barry)	1·00	1·25
	a. Horiz strip of 4. Nos. 1606/9	3·50	4·50
	b. Booklet pane. No. 1606×4, with margins all round	4·25	
1607	48c. "Man writing a Letter" (Gabriel Metsu)	1·00	1·25
	b. Booklet pane. Nos. 1607/8, each ×2, with margins all round	2·75	
1608	48c. "Woman reading a Letter" (Gabriel Metsu)	1·00	1·25
1609	48c. "Woman seen from the Back" (Jean-Antoine Watteau)	1·00	1·25
	b. Booklet pane. No. 1609×4, with margins all round	4·25	
1606/9	Set of 4	3·50	4·50

Nos. 1606/9 were printed together, *se-tenant*, as horizontal strips of 4 in sheets of 16.

440 Frank O'Connor   **441** E. T. S. Walton

(Des G. Garland. Litho Walsall)

2003 (16 Sept). Birth Centenary of Frank O'Connor (writer). Chalk-surfaced paper. Phosphor frame. P 14×14½.

| 1610 | **440** | 50c. multicoloured | 1·00 | 1·00 |

(Des FOR Design. Litho Walsall)

2003 (16 Sept). Birth Centenary of E. T. S. Walton (Nobel Prize for Physics, 1951). Chalk-surfaced paper. Phosphor frame. P 14×14½.

| 1611 | **441** | 57c. cream, brownish black and grey-brown | 1·00 | 1·00 |

442 Admiral William Brown
(founder of the Argentine Navy)

(Des G. Garland)

2003 (30 Sept). Irish Mariners. T **442** and similar horiz designs. Multicoloured. Chalk-surfaced paper.

(a) Litho Walsall. PVA gum. Size 40×29 mm. Phosphor bars. P 14½×14
1612	48c. Type **442**	1·25	1·25
	a. Horiz pair. Nos. 1612/13	2·50	2·50
1613	48c. Commodore John Barry (Commanding Officer of US Navy, 1794–1803)	1·25	1·25
1614	57c. Captain Robert Halpin (Commander of cable ship *Great Eastern*)	1·40	1·40
	a. Horiz pair. Nos. 1614/15	2·75	2·75
1615	57c. Captain Richard Roberts (captain of *Sirius*, first scheduled passenger steamship London to New York voyage)	1·40	1·40
1612/15 *Set of 4*		4·75	4·75
MS1616 150×90 mm. €5 Commodore John Barry		8·00	8·50

(b) Litho SNP Ausprint. Self-adhesive. Size 36×25 mm. Phosphor frame. P 11×11½
1617	48c. Commodore John Barry	1·10	1·40
	a. Horiz strip of 4. Nos. 1617/20	4·00	5·00
1618	48c. Admiral William Brown	1·10	1·40
1619	48c. Captain Robert Halpin	1·10	1·40
1620	48c. Captain Richard Roberts	1·10	1·40
1617/20 *Set of 4*		4·00	5·00

Nos. 1612/13 and 1614/15 were each printed together, *se-tenant*, in horizontal pairs throughout the sheets.

Nos. 1617/20 occur, *se-tenant*, as strips of 4 and rolls of 100 with the surplus self-adhesive paper around each stamp removed.

443 Pope John Paul II

(Des FOR Design Ltd. Litho Irish Security Stamp Ptg Ltd)

2003 (16 Oct). 25th Anniv of the Election of Pope John Paul II. T **443** and similar designs. Multicoloured. Chalk-surfaced paper. Phosphor frame. P 14×15.
1621	48c. Type **443**	1·25	90
1622	50c. Pope in St. Peter's Square, Rome	1·40	95
1623	57c. Making speech at United Nations	1·50	1·40
1621/3 *Set of 3*		3·75	3·00

444 Angel

(Des Olwyen Whelan)

2003 (10 Nov). Christmas. T **444** and similar multicoloured designs. Chalk-surfaced paper. Phosphor frame.

(a) Litho Irish Security Stamp Ptg Ltd. PVA gum. P 13½ (48c.) or 15×14 (50, 57c.)
1624	48c. Flight into Egypt (35×35 mm)	90	80
1625	50c. Type **444**	95	80
1626	57c. Three Kings	1·10	1·25
1624/6 *Set of 3*		2·75	2·50

(b) Litho SNP Ausprint. Self-adhesive. Size 29×24 mm. P 11½×11
1627	48c. Nativity	1·00	70
	a. Booklet pane. No. 1627×24	23·00	

No. 1627 was only available from €11.04 stamp booklets, No. SB115, in which the self-adhesive backing paper around each stamp was retained.

445 Boyne Bridge   **446** "Monkeys in Love"

(Des Red Dog Design Consultants. Litho Irish Security Stamp Ptg Ltd)

2004 (15 Jan). Ireland's Presidency of European Union. Chalk-surfaced paper. Phosphor frame. P 14×15.
1628	**445**	48c. multicoloured	1·50	1·00

(Des Wendy Shea and Q. Design)

2004 (30 Jan). Greetings Stamps. Animals. T **446** and similar vert designs. Multicoloured. Chalk-surfaced paper. Phosphor frame.

(a) Litho Irish Security Stamp Ptg Ltd. PVA gum. Design 29×39 mm. P 14×15
1629	48c. Type **446**	1·50	1·25
MS1630 124×74 mm. 60c. Type **446**; 60c. "Jolly Panda"; 60c. "Cute Koalas"		3·50	3·75

(b) Litho SNP Ausprint. Self-adhesive. Designs 24×29 mm. P 11×11½
1631	48c. Type **446**	1·00	1·00
	a. Booklet pane. Nos. 1631/2, each ×3, and 1633/4, each ×2	9·00	
1632	48c. "Jolly Panda"	1·00	1·00
1633	48c. "Cute Koalas"	1·00	1·00
1634	48c. "Happy Hippo"	1·00	1·00
1631/4 *Set of 4*		3·50	3·50

Nos. 1631/4 were only available in €4.80 stamp booklets, No. SB118, in which the surplus self-adhesive paper around each stamp was retained.

447 St. Patrick and Stained Glass Window from Church of the Holy and Undivided Trinity, Magheralin, Co. Down

448 Abbey Theatre Logo

(Des FOR Design Ltd. Litho Irish Security Stamp Ptg Ltd.)

2004 (27 Feb). St. Patrick's Day. Chalk-surfaced paper. Phosphor frame. P 14×15.
1635	**447**	65c. multicoloured	1·50	1·50

(Des Zeus Creative. Litho Irish Security Stamp Ptg Ltd)

2004 (27 Feb). Centenary of Abbey Theatre, Dublin. Chalk-surfaced paper. Phosphor frame. P 14×15.
1636	**448**	48c. multicoloured	1·10	1·10

449 Expedition Members, Dogs and *Endurance* trapped in Ice

450 Flags, Football and Globe

(Des G. Garland. Litho Irish Security Stamp Ptg Ltd)

2004 (19 Mar). 90th Anniv of Shackleton's Antarctic Expedition. T **449** and similar square designs. Multicoloured. Chalk-surfaced paper. Phosphor frame* (Nos. 1637/40). P 13½.

1637	48c. Type **449**	1·75	1·50
	a. Horiz pair. Nos. 1637/8	3·50	3·00
1638	48c. Two crew members, huskies and bow of *Endurance*	1·75	1·50
1639	65c. Crew member looking out of tent	2·50	2·25
	a. Horiz pair. Nos. 1639/40	5·00	4·50
1640	65c. Crew members and tented camp on ice..	2·50	2·25
1637/40	*Set of 4*	7·75	6·75
MS1641	149×90 mm. €1 As No. 1639; €1 As No. 1640	6·50	5·50

Nos. 1637/8 and 1639/40 were each printed together, *se-tenant*, in horizontal pairs in sheets of 16, each pair forming a composite design.

*Nos. 1637/40 had phosphor frames around each horizontal pair, giving individual stamps with phosphor frames at top, left and bottom (Nos. 1637 and 1639) or at top, right and bottom (Nos. 1638 and 1640).

Nos. 1637/40 were also sold in premium booklets, No. SP1, sold at €9.50.

(Des P. Raftery. Litho Walsall)

2004 (31 Mar). Centenary of FIFA (Fédération Internationale de Football Association). Chalk-surfaced paper. Phosphor frame. P 13½×13.

1642	**450** 60c. multicoloured	1·40	1·40

451 Map of Europe showing Acceding Countries

(Des Red Dog Design Consultants. Litho Irish Security Stamp Ptg Ltd)

2004 (1 May). Enlargement of the European Union. Chalk-surfaced paper. Phosphor frame. P 15×14.

1643	**451** 65c. multicoloured	1·25	1·40

452 Tufted Duck

(Des K. Mullarney and P. Raftery. Litho Walsall)

2004 (11 May). Ducks. T **452** and similar horiz designs. Multicoloured. Chalk-surfaced paper. Phosphor frame. P 13×13½.

1644	48c. Type **452**	1·00	70
1645	60c. Red-breasted Merganser	1·50	1·25
1646	65c. Gadwall	1·50	1·25
1647	€1 Garganey	2·50	2·00
1644/7	*Set of 4*	6·00	4·75
MS1648	150×90 mm. Nos. 1644/7	6·00	6·00

453 Ross Castle, Co. Kerry

454 Emblem

(Des Q. Design. Litho Walsall)

2004 (11 May). Europa. Holidays. T **453** and similar vert designs. Multicoloured. Chalk-surfaced paper. Phosphor frame. P 14.

1649	48c. Type **453**	1·25	70
1650	65c. Cliffs of Moher, Co. Clare	1·50	1·50

Nos. 1649/50 were each printed in sheets of 10 (4×3) which contain two stamp-size labels in the centre of the top row.

(Des P. Raftery. Litho Walsall)

2004 (15 May). Tenth Anniv of UN International Year of the Family. Chalk-surfaced paper. Phosphor frame. P 13½×13.

1651	**454** 65c. bright scarlet, greenish yellow and deep green	1·25	1·50

455 "Frog" (Daire Lee)   **456** "James Joyce" (Tullio Pericoli)

(Des FOR Design Ltd. Litho Irish Security Stamp Ptg Ltd)

2004 (19 May). Winning Entries in Children's Painting Competition. T **455** and similar multicoloured designs. Chalk-surfaced paper. Phosphor frame. P 14×15 (vert) or 15×14 (horiz).

1652	48c. Type **455**	90	70
1653	60c. "Marmalade Cat" (Cian Colman)	1·25	1·25
1654	65c. "Ralleshin Dipditch" (Daire O'Rourke)	1·25	1·25
1655	€1 "Fish on a Dish" (Ailish Fitzpatrick) (horiz)	1·90	2·00
1652/5	*Set of 4*	4·75	4·75

(Des Q. Design. Litho Irish Security Stamp Ptg Ltd)

2004 (16 June). Centenary of "Leopold Bloom's Adventure" (from *Ulysses* by James Joyce). T **456** and similar vert design. Multicoloured. Chalk-surfaced paper. Phosphor frame. P 13½.

1656	48c. Type **456**	80	70
1657	65c. James Joyce	1·10	1·40

457 College Entrance   **458** LUAS Tram

(Des Q. Design. Litho Irish Security Stamp Ptg Ltd)

2004 (26 June). 426th Anniv of Irish College, Paris. Chalk-surfaced paper. Phosphor frame. P 14×15.

1658	**457** 65c. multicoloured	1·00	1·00

(Des V. Killowry. Litho Irish Security Stamp Ptg Ltd)

2004 (30 June). Introduction of LUAS Tram System, Dublin. T **458** and similar square design. Multicoloured. Chalk-surfaced paper. Phosphor frame. P 13½.

1659	48c. Type **458**	80	85
1660	48c. People accessing LUAS tram	80	85

459 Javelin Thrower and Olympic Flame   **460** Two Camogie Players and O'Duffy Cup

(Des F. O'Connor. Litho Walsall)

2004 (22 July). Olympic Games, Athens. T **459** and similar horiz design. Multicoloured. Chalk-surfaced paper. Phosphor frame. P 14 (48c.) or 14½×14 (60c.).

1661	48c. Type **459**	1·25	70
1662	60c. Discobolus (sculpture, Myron) and Olympic flame	1·50	1·60

(Des F. O'Connor. Litho Irish Security Stamp Ptg)

2004 (22 July). Centenary of Camogie (Gaelic game for women). T **460** and similar horiz design. Multicoloured. Chalk-surfaced paper. Phosphor frame. P 15×14.

1663	48c. Type **460**	95	1·10
	a. Pair. Nos. 1663/4	1·90	2·10
1664	48c. Two players and Camogie emblem	95	1·10

Nos. 1663/4 were printed together, se-tenant, in horizontal or vertical pairs throughout sheets of 16.

461 Common Dog-violet

(Des Susan Sex. Litho Irish Security Stamp Ptg Ltd (Nos. 1665/92), SEP Sprint, Australia (Nos. 1693/9ba) or Ashton-Potter, USA (Nos. 1697c, 1699c/ea))

2004 (9 Sept)–09. Wild Flowers. T **461** and similar multicoloured designs. Phosphor frame (48, 55, 60, 65, 75, 78, 82, 90, 95c). Chalk-surfaced paper.

(a) PVA gum. P 15×14 (€1, €2) or 14×15 (others)

(i) 23×26 mm

1665	1c. Bloody Crane's-bill (12.4.05)	10	30
1666	2c. Irish Orchid (12.4.05)	10	30
1667	3c. Yellow Flag (1.3.07)	15	30
1668	4c. Type **461**	20	30
1669	5c. Dandelion	1·00	30
1670	7c. Fly Orchid (12.4.05)	50	40
1671	10c. Mountain Avens (12.4.05)	1·00	40
1672	12c. Autumn Gorse (20.2.06)	25	40
1673	20c. Thrift (3.8.08)	40	40
1674	25c. Common Knapweed (20.2.06)	50	50
1675	48c. Daisy	2·50	1·50
	a. Booklet pane. Nos. 1675/6 each ×5	15·00	
1676	48c. Primrose	1·00	70
1677	50c. Biting Stonecrop (3.8.08)	1·00	75
1678	55c. Large-flowered Butterwort (1.3.07)	1·20	1·20
	a. Booklet pane. No. 1678×10 (20.4.07)	12·50	
1679	60c. Hawthorn	1·25	85
1680	65c. Bluebell	1·25	95
1681	75c. Navelwort (20.2.06)	1·50	1·10
1682	78c. Black Bog-rush (1.3.07)	2·00	1·90
1683	82c. Sea Aster (3.3.08)	1·75	1·40
	a. Booklet pane. No. 1683×10	17·00	
1684	90c. Viper's Bugloss (20.2.06)	1·75	1·60
1685	95c. Purple Loosestrife (1.3.07)	2·25	2·25

(ii) 26×47 mm (€1, €2) or 47×26 mm (others)

1686	€1 Foxglove (20.2.06)	2·50	1·50
1687	€2 Lords-and-ladies	2·75	3·00
1688	€5 Dog-rose	7·00	7·00
1689	€10 Spring Gentian (12.4.05)	14·00	14·00
1665/89	Set of 25	38·00	38·00

(b) Booklet stamps. PVA gum. Size 20×23 mm. Phosphor frame (55c. only). Chalk-surfaced paper. P 15×14

1690	5c. Dandelion (20.4.07)	45	1·00
	a. Booklet pane. Nos. 1690×2, 1691 and 1692×3	6·25	
	b. Booklet pane. Nos. 1690×2, 1691a and 1692×3 (2009)	35·00	
1691	25c. Common Knapweed (20.4.07)	1·75	2·50
	a. Phosphor frame (2009)	28·00	35·00
1692	55c. Large-flowered Butterwort (20.4.07)	1·40	1·40

(c) Size 23×29 mm. Self-adhesive. Phosphor frame. Chalk-surfaced paper. P 11 (1697) or 11½ (others)

1693	48c. Daisy	1·75	2·00
	a. Vert pair. Nos. 1693/4	3·50	4·00
	b. Booklet pane. Nos. 1693/4 each ×5	15·00	
	c. Perf 13		
	ca. Booklet pane. Nos. 1693/4c		
1694	48c. Primrose	1·75	2·00
	c. Perf 13		
1695	(N) Large-flowered Butterwort (1.3.07)	1·75	1·75
	a. Vert pair. Nos. 1695/6	3·50	3·50
	b. Booklet pane. Nos. 1695/6, each ×5	15·00	
1696	(N) Blue-eyed Grass (1.3.07)	1·75	1·75
1697	55c. Large-flowered Butterwort (20.4.07)	1·25	1·50
	a. Booklet pane. No. 1697×10	12·50	
	b. Perf 13 (20.4.07)	2·00	2·00
	c. Perf 11 (2011)	1·25	1·50

1698	75c. Navelwort (27.3.06)	1·75	1·75
	a. Booklet pane. No. 1698×10	17·00	
1699	78c. Black Bog-rush (20.4.07)	2·25	2·25
	a. Booklet pane. No. 1699×10	20·00	
	b. Inscr "black Bog-rush" (R. 4/2, first printing only)	10·00	13·00
1699c	82c. Sea Aster (18.3.08)	2·25	2·25
	ca. Booklet pane. No. 1699b×10	20·00	

(d) Size 20×24 mm. Self-adhesive. Phosphor frame. Chalk-surfaced paper. P 14

1699d	(N) Yellow Horned-poppy (5.12.08)	1·75	1·75
	da. Booklet pane. No. 1696c×10	17·00	
1699e	55c. Large-flowered Butterwort (16.10.09)	1·75	1·75
	ea. Booklet pane. No. 1699d×10	17·00	
1699f	82c. Sea Aster (7.8.09)	2·40	2·40
	fa. Booklet pane. No. 1699e×10	24·00	

Nos. 1675 and 1693/4 were only available from €4.80 stamp booklets in which the surplus self-adhesive paper around Nos. 1693/4 was retained.

Booklet panes Nos. 1678a and 1683a (from €5.50 and €8.20 booklets, Nos. SB134 and SB142) have margins at either end and horizontal edges, giving stamps imperforate at either top or bottom.

Booklet pane No. 1690a (from €2 booklet, No. SB133) has the vertical edges of the pane imperforate, giving stamps imperforate at either left or right.

Nos. 1695/6 were each sold for 55c. each. They were produced in rolls of 100 containing the two designs, and also in stamp booklets sold for €5.50, No. SB132.

Nos. 1697 and 1699 come from separate €5.50 and €7.80 stamp booklets, Nos. SB135/6, with the surplus self-adhesive paper around each stamp retained.

Nos. 1697b/c comes from rolls of 100 with the surplus paper around each stamp removed.

Nos. 1698 and 1699b were only issued in €7.50 and €8.20 stamp booklets, Nos. SB127 and SB143, in which the surplus self-adhesive paper around each stamp was retained.

No. 1699d was valid for 55c. each. It was only issued in booklets of ten (SB146) sold for €5.50. The inscription is towards the top of the stamp.

No. 1699e was issued in €5.50 booklets, No. SB152.

No. 1699f was issued in €8.20 booklets, No. SB151.

(Des Q. Design. Litho Irish Security Stamp Ptg Ltd)

2004 (16 Sept). 140th Anniv of National Gallery of Ireland (3rd issue). Horiz designs as T **426**. Multicoloured. Chalk-surfaced paper. Phosphor frame. P 15×14.

1700	48c. "The House Builders" (Walter Osborne)	80	80
	a. Horiz strip of 4. Nos. 1700/3	3·00	3·00
	b. Booklet pane. No. 1700×4 with margins all round	3·00	
1701	48c. "Kitchen Maid with the Supper at Emmaus" (Diego Velázquez)	80	80
	b. Booklet pane. No. 1701×4 with margins all round	3·00	
1702	48c. "The Lamentation over the Dead Christ" (Nicolas Poussin)	80	80
	b. Booklet pane. No. 1702×4 with margins all round	3·00	
1703	48c. "The Taking of Christ" (Caravaggio)	80	80
	b. Booklet pane. No. 1703×4 with margins all round	3·00	
1700/3	Set of 4	3·00	3·00

Nos. 1700/3 were printed together, se-tenant, as horizontal strips of 4 in sheets of 16.

462 William Butler Yeats

(Des G. Malmfors. Eng L. Sjooblom. Recess and litho Sweden Post)

2004 (1 Oct). Irish Winners of Nobel Prize for Literature. T **462** and similar horiz designs. Multicoloured. Phosphor frame. P 12½×13½.

1704	(N) Type **462**	1·00	1·00
	a. Block of 4. Nos. 1704/7	3·50	3·50
	b. Booklet pane. Nos. 1704/7	3·50	
1705	(N) George Bernard Shaw	1·00	1·00
1706	(N) Samuel Beckett	1·00	1·00
1707	(N) Seamus Heaney	1·00	1·00
1704/7	Set of 4	3·50	3·50

Nos. 1704/7 were printed together, se-tenant, in blocks of four stamps within sheets of 16. They were also issued in €1.92 stamp booklets (No. SB122).

Nos. 1704/7 were inscribed "N" and sold for 48c. each. Stamps of similar designs were issued by Sweden.

463 George Fox (Founder of The Society of Friends ("Quakers"))

464 Patrick Kavanagh

(Des P. Raftery. Litho Walsall)

2004 (21 Oct). 350th Anniv of Quakers in Ireland. Chalk-surfaced paper. Phosphor frame. P 13×13½.
1708　**463**　60c. multicoloured .... 1·00　1·00

(Des P. Raftery. Litho Walsall)

2004 (21 Oct). Birth Centenary of Patrick Kavanagh (poet). Chalk-surfaced paper. Phosphor frame. P 13×13½.
1709　**464**　48c. bronze-green and dull yellowish green .... 1·00　75

465 The Holy Family　　**466** Lovebirds

(Des F. O'Connor. Litho Irish Security Stamp Ptg Ltd)

2004 (10 Nov). Christmas. T **465** and similar vert designs. Multicoloured. Chalk-surfaced paper. Phosphor frame.

(a) PVA gum. P 14×15

1710		48c. Type **465**	85	50
1711		60c. The flight into Egypt	1·10	1·25
1712		65c. The Adoration of the Magi	1·25	1·40
1710/12 Set of 3			2·40	2·50

(b) Size 24×29 mm. Self-adhesive. P 11

1713		48c. The Holy Family	1·00	70
	a.	Booklet pane. No. 1713×24	22·00	

No. 1713 was only issued in €11.04 stamp booklets.

(Des Wendy Shea and Q. Design)

2005 (28 Jan). Love, Greetings and Chinese New Year of the Rooster. T **466** and similar horiz designs. Multicoloured. Chalk-surfaced paper. Phosphor frame.

(a) Litho Irish Security Stamp Ptg Ltd. PVA gum. Designs 40×30 mm. P 15×14

1714		48c. Type **466**	1·00	1·00
MS1715		130×74 mm. 60c. Rooster; 60c. Type **466**; 60c. Owl	6·50	6·50

(b) Litho SEP Sprint. Self-adhesive. Designs 30×25 mm. P 11

1716		48c. Rooster	1·50	1·50
	a.	Booklet pane. No. 1716; No. 1718×3; No. 1717; No. 1719×2	7·50	
1717		48c. Stork	1·50	1·50
1718		48c. Type **466**	1·00	1·00
1719		48c. Owl	1·25	1·25
1716/19 Set of 4			4·75	4·75

No. 1714 was available from sheets of 16. Nos. 1716/19 were only available in €4.80 stamp booklets, No. SB124, in which the surplus self-adhesive paper around each stamp was retained.

467 St. Patrick

468 "Landscape, Co. Wicklow" (Evie Hone)

(Des P. Raftery. Litho Irish Security Stamp Ptg Ltd)

2005 (17 Feb). St. Patrick's Day. Phosphor frame. Chalk-surfaced paper. P 14×15.
1720　**467**　65c. multicoloured .... 1·25　1·25

(Des Q. Design. Litho Irish Security Stamp Ptg Ltd)

2005 (24 Feb). Female Artists. T **468** and similar multicoloured designs. Phosphor frame. Chalk-surfaced paper. P 15×14 (48c.) or 14×15 (65c.).

1721		48c. Type **468**	85	95
	a.	Pair. Nos. 1721/2	1·70	1·90
1722		48c. "Seabird and Landmarks" (Nano Reid)	85	95
1723		65c. "Three Graces" (Gabriel Hayes) (*vert*)	1·10	1·25
	a.	Pair. Nos. 1723/4	2·20	2·00
1724		65c. "Threshing" (Mildred Anne Butler) (*vert*).	1·10	1·25
1721/4 Set of 4			3·50	4·00

Nos. 1721/2 and 1723/4 were printed together, *se-tenant*, as horizontal and vertical pairs in sheets of 16.

469 Statue, City Hall and Churches

(Des P. Murray. Litho Irish Security Stamp Ptg Ltd)

2005 (7 Mar). Cork — European Capital of Culture 2005. T **469** and similar square design. Multicoloured. Phosphor frame. P 13½.

1725		48c. Type **469**	80	80
	a.	Horiz pair. Nos. 1725/6	1·60	1·60
1726		48c. Court House and Shandon Steeple (clock tower)	80	80

Nos. 1725/6 were printed together, *se-tenant*, in horizontal pairs in sheets of 16, each pair forming a composite design showing Patrick's Bridge and a montage of landmark buildings and monuments of the city of Cork.

470 William Rowan Hamilton (birth bicentenary)

(Des G. Garland. Litho Irish Security Stamp Ptg Ltd)

2005 (14 Mar). UNESCO World Year of Physics. T **470** and similar horiz designs. Multicoloured. Phosphor frame. P 13½.

1727		48c. Type **470**	85	70
1728		60c. UNESCO Headquarters, Paris, trees and reflections of sunlight	1·10	1·25
1729		65c. Albert Einstein (50th death anniv)	1·25	1·40
1727/9 Set of 3			3·00	3·00

471 SOTW/CR 201 Class Diesel Locomotive pulling "Enterprise Express" Train

(Des V. Killowry and P. Raftery. Litho Irish Security Stamp Ptg Ltd)

2005 (5 Apr). 150th Anniv of Dublin–Belfast Railway. T **471** and similar horiz designs. Multicoloured. Chalk-surfaced paper. Phosphor frame. P 15×14½.

1730		48c. Type **471**	1·25	1·25
	a.	Pair. Nos. 1730/1	2·50	2·50
1731		48c. V Class 3 steam locomotive No. 85, *Merlin*, arriving at Amiens Street (now Connolly) Station, Dublin, c. 1951	1·25	1·25
1732		60c. Q Class steam locomotive No. 131 crossing Boyne Valley viaduct, Drogheda	1·60	1·60
1733		65c. Modern "Enterprise Express" leaving Belfast Central Station	1·60	1·60
1730/3 Set of 4			5·00	5·00
MS1734 150×90 mm. Nos. 1730/3			5·00	5·50

Nos. 1730/1 were printed together, *se-tenant*, in horizontal and vertical pairs in sheets of 16 stamps.

Nos. 1730/3 also exist as separate panes of four from a premium stamp booklet, No. SP3, containing stamps with a face value of €8.84 but sold at €9.

472 Red Deer Stags, Killarney National Park, Ireland

(Des J. Spokes (65c.) or F. O'Connor (others). Litho Cartor)

2005 (22 Apr). Biosphere Reserves. T **472** and similar horiz design. Multicoloured. Chalk-surfaced paper. Phosphor frame. P 13½.

1735	48c. Type **472**	85	70
1736	65c. Saskatoon Berries and Osprey, Waterton Lakes National Park, Alberta, Canada	1·75	1·50
MS1737	150×90 mm. Nos. 1735/6	2·50	2·50

Stamps in similar designs were issued by Canada.

473 Lamb, Cabbage, Carrots and Potato (ingredients of Irish Stew)

474 Small Copper

(Des Dialogue. Litho Cartor)

2005 (9 May). Europa. Gastronomy. T **473** and similar horiz design. Multicoloured. Chalk-surfaced paper. Phosphor frame. P 14½.

1738	48c. Type **473**	75	70
1739	65c. Oysters	1·00	1·25

Nos. 1738/9 were each printed in sheetlets of 10 stamps with enlarged illustrated left margins.

(Des I. Loe and P. Raftery. Litho Irish Security Stamp Printing Ltd)

2005 (24 May). Butterflies. T **474** and similar square designs. Multicoloured. Chalk-surfaced paper. Phosphor frame (Nos. 1740/3). P 13½.

1740	48c. Type **474**	1·00	70
1741	60c. Green Hairstreak	1·40	1·25
1742	65c. Painted Lady	1·40	1·25
1743	€1 Pearl-bordered Fritillary	2·25	2·50
1740/3	*Set of 4*	5·50	5·00
MS1744	150×67 mm. €5 As No. 1742. Ordinary paper.	9·00	11·00

475 *Dunbrody*

476 Glendalough, Co. Wicklow

(Des V. Killowry and P. Raftery. Litho Irish Security Stamp Ptg Ltd)

2005 (4 July). Cutty Sark International Tall Ships Race, Waterford. T **475** and similar square designs. Multicoloured. Phosphor frame. Chalk-surfaced paper. P 13½.

1745	48c. Type **475**	1·10	1·00
1746	60c. *Tenacious*	1·25	1·25
1747	65c. USCG *Eagle*	1·25	1·25
1745/7	*Set of 3*	3·25	3·25

(Des M. Craig. Litho Irish Security Stamp Ptg Ltd)

2005 (27 July). Round Towers of Ireland. T **476** and similar vert designs, each black. Phosphor frame. Chalk-surfaced paper. P 13½.

1748	48c. Type **476**	75	85
	a. Horiz strip of 4. Nos. 1748/51	2·75	3·00
1749	48c. Ardmore, Co. Waterford	75	85
1750	48c. Clones, Co. Monaghan	75	85
1751	48c. Kilmacduagh, Co. Galway	75	85
1748/51	*Set of 4*	2·75	3·00

Nos. 1748/51 were printed together, *se-tenant*, in horizontal strips of 4 in sheetlets of 12 (4×3), with the centre strip having the stamps in reverse order. They commemorate the 75th Anniversary of the Monuments of Ireland Act.

477 Bees on Honeycomb

478 Eamonn Darcy, Christy O'Connor Jnr and Philip Walton holding Ryder Cup

(Des S. Simpson. Litho Cartor)

2005 (19 Aug). Apimondia 2005 (international bee-keeping conference and exhibition), Dublin. Phosphor frame. Chalk-surfaced paper. P 13½×13.

1752	**477**	65c. multicoloured	1·25	1·25

(Des P. Raftery. Litho Irish Security Stamp Ptg Ltd)

2005 (27 Sept). Ireland and the Ryder Cup (golf tournament). T **478** and similar horiz designs. Multicoloured. Phosphor frame. Chalk-surfaced paper. P 15×14½.

1753	48c. Type **478**	1·25	1·25
	a. Pair. Nos. 1753/4	2·50	2·50
1754	48c. Darren Clarke, Paul McGinley and Pádraig Harrington with Ryder Cup	1·25	1·25
1755	60c. Harry Bradshaw, Ronan Rafferty and Christy O'Connor Snr	1·50	1·50
1756	65c. The K Club, Straffan, Co. Kildare (venue of 2006 Ryder Cup)	1·50	1·50
1753/6	*Set of 4*	5·00	5·00

Nos. 1753/4 were printed together, *se-tenant*, in horizontal and vertical pairs in sheets of 16.

Nos. 1753/4 were also issued in €9.50 premium booklets, No. SP4.

479 Erskine Childers

480 An Garda Síochána on Overseas Duty

(Des P. Raftery. Litho Irish Security Stamp Ptg Ltd)

2005 (10 Oct). Birth Centenary of Erskine Childers (President of Ireland 1973–4). Phosphor frame. Chalk-surfaced paper. P 14×15.

1757	**479**	48c. multicoloured	1·00	1·00

(Des G. Garland. Litho Irish Security Stamp Ptg Ltd)

2005 (14 Oct). 50th Anniv of Ireland's Membership of United Nations. T **480** and similar horiz designs. Multicoloured. Phosphor frame. Chalk-surfaced paper. P 15×14.

1758	48c. Type **480**	1·00	1·00
	a. Pair. Nos. 1758/9	2·00	2·00
1759	48c. Irish Army medical aid in East Timor	1·00	1·00
1760	60c. F.H. Boland (signatory of Ireland's membership), 1955	1·25	1·25
1761	65c. Member of Irish Defence Force in classroom, Lebanon	1·25	1·25
1758/61	*Set of 4*	4·00	4·00

Nos. 1758/9 were printed together, *se-tenant*, in horizontal and vertical pairs in sheets of 16 stamps.

481 "Arthur Griffith" (Leo Whelan) and Title Page of Essay

482 Nativity

(Des G. Garland. Litho Irish Security Stamp Ptg Ltd)

2005 (21 Nov). Centenary of Arthur Griffith's Essays "The Resurrection of Hungary: A Parallel for Ireland". Phosphor frame. Chalk-surfaced paper. P 13½×14.

1762	**481**	48c. multicoloured	1·00	1·00

(Des Pamela Leonard)

2005 (21 Nov). Christmas. T **482** and similar vert designs. Multicoloured. Chalk-surfaced paper.

(a) Litho Irish Security Stamp Ptg Ltd. PVA gum. Fluorescent paper. P 14½×15

1763	48c. Type **482**		80	50
1764	60c. Choir of angels with harp		1·10	1·25
1765	65c. Choir of angels with tambourine and trumpet		1·25	1·50
1763/5	*Set of 3*		2·75	3·00

(b) Litho SEP Sprint, Australia. Size 24×29 mm. Self adhesive. Phosphor frame. P 11½

1766	48c. Type **482**	85	80
	a. Booklet pane. No. 1766×26	21·00	

No. 1766 was only issued in €12 stamp booklets, No. SB125.

483 Patrick Gallagher (founder) and Templecrone Co-operative Store

484 Red Setter and Couple Embracing

(Des S. Simpson. Litho Irish Security Stamp Ptg Ltd)

2006 (16 Jan). Centenary of the Templecrone Co-operative Agricultural Society ("The Cope"). Phosphor frame. Chalk-surfaced paper. P 15×14½.

1767	**483**	48c. multicoloured	1·00	1·00

(Des Amanda Brady)

2006 (25 Jan). Love, Greetings and Chinese New Year of the Dog. T **484** and similar horiz designs. Multicoloured. Phosphor frame. Chalk-surfaced paper.

(a) Litho Irish Security Stamp Ptg Ltd. PVA gum. P 15×14½

1768	48c. Type **484**	1·00	85
MS1769 130×74 mm. 65c. Two Chinese crested dogs; 65c. As No. 1768; 65c. Golden Labrador		5·00	5·00

(b) Litho SEP Sprint, Australia. Self-adhesive. Size 29×24 mm. P 11½

1770	48c. Two Chinese crested dogs	1·75	1·75
	a. Booklet pane. No. 1770×3, 1771×2, 1772×3 and 1773×2 plus 10 greetings labels	16·00	
1771	48c. Golden Labrador	1·75	1·75
1772	48c. Type **484**	1·75	1·75
1773	48c. Red Setter puppy	1·75	1·75
1770/3	*Set of 4*	6·25	6·25

Nos. 1770/3 were only issued in €4.80 stamp booklets, No. SB126, in which the surplus self-adhesive paper around each stamp was retained.

485 "St. Patrick lights the Paschal Fire at Slane" (Seán Keating)

(Des P. Raftery. Litho Irish Security Stamp Ptg Ltd)

2006 (16 Feb). St. Patrick's Day. Phosphor frame. Chalk-surfaced paper. P 15×14½.

1774	**485**	65c. multicoloured	1·75	1·25

486 Sessile Oak (*Quercus petraea*)

(Des Susan Sex and Q. Design. Litho Irish Security Stamp Ptg Ltd)

2006 (7 Mar). Trees of Ireland. T **486** and similar square designs. Multicoloured. Phosphor frame. Chalk-surfaced paper. P 13½.

1775	48c. Type **486**	60	85
1776	60c. Yew (*Taxus baccata*)	1·10	1·10
1777	75c. Ash (*Fraxinus excelsior*)	1·40	1·40
1778	€1 Strawberry-tree (*Arbutus unedo*)	1·75	2·00
1775/8	*Set of 4*	4·75	5·25
MS1779 150×90 mm. Nos. 1775/8		6·50	6·50

No. MS1779 was reissued on 27 May 2006 additionally inscribed on the sheet margin for Washington 2006 International Stamp Exhibition, and sold for €3.

487 St. Hubert, Church of Ireland, Carnalway, Co. Kildare

488 General Post Office, Dublin

(Des S. Simpson. Litho Irish Security Stamp Ptg Ltd)

2006 (21 Mar). 75th Death Anniv of Harry Clarke (stained glass artist). Phosphor frame. Chalk-surfaced paper. P 13½.

1780	**487**	48c. multicoloured	1·00	85

(Des Ger Garland. Litho Irish Security Stamp Ptg Ltd)

2006 (12 Apr). 90th Anniv of the Easter Rising. Phosphor frame. Chalk-surfaced paper. P 13½.

1781	**488**	48c. multicoloured	1·00	85

489 Children waving Irish and EU Flags (Katie McMillan)

490 EU Flag

(Adapted Q. Design. Litho Cartor)

2006 (9 May). Europa. Winning Entries in Children's Stamp Design Competition. T **489** and similar vert design. Multicoloured. Phosphor frame. Chalk-surfaced paper. P 14×14½.

1782	48c. Type **489**	1·25	60
1783	75c. Flags of EU members in flowers (Sarah Naughter)	1·60	2·25

(Des Ger Garland. Litho Cartor)

2006 (9 May). Tenth Anniv of European Union Flag. Phosphor frame. Chalk-surfaced paper. P 14½×14.

1784	**490**	48c. multicoloured	1·00	85

491 Interior of University Church (Dr. Thomas Ryan)

492 Máirtín Ó Cadhain (Irish language writer) (birth centenary)

(Des S. Simpson. Litho Irish Security Stamp Ptg Ltd)

2006 (25 May). 150th Anniv of University Church, St. Stephen's Green, Dublin. Phosphor frame. Chalk-surfaced paper. P 14×15.

1785	**491**	48c. multicoloured	1·00	75

(Des S. O'Sullivan (1786), J. Hanley (1787). Litho Irish Security Stamp Ptg Ltd)

2006 (6 June). Celtic Scholars. T **492** and similar vert design. Multicoloured. Phosphor frame. Chalk-surfaced paper. P 14×15.

1786		48c. Type **492**	1·00	1·00
	a.	Pair. Nos. 1786/7	2·00	2·00
1787		48c. Johann Caspar Zeus (Celtic languages researcher) (birth bicentenary)	1·00	1·00

Nos. 1786/7 were printed together, *se-tenant*, in horizontal and vertical pairs in sheetlets of 16 stamps.

493 Pebbles and Typewriter Keyboard

(Des Zinc Design Consultants. Litho Cartor)

2006 (6 June). Tenth Anniv of the Department of the Gaeltacht. Phosphor frame. Chalk-surfaced paper. P 13½.

1788	**493**	48c. multicoloured	1·00	75

494 Emblem

495 *St. David* (ferry), 1906

(Des Zinc Design Consultants. Litho Irish Security Stamp Ptg Ltd)

2006 (6 June). Tenth Anniv of TG4 (Teilifíse Gaeilge 4) Television Channel. Phosphor frame. Chalk-surfaced paper. P 13½.

1789	**494**	48c. multicoloured	1·00	75

(Des V. Killowry and P. Raftery. Litho Irish Security Stamp Ptg Ltd)

2006 (20 June). Centenary of the Rosslare–Fishguard Ferry Service. T **495** and similar horiz design. Multicoloured. Phosphor frame (Nos. 1790/1). Chalk-surfaced paper. P 15×14.

1790		48c. Type **495**	1·50	1·50
	a.	Pair. Nos. 1790/1	3·00	3·00
1791		48c. *Stena Lynx* (ferry), 2006	1·50	1·50
MS1792	150×90 mm. Nos. 1790/1		3·50	3·50

Nos. 1790/1 were printed together, *se-tenant*, in horizontal and vertical pairs in sheets of 16 stamps.

496 "The Battle of the Somme (36th Ulster Division)" (J. P. Beadle)

(Des Ger Garland. Litho Irish Security Stamp Ptg Ltd)

2006 (26 June). 90th Anniv of the Battle of the Somme. Phosphor frame. Chalk-surfaced paper. P 13½.

1793	**496**	75c. multicoloured	3·00	2·50

497 Guide Dog

498 Golf Ball on Tee

(Des S. Simpson. Litho and embossing Cartor)

2006 (7 July). 30th Anniv of Irish Guide Dogs for the Blind. Phosphor frame. Chalk-surfaced paper. P 13½×13.

1794	**497**	48c. multicoloured	1·75	1·25

(Des Javelin)

2006 (25 July). Ryder Cup Golf Tournament, K Club, Straffan, Co. Kildare (1st issue). T **498** and similar vert designs. Multicoloured. Phosphor frame (Nos. 1795/8, 1800/3 only). Chalk-surfaced paper.

(a) Litho Irish Security Stamp Ptg Ltd. PVA gum. P 14×15

1795		48c. Type **498**	1·40	1·40
	a.	Horiz strip of 4. Nos. 1795/8	5·00	5·00
1796		48c. Golf ball in the rough	1·40	1·40
1797		48c. Golf ball in bunker	1·40	1·40
1798		48c. Golf ball at edge of green	1·40	1·40
1795/8	*Set of 4*		5·00	5·00
MS1799	150×90 mm. Nos. 1795/8		5·00	5·00

(b) Litho SEP Sprint, Australia. Self-adhesive. Size 24×29 mm. P 11½

1800		48c. Type **498**	1·40	1·40
	a.	Vert strip of 4. Nos. 1800/3	5·00	5·00
1801		48c. As No. 1796	1·40	1·40
1802		48c. As No. 1797	1·40	1·40
1803		48c. As No. 1798	1·40	1·40
1800/3	*Set of 4*		5·00	5·00

Nos. 1795/8 were printed together, *se-tenant*, in horizontal strips of four stamps in sheetlets of 16.

Nos. 1800/3 occur, *se-tenant*, in strips of four and rolls of 100 with the surplus self-adhesive paper around each stamp removed.

See also No. **MS**1808.

499 "Ronnie Delany" (Dr. Thomas Ryan)

500 Michael Cusack

(Des S. Simpson. Litho Irish Security Stamp Ptg Ltd)

2006 (16 Aug). 50th Anniv of Ronnie Delany's Gold Medal for 1500 Metres at Olympic Games, Melbourne. Phosphor frame. Chalk-surfaced paper. P 13½.

1804	**499**	48c. multicoloured	1·00	75

(Des T. Ryan and Q. Design. Litho Irish Security Stamp Ptg Ltd)

2006 (23 Aug). Death Centenary of Michael Cusack (founder of Gaelic Athletic Association). Phosphor frame. Chalk-surfaced paper. P 14×15.

1805	**500**	48c. multicoloured	1·00	75

501 "Michael Davitt" (Sir William Orpen)

502 RTÉ National Symphony Orchestra

(Des Q. Design. Litho Irish Security Stamp Ptg Ltd)

2006 (5 Sept). Death Centenary of Michael Davitt (founder of Irish National Land League). Phosphor frame. Chalk-surfaced paper. P 14×15.

| 1806 | **501** | 48c. multicoloured | 1·00 | 75 |

(Des S. Simpson. Litho Irish Security Stamp Ptg Ltd)

2006 (8 Sept). 25th Anniv of National Concert Hall, Dublin. Phosphor frame. Chalk-surfaced paper. P 14×15.

| 1807 | **502** | 48c. multicoloured | 1·00 | 75 |

503 Teeing Off

(Des Javelin Y & R. Lenticular Outer Aspect, New Zealand and litho SEP Sprint, Australia)

2006 (19 Sept). Ryder Cup Golf Tournament, K Club, Straffan, Co. Kildare (2nd issue). Sheet 140×102 mm containing T **503** and similar horiz design. Multicoloured. Self-adhesive. P 9½.

| MS1808 | Type **503**; 75c. In bunker | 4·50 | 5·00 |

504 River Barrow at Graiguenamanagh, Co. Kilkenny

(Des Q. Design. Litho Irish Security Stamp Ptg Ltd)

2006 (20 Oct). Inland Waterways (1st series). T **504** and similar horiz designs. Multicoloured. Phosphor frame. Chalk-surfaced paper. P 13½.

1809	75c. Type **504**	1·60	1·90
	a. Booklet pane. No. 1809×4 with margins all round	5·50	
1810	75c. Belturbet Marina, River Erne, Co. Cavan	1·60	1·90
	a. Booklet pane. No. 1810×4 with margins all round	5·50	
1811	75c. Lock-keepers cottage on Grand Canal, Cornalour, Co. Offaly	1·60	1·90
	a. Booklet pane. No. 1811×4 with margins all round	5·50	
1812	75c. River Shannon at Meelick Quay	1·60	1·90
	a. Booklet pane. No. 1812×4 with margins all round	5·50	
1809/12	Set of 4	6·25	7·50

See also Nos. 1919a/1919d.

505 The Chieftains

(Des Detail Design Studio. Litho Irish Security Stamp Ptg Ltd)

2006 (7 Nov). Irish Music (1st series). T **505** and similar horiz designs. Multicoloured. Phosphor frame (Nos. 1813/16 only). Chalk-surfaced paper. P 13½×14.

1813	48c. Type **505**	1·25	1·00
1814	48c. The Dubliners	1·25	1·00
1815	75c. The Clancy Brothers and Tommy Makem	1·50	2·25
1816	75c. Altan	1·50	2·25
1813/16	Set of 4	5·00	6·00
MS1817	150×90 mm. Nos. 1813/16. Ordinary paper	5·50	6·50

Nos. 1813/16 were also issued in €10 premium booklets, No. SP6.
See also Nos. 1919/MS1923.

506 Madonna and Child

507 "The Nativity" (Simon Bening)

(Des P. J. Lynch (Nos. 1818/19) and Q. Design)

2006 (9 Nov). Christmas. Multicoloured. Phosphor frame. Chalk-surfaced paper.

(a) Litho Irish Security Stamp Ptg Ltd. PVA gum. T **506** *and similar vert design. P* 14×15

| 1818 | 48c. Type **506** | 1·00 | 50 |
| 1819 | 75c. Shepherd with lamb | 1·75 | 2·25 |

(b) Litho SEP Sprint, Australia. Self-adhesive. Size 22×30 mm. P 11½

| 1820 | 48c. Type **507** | 1·25 | 60 |
| | a. Booklet pane. No. 1820×26 | 26·00 | |

No. 1820 was only issued in €12 stamp booklets, No. SB129.

2006 (16 Nov). Belgica 2006 International Stamp Exhibition, Brussels. No. **MS**1817 with Belgica '06 emblem and "16–20 November, 2006" added to the sheet margin.

| MS1821 | 150×90 mm. Nos. 1813/16 | 5·50 | 6·50 |

2006 (1 Dec). MonacoPhil 2006 International Stamp Exhibition. No. **MS**1817 with MonacoPhil 2006 emblem and "1–3 December, 2006" added to the sheet margin.

| MS1822 | 150×90 mm. Nos. 1813/16 | 5·50 | 6·50 |

508 Franciscan and Door to Auditorium of Irish College

(Des T. Ryan and P. Raftery. Litho Irish Security Stamp Ptg Ltd)

2007 (24 Jan). 400th Anniv of the Irish Franciscan College, Louvain, Belgium. Phosphor frame. Chalk-surfaced paper. P 14×15.

| 1823 | **508** | 75c. multicoloured | 1·75 | 2·25 |

509 Father Luke Wadding

510 Linked Hands

(Des T. Ryan and S. Simpson. Litho Irish Security Stamp Ptg Ltd)

2007 (24 Jan). 350th Death Anniv of Father Luke Wadding (theologian). Phosphor frame. Chalk-surfaced paper. P 14×15.

| 1824 | **509** | 75c. multicoloured | 1·75 | 2·25 |

(Des Q. Design. Litho SEP Sprint, Australia)

2007 (26 Jan). Weddings (1st issue). Phosphor frame. Chalk-surfaced paper. Self-adhesive. P 11½.

| 1825 | **510** | (N) multicoloured | 1·00 | 70 |
| | | a. Booklet pane. No. 1825×10 | 9·00 | |

No. 1825 is inscribed "N" and was sold for 48c. each. It was issued in booklets of ten, No. SB130, sold for €4.80.
See also Nos. 1862, 1880, 1929, 1990, 2047, 2101, and 2151.

511 Cartoon Stamp and Heart

512 Two Pigs

(Des S. Simpson. Litho SEP Sprint, Australia)

2007 (26 Jan). Greetings Stamps. T **511** and similar vert design. Multicoloured. Phosphor frame. Chalk-surfaced paper. Self-adhesive. P 11½.

1826	(48c.) Type **511**	1·10	70
	a. Booklet pane. Nos. 1826/7, each ×5	10·00	
1827	(48c.) Birthday cake	1·10	70

Nos. 1826/7 are inscribed "N" and sold for 48c. each. They were issued in booklets of ten, No. SB131, sold for €4.80.

(Des Hu Zhenyuan and S. Simpson. Litho Irish Security Stamp Ptg Ltd)

2007 (9 Feb). Chinese New Year ("Year of the Pig"). Phosphor frame. Chalk-surfaced paper. P 15×14.

1828	**512** 75c. multicoloured	1·75	2·25
MS1829	130×74 mm. 75c.×2 Type **512**; 75c. As Type **512** but vermilion background	5·25	6·75

513 Shamrock

514 Hugh O'Neill, Earl of Tyrone

(Des Ger Garland. Litho Irish Security Stamp Ptg Ltd)

2007 (9 Feb). St. Patrick's Day. Phosphor frame. Chalk-surfaced paper. P 13½.

1830	**513** 75c. multicoloured	2·00	2·50

(Des S. Ó Brógáin and S. Simpson. Litho Irish Security Stamp Ptg Ltd)

2007 (23 Feb). 400th Anniv of the Flight of the Earls. T **514** and similar vert designs. Multicoloured. Phosphor frame*. Chalk-surfaced paper. P 14×15.

1831	48c. Type **514**	1·00	1·25
	a. Horiz pair. Nos. 1831/2	2·00	2·50
1832	48c. Rory O'Donnell, Earl of Tyrconnell	1·00	1·25
MS1833	150×90 mm. Nos. 1831/2	2·25	2·50

Nos. 1831/2 were printed together, *se-tenant*, as horizontal pairs in sheetlets of 16 stamps, each pair forming a composite background design showing Lough Swilly and map of Europe.

*Nos. 1831/2 and the stamps within **MS**1833 had a phosphor frame around the horizontal pair, giving No. 1831 a phosphor frame at top, left and bottom and No. 1832 a phosphor frame at top, right and bottom.

Collectors who purchased **MS**1833 from An Post received a free souvenir print of the miniature sheet artwork.

515 Trim Castle, Co. Meath

(Des Q. Design. Litho Irish Security Stamp Ptg Ltd)

2007 (9 Mar). Castles. T **515** and similar horiz designs. Multicoloured. Phosphor frame. Chalk-surfaced paper. P 15×14.

1834	55c. Type **515**	1·50	1·50
	a. Block of 4. Nos. 1834/7	5·50	5·50
1835	55c. Dunluce Castle, Co. Antrim	1·50	1·50
1836	55c. Lismore Castle, Co. Waterford	1·50	1·50
1837	55c. Portumna Castle, Co. Galway	1·50	1·50
1834/7	Set of 4	5·50	5·50

MS1838	150×90 mm. Nos. 1834/7	5·50	5·50

Nos. 1834/7 were printed together, *se-tenant*, in blocks of 4 in sheetlets of 16.

516 EU Flag, Signatures and Palazzo dei Conservatori, Rome

517 Girl Scout at Campsite, c. 2007

(Des S. Simpson. Litho Irish Security Stamp Ptg Ltd)

2007 (28 Mar). 50th Anniv of the Treaty of Rome. Phosphor frame. Chalk-surfaced paper. P 14×15.

1839	**516** 55c. multicoloured	1·25	1·25

(Des Red & Grey Design. Litho Cartor)

2007 (9 May). Europa. Centenary of Scouting. T **517** and similar horiz design. Multicoloured. Phosphor frame. Chalk-surfaced paper. P 14½×14.

1840	55c. Type **517**	1·50	75
1841	78c. Boy scout camping, c. 1907	2·00	2·50

518 Jupiter

(Des Design Factory. Litho Cartor)

2007 (25 May). The Planets. T **518** and similar horiz designs. Multicoloured. Phosphor frame*. Chalk-surfaced paper. P 13½.

1842	55c. Type **518**	1·40	1·50
	a. Horiz pair. Nos. 1842/3	2·75	3·00
1843	55c. Neptune	1·40	1·50
1844	78c. Saturn	1·90	2·25
	a. Horiz pair. Nos. 1844/5	3·75	4·50
1845	78c. Uranus	1·90	2·25
1842/5	Set of 4	6·00	6·75
MS1846	150×90 mm. Nos. 1842/5	6·00	6·75

Nos. 1842/3 and 1844/5 were printed together, *se-tenant*, in horizontal pairs in sheetlets of 16, each pair forming a composite design showing Planet Earth.

*Nos. 1842/3, 1844/5 and the stamps within **MS**1846 have a phosphor frame around the horizontal pair, giving Nos. 1842 and 1844 a phosphor frame at top, left and bottom and Nos. 1843 and 1845 a phosphor frame at top, right and bottom.

Nos. 1842/5 were also issued in €12 premium booklets, No. SP7.

519 St. Charles of Mount Argus, Dublin

520 Anniversary Emblem

(Des James Hanley and Steve Simpson. Litho Irish Security Stamp Ptg Ltd)

2007 (5 June). Canonisation of Blessed Charles of Mount Argus. Phosphor frame. Chalk-surfaced paper. P 13½.

1847	**519** 55c. multicoloured	1·25	1·25

(Des Zinc Design. Litho Irish Security Stamp Ptg Ltd)

2007 (13 June). 50th Anniv of the IPA (Institute of Public Administration). Phosphor frame. Chalk-surfaced paper. P 13½.

1848	**520** 55c. multicoloured	1·25	1·25

521 RTÉ National Symphony
Orchestra

(Des Zinc Design. Litho Irish Security Stamp Ptg Ltd)

2007 (19 June). RTÉ Performing Groups. T **521** and similar horiz designs. Multicoloured. Phosphor frame. Chalk-surfaced paper.

(a) Litho Irish Security Stamp Ptg Ltd. PVA gum. P 13½

1849	55c. Type **521**	1·40	1·50
	a. Horiz strip of 5. Nos. 1849/53	6·25	6·75
1850	55c. RTÉ Concert Orchestra	1·40	1·50
1851	55c. RTÉ Vanbrugh Quartet	1·40	1·50
1852	55c. RTÉ Philharmonic Choir	1·40	1·50
1853	55c. RTÉ Cór na nÓg children's choir	1·40	1·50
1849/53	*Set of 5*	6·25	6·75

(b) Litho SEP Sprint, Australia. Self-adhesive. P 11½

1854	55c. As No. 1853	1·10	1·60
	a. Booklet pane. Nos. 1854/8, each ×2	10·00	
1855	55c. As No. 1850	1·10	1·60
1856	55c. As No. 1852	1·10	1·60
1857	55c. As No. 1849	1·10	1·60
1858	55c. As No. 1851	1·10	1·60
1854/8	*Set of 5*	5·00	7·25

Nos. 1849/53 were printed together, *se-tenant*, in horizontal strips of five stamps in sheetlets of 20.

Nos. 1849/53 were also issued in premium booklets, No. SP8.

Nos. 1854/8 were only issued in €5.50 stamp booklets, No. SB137.

522 Society Seal and
Gandon Façade of King's
Inns Building

523 Bound Books containing
Records in Registry of Deeds

(Des Ger Garland. Litho Irish Security Stamp Ptg Ltd)

2007 (10 July). 400th Anniv of Revival of the Honourable Society of King's Inns. Phosphor frame. Chalk-surfaced paper. P 13½.

1859	**522**	55c. multicoloured	1·25	1·25

(Des Ger Garland. Litho Irish Security Stamp Ptg Ltd)

2007 (10 July). 300th Anniv of the Registry of Deeds Act. Phosphor frame. Chalk-surfaced paper. P 15×14.

1860	**523**	78c. multicoloured	1·75	1·75

524 Girls Choir from Coláiste Iosagáin,
Co. Dublin

(Des Ger Garland. Litho Irish Security Stamp Ptg Ltd)

2007 (17 July). Centenary of the National Anthem. Phosphor frame. Chalk-surfaced paper. P 13½.

1861	**524**	55c. multicoloured	1·25	1·25

2007 (25 July). Weddings (2nd issue). As T **510** but new value. Phosphor frame. Chalk-surfaced paper. Self-adhesive. P 11½.

1862	55c. As Type **510**	1·25	1·25
	a. Booklet pane. No. 1862×10	11·00	

No. 1862 was only issued in €5.50 stamp booklets, No. SB138.

525 *Skuldelev 2* (Viking longship)

(Des Vincent Killowry and Paul Raftery. Litho Irish Security Stamp Ptg Ltd)

2007 (7 Aug). Voyage of the *Havhingsten fra Glendalough* (replica of Viking longship *Skuldelev 2*) from Denmark to Dublin. T **525** and similar horiz design. Multicoloured. Phosphor frame. Chalk-surfaced paper. P 15×14.

1863	55c. Type **525**	1·25	1·25
MS1864	150×90 mm. €3 *Havhingsten fra Glendalough* (replica Viking longship). Ordinary paper	6·75	7·50

526 Paul O'Connell   **527** 'Fat Cat'

(Des Design Factory. Litho Irish Security Stamp Ptg Ltd)

2007 (20 Aug). Rugby World Cup, France. T **526** and similar horiz design. Multicoloured. Phosphor frame. Chalk-surfaced paper. P 13½.

1865	55c. Type **526**	1·00	1·25
1866	78c. Irish players in lineout, Croke Park, 2007	1·75	2·50
MS1867	Two sheets, each 150×90 mm. (a) No. 1865.	2·75	3·50
	(b) No. 1866 *Set of 2 sheets*		

(Des Steve Simpson. Litho Irish Security Stamp Ptg Ltd)

2007 (6 Sept). 'Celtic Cats'. T **527** and similar multicoloured designs showing cartoons by Martyn Turner. Phosphor frame. Chalk-surfaced paper. P 14×15.

1868	55c. Type **527**	1·00	1·50
	a. Horiz pair. Nos. 1868/9	2·00	3·00
1869	55c. 'Celtic Tigress'	1·00	1·50
1870	78c. 'Cool Cats'	1·75	2·25
	a. Horiz pair. Nos. 1870/1	3·50	4·50
1871	78c. 'Kilkenny Cat'	1·75	2·25
1868/71	*Set of 4*	5·00	6·75
MS1872	150×90 mm. As Nos. 1868/71 but 18×18 mm. P 13½	5·00	6·75

Nos. 1868/9 and 1870/1 were each printed together, *se-tenant*, in horizontal pairs in sheetlets of 16 stamps.

528 Fr. Joseph Mullooly in   **529** James Fintan Lalor
4th-century Basilica, San
Clemente, Rome

(Des Paul Raftery. Litho Irish Security Stamp Ptg Ltd)

2007 (12 Sept). 150th Anniv of Archaeological Discoveries, San Clemente, Rome. Phosphor frame. Chalk-surfaced paper. P 15×14.

1873	**528**	55c. multicoloured	1·25	1·25

(Des John Conway. Litho Irish Security Stamp Ptg Ltd)

2007 (18 Sept). Birth Bicentenary of James Fintan Lalor (nationalist and journalist). Phosphor frame. Chalk-surfaced paper. P 14×15.

1874	**529**	55c. multicoloured	1·25	1·25

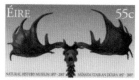

530 Giant Elk Antlers

(Des Steve Simpson. Litho Irish Security Stamp Ptg Ltd)

2007 (25 Oct). 150th Anniv of the Natural History Museum, Dublin. Phosphor frame. Chalk-surfaced paper. P 13½.

1875 **530** 55c. multicoloured .... 1·25   1·25

531 The Presentation in the Temple

532 Charles Wesley (*The Lily Portrait*)

(Des Seán Ó Brógáin and Steve Simpson)

2007 (8 Nov). Christmas. T **531** and similar multicoloured designs. Phosphor frame. Chalk-surfaced paper.

(a) Litho Irish Security Stamp Ptg Ltd. PVA gum. P 15×14.

1876   55c. Type **531** .... 1·25   75
1877   78c. The Three Magi .... 2·00   3·50

(b) Litho SEP Sprint, Australia. Self-adhesive. Size 24×29 mm. P 11½

1878   55c. The Adoration of the Shepherds .... 1·25   1·25
   a. Booklet pane. No. 1878×26 .... 26·00
No. 1878 was only issued in €13.75 stamp booklets, No. SB139.

(Des Steve Simpson. Litho Irish Security Stamp Ptg Ltd)

2007 (15 Nov). 300th Birth Anniv of Charles Wesley (founder of Methodism and hymn writer). Phosphor frame. Chalk-surfaced paper. P 14×15.

1879 **532** 78c. multicoloured .... 1·90   2·25

533 Bride and Groom Embracing

534 Rat and Candle

(Des Amanda Brady. Litho SEP Sprint, Australia)

2008 (16 Jan). Weddings (3rd issue). Phosphor frame. Chalk-surfaced paper. Self-adhesive. P 11½.

1880 **533** 55c. multicoloured .... 1·25   1·40
   a. Booklet pane. No. 1880×10 .... 11·00
No. 1880 was only issued in €5.50 stamp booklets, No. SB140.

(Des Renze Zhou. Litho Irish Security Stamp Ptg Ltd)

2008 (23 Jan). Chinese New Year ("Year of the Rat"). Phosphor frame. Chalk-surfaced paper. P 15×14.

1881 **534** 78c. multicoloured .... 2·00   2·25
MS1882 130×74 mm. No. 1881×3 .... 5·75   6·50

535 Liam Whelan and Munich Memorial Clock, Old Trafford, Manchester

(Des RMG Target. Litho Irish Security Stamp Ptg Ltd)

2008 (4 Feb). 50th Anniv of the Munich Air Disaster. Phosphor frame. Chalk-surfaced paper. P 13½.

1883 **535** 55c. multicoloured .... 2·00   1·40

536 Juggling Frog

537 St. Patrick (line engraving by Leonard Gaultier)

(Des Steve Simpson. Litho SEP Sprint, Australia)

2008 (11 Feb). Greeting Stamps. T **536** and similar vert design. Multicoloured. Self-adhesive. Phosphor frame. Chalk-surfaced paper. P 11½.

1884   55c. Type **536** .... 1·40   1·40
   a. Booklet pane. Nos. 1884/5, each ×5 ...... 12·50
1885   55c. Trumpeting elephant .... 1·40   1·40
Nos. 1884/5 were only issued in €5.50 stamp booklets, No. SB141.

(Des Ger Garland. Litho Irish Security Stamp Ptg Ltd)

2008 (11 Feb). St. Patrick's Day. Phosphor frame. Chalk-surfaced paper. P 13½.

1886 **537** 78c. multicoloured .... 2·00   2·25
No. 1886 is based on a drawing made in 1619 by Thomas Messingham.

538 Logo

539 Hugh Lane (Antonio Mancini)

(Des Ger Garland. Litho Irish Security Stamp Ptg Ltd)

2008 (7 Mar). European Year of Intercultural Dialogue. Phosphor frame. Chalk-surfaced paper. P 13½.

1887 **538** 55c. multicoloured .... 1·40   1·40

(Des Ger Garland. Litho Irish Security Stamp Ptg Ltd)

2008 (28 Mar). Centenary of Hugh Lane Gallery, Dublin. Phosphor frame. Chalk-surfaced paper. P 13½.

1888 **539** 55c. multicoloured .... 1·40   1·40

540 West of Ireland Landscape

541 Logo of Irish League of Credit Unions (ILCU)

(Des Ger Garland. Litho Irish Security Stamp Ptg Ltd)

2008 (17 Apr). Paul Henry Landscape Paintings. T **540** and similar horiz designs. Multicoloured. Phosphor frame*. Chalk-surfaced paper. P 13½.

1889   55c. Type **540** (signature at left) .... 1·40   1·50
   a. Horiz pair. Nos. 1889/90 .... 2·75   3·00
1890   55c. West of Ireland Landscape (rocks in foreground, signature at right) .... 1·40   1·50
1891   55c. A Connemara Village (signature at left) 1·40   1·50
   a. Horiz pair. Nos. 1891/2 .... 2·75   3·00
1892   55c. A Connemara Village (signature at right) .... 1·40   1·50
1889/92 Set of 4 .... 5·00   5·50
Nos. 1889/90 and 1891/2 were each printed together, *se-tenant*, as horizontal pairs in sheetlets of 16, each pair forming a composite design showing the complete painting.
Nos. 1889/92 were also issued in €9 premium booklets, No. SP9.

*Nos. 1889/90, 1891/2 and the stamps within SP9 have a phosphor frame around the horizontal pair, giving Nos. 1889 and 1891 a phosphor frame at top, left and bottom, and Nos. 1890 and 1892 a phosphor frame at top, right and bottom.
Nos. 1889/92 commemorate the 50th death anniversary of Paul Henry.

(Des Ger Garland. Litho Irish Security Stamp Printing Ltd)

2008 (23 Apr). 50th Anniv of the Credit Union Movement in Ireland. Phosphor frame. Chalk-surfaced paper. P 15×14.
1893 **541** 55c. multicoloured .... 1·50 1·50

542 World Map showing Africa and Asia (Mohammed Rahman)

(Des Richard Chaney. Litho Irish Security Stamp Ptg Ltd)

2008 (28 Apr). International Year of Planet Earth. T **542** and similar circular design showing children's plasticine models of Planet Earth. Multicoloured. Phosphor frame. Chalk-surfaced paper. Self-adhesive. P 13.
1894 55c. Type **542** .... 1·50 1·50
a. Booklet pane. Nos. 1894/5, each×5 .... 13·50
1895 55c. World map showing the Americas and Atlantic Ocean (Conor Reid) .... 1·50 1·50
Nos. 1894/5 were issued in €5.50 stamp booklets.
They were also available in self-adhesive sheetlets of ten stamps, five of each design, sold at €7.50 per sheetlet.

543 '50'

(Des Kasia Ozmin. Litho Irish Security Stamp Ptg Ltd)

2008 (23 May). 50th Anniv of the Institute of Creative Advertising and Design (ICAD). Phosphor frame. Chalk-surfaced paper. P 13½.
1896 **543** 55c. multicoloured .... 1·50 1·50

544 RMS *Leinster*

(Des Vincent Killowry and Steve Simpson. Litho Irish Security Stamp Ptg Ltd)

2008 (30 May). 90th Anniv of the Sinking of RMS *Leinster*. Phosphor frame. Chalk-surfaced paper. P 15×14.
1897 **544** 55c. multicoloured .... 2·00 1·50

545 Boy writing Letter

546 Aughrim, Co. Wicklow (2007 winner)

(Des Bold Design. Litho Irish Security Stamp Ptg Ltd)

2008 (9 June). Europa. The Letter. T **545** and similar vert design. Multicoloured. Phosphor frame. Chalk-surfaced paper. P 14×15.
1898 55c. Type **545** .... 1·50 1·50
1899 82c. Girl writing letter .... 2·00 2·00
Nos. 1898/9 were each printed in sheetlets of ten stamps with enlarged illustrated top margins.

(Des Steve Simpson. Litho Irish Security Stamp Ptg Ltd)

2008 (19 June). 50th Anniv of the Tidy Towns Competition. Phosphor frame. Chalk-surfaced paper. P 14×15.
1900 **546** 55c. multicoloured .... 1·50 1·50

547 Lt. Col. McCarthy, Comdt. Higgins, Capt. Lavelle, Comdt. Coughlan and Capt. Henderson

(Des Paul Raftery. Litho Irish Security Stamp Ptg Ltd)

2008 (26 June). 50th Anniv of the First Irish Defence Forces Mission to the UN. Phosphor frame. Chalk-surfaced paper. P 15×14.
1901 **547** 55c. multicoloured .... 2·00 1·50

548 Colm Meaney in *Kings*

(Des Gospel TM. Litho Irish Security Stamp Ptg Ltd)

2008 (8 July). 'Filmed in Ireland'. T **548** and similar vert designs. Multicoloured. Phosphor frame. Chalk-surfaced paper. P 15×14.
1902 55c. Type **548** .... 1·25 1·50
1903 55c. Bríd Ní Neachtáin in *Cré Na Cille* .... 1·25 1·50
1904 82c. Cillian Murphy in *The Wind that Shakes the Barley* .... 1·60 2·10
1905 82c. Pat Shortt in *Garage* .... 1·60 2·10
1902/5 *Set of 4* .... 5·00 6·50
MS1906 150×90 mm. Nos. 1902/5 .... 5·50 7·00
Nos. 1902/5 were each printed in separate sheetlets of 12 (4×3), with the vertical rows of stamps separated by gutters.
Nos. 1902/5 were also issued in €12 premium booklets, No. SP10.

549 Rowing

(Des Graham Knuttel and Pure Communications. Litho Irish Security Stamp Ptg Ltd)

2008 (15 July). Olympic Games, Beijing. T **549** and similar horiz design. Multicoloured. Phosphor frame. Chalk-surfaced paper. P 15×14.
1907 55c. Type **549** .... 1·50 1·50
1908 82c. Shot-putt .... 2·00 2·00
MS1909 150×90 mm. As Nos. 1907/8 optd 'Olympex 2008' .... 3·50 4·00

549a Lock-keeper's Cottage on Grand Canal, Cornalour, Co. Offaly

(Des Steve Simpson. Digital/thermal transfer Label Art Ltd)

2008 (21 July–6 Oct). Inland Waterways (2nd series). T **549a** and similar horiz designs as Nos. 1809/12. Multicoloured. Self-adhesive. Phosphor frame. Die-cut perf 11.

1909a	55c. Type **549a**.		1·60	1·60
	ab. Vert strip of 4. Nos. 1909a/d		6·25	6·25
	ac. Three phosphor bars (6 Oct)		3·00	3·00
	aca. Vert strip of 4. Nos. 1909 ac/dc		11·00	11·00
1909b	55c. Belturbet Marina, River Erne, Co. Cavan		1·60	1·60
	bc. Three phosphor bars (6 Oct)		3·00	3·00
1909c	55c. River Barrow at Graiguenamanagh, Co. Kilkenny		1·60	1·60
	cc. Three phosphor bars (6 Oct)		3·00	3·00
1909d	55c. River Shannon, Meelick Quay		1·60	1·60
	dc. Three phosphor bars (6 Oct)		3·00	3·00
1909a/d Set of 4			6·25	6·25
1909ac/dc Set of 4			11·00	11·00

Nos. 1909a/dc were only available from machines and from the Philatelic Bureau. Four standard values were available from machines: 55c., 82c., 95c. and €1·50, but other values (minimum 55c.) could be obtained, depending on the weight of the item and its destination.

550 Parasol (*Macrolepiota procera*)

(Des Ian Loe and Steve Simpson. Litho Irish Security Stamp Ptg Ltd)

2008 (1 Aug). Fungi. T **550** and similar vert designs. Multicoloured. Phosphor frame. Chalk-surfaced paper. P 14×15.

1910	55c. Type **550**		1·50	1·50
	a. Pair. Nos. 1910/11		3·00	3·00
1911	55c. Orange Birch Bolete (*Leccinum versipelle*)		1·50	1·50
1912	82c. Pink Waxcap (*Hygrocybe calyptriformis*).		2·00	2·00
1910/12 Set of 3			4·50	4·50
MS1913 150×67 mm. 95c. Scarlet Elfcup (*Sarcoscypha austriaca*)			3·00	4·00

Nos. 1910/11 were printed together, *se-tenant*, as horizontal and vertical pairs in sheetlets of 16.

551 HMS *Agamemnon* and USS *Niagra* laying Cable, 1858

(Des Vincent Killowry and Steve Simpson. Litho Irish Security Stamp Ptg Ltd)

2008 (15 Aug). 150th Anniv of the First Transatlantic Cable Message. Phosphor frame. Chalk-surfaced paper. P 13½.

1914	**551**	82c. multicoloured	2·75	2·75

552 'STATE PENSIOON'

(Des Bold Design. Litho Irish Security Stamp Ptg Ltd)

2008 (19 Sept). Centenary of the Old Age Pensions Act. Phosphor frame. Chalk-surfaced paper. P 13½.

1915	**552**	55c. multicoloured	1·50	1·50

553 Open Books forming Star

(Des Catherine Pearson. Litho Irish Security Stamp Ptg Ltd)

2008 (19 Sept). Centenary of the National University of Ireland. Phosphor frame. Chalk-surfaced paper. P 13½.

1916	**553**	55c. multicoloured	1·50	1·50

554 Pádraic Mac Piarais and Cullenswood House, Ranelagh, Dublin, 1908–10

(Des Thomas Ryan and Paul Raftery. Litho Irish Security Stamp Ptg Ltd)

2008 (25 Sept). Centenary of Opening of Scoil Éanna (bilingual Irish/English school). T **554** and similar horiz design showing founder and school premises. Phosphor frame. Chalk-surfaced paper. P 15×14.

1917	55c. Type **554**	1·50	1·50
1918	55c. Pádraic Mac Piarais and The Hermitage, Rathfarnham, 1910–35	1·50	1·50

555 Planxty

(Des Finbarr O'Connor and Steve Simpson. Litho Irish Security Stamp Ptg Ltd)

2008 (10 Oct). Irish Music (2nd series). T **555** and similar horiz designs. Multicoloured. Phosphor frame. Chalk-surfaced paper. P 13½.

1919	55c. Type **555**		1·40	1·50
1920	55c. De Dannan		1·40	1·50
1921	82c. Tulla Céilí Band		1·75	2·00
1922	82c. The Bothy Band		1·75	2·00
1919/22 Set of 4			5·50	6·25
MS1923 150×90 mm. Nos. 1919/22			5·50	6·50

556 Irish Dancer   **557** The Flight into Egypt

(Des Conor Walton and Design Tactics. Litho Irish Security Stamp Ptg Ltd)

2008 (7 Nov). Traditional Dances. T **556** and similar vert design. Multicoloured. Phosphor frame. Chalk-surfaced paper. P 13½.

1924	55c. Type **556**	1·50	1·50
MS1925 150×90 mm. No. 1924; 82c. Flamenco dancer		3·50	4·25

Stamps in a similar design were issued by Spain.

(Des James Hanley and Steve Simpson. Litho Irish Security Stamp Ptg Ltd)

2008 (7 Nov). Christmas. T **557** and similar multicoloured designs. Phosphor frame. Chalk-surfaced paper.

(a) Litho Irish Security Stamp Ptg Ltd. PVA gum. P 14×15

1926	55c. Type **557**	1·50	1·00
1927	82c. The Annunciation	2·00	2·25

(b) Litho Walsall. Self-adhesive. Size 25×30 mm. P 11½

1928	55c. Infant Jesus in manger	1·50	1·50
	a. Booklet pane. No. 1928×26	30·00	

No. 1928 was only issued in €13.75 stamp booklets, No. SB145.

558 Pair of Wedding Rings

(Des Zinc Design. Litho Irish Security Stamp Ptg Ltd)

2009 (23 Jan). Weddings (4th issue). Phosphor frame. Chalk-surfaced paper. Self-adhesive. P 13.

1929	55c. multicoloured	1·60	1·60
	a. Booklet pane. No. 1929×10	14·50	

No. 1929 was only issued in €5.50 stamp booklets, No. SB147.

559 Eye   **560** Ox

(Des Red Dog Design Consultants. Litho and embossed Irish Security Stamp Ptg Ltd)

2009 (23 Jan). Birth Bicentenary of Louis Braille (inventor of Braille writing for the blind). Phosphor frame. Chalk-surfaced paper. P 14.

1930	**559**	55c. black	1·90	1·60

No. 1930 has 'Éire' and '55c' in Braille.

(Des Renze Zhou. Litho Irish Security Stamp Ptg Ltd)

2009 (23 Jan). Chinese New Year ("Year of the Ox"). Phosphor frame. Chalk-surfaced paper. P 14½×14.

1931	**560**	82c. multicoloured	2·50	2·50
MS1932	130×74 mm. No. 1931×3		6·50	8·00

561 St. Patrick Climbs Croagh Patrick (Margaret Clarke)   **562** Little Girl posting Card, helped by her Father

(Des Ger Garland. Litho Irish Security Stamp Ptg Ltd)

2009 (19 Feb). St. Patrick's Day. Phosphor frame. Chalk-surfaced paper. P 14×14½.

1933	**561**	82c. multicoloured	2·50	2·50

(Des Cathy Dineen and Steve Simpson. Litho Irish Security Stamp Ptg Ltd)

2009 (6 Mar). Greetings Stamps. T **562** and similar vert design. Multicoloured. Self-adhesive. Phosphor frame. Chalk-surfaced paper. P 12½×13.

1934	55c. Type **562**	1·60	1·60
	a. Booklet pane. Nos. 1934/5, each ×5	14·50	

1935	55c. Girl with opened birthday card and dog.	1·60	1·60

Nos. 1934/5 were only issued in €5.50 booklets, No. SB148.

563 Charles Darwin (pen and ink drawing, Harry Furniss)   **564** Scene from *The Playboy of the Western World* (Seán Keating)

(Des Steve Simpson. Litho Irish Security Stamp Ptg Ltd)

2009 (20 Mar). Birth Bicentenary of Charles Darwin (naturalist and evolutionary theorist). Phosphor frame. Chalk-surfaced paper. P 13½.

1936	**563**	82c. multicoloured	2·40	2·40

(Des Paul Raftery. Litho Irish Security Stamp Ptg Ltd)

2009 (24 Mar). Death Centenary of John Millington Synge (writer). Phosphor frame. Chalk-surfaced paper. P 14×14½.

1937	**564**	55c. multicoloured	1·60	1·60

565 *Irish Times* Clock

(Des Richard Chaney. Litho Irish Security Stamp Ptg Ltd)

2009 (27 Mar). 150th Anniv of the *Irish Times* (newspaper). Phosphor frame. Chalk-surfaced paper. P 13.

1938	**565**	55c. multicoloured	1·60	1·60

566 Girl writing Letter   **567** Self-portrait, 1969

(Des Zinc Design. Litho Ashton-Potter, USA)

2009 (3 Apr). 25th Anniv of An Post. T **566** and similar vert designs. Multicoloured. Phosphor band at top of stamp. Chalk-surfaced paper. Self-adhesive.

(a) Coil stamps. Size 25×30 mm. P 11

1939	55c. Type **566**	2·00	2·00
	a. Vert strip of 5. Nos. 1939/43	9·00	9·00
1940	55c. Girl posting letter	2·00	2·00
1941	55c. Postman emptying pillar box	2·00	2·00
1942	55c. Woman at post office counter	2·00	2·00
1943	55c. An Post van and lorry	2·00	2·00
1944	55c. Flying letters	2·00	2·00
	a. Vert strip of 5. Nos. 1944/8	9·00	9·00
1945	55c. Postman with trolley	2·00	2·00
1946	55c. Postman with mail	2·00	2·00
1947	55c. Seán Kelly cycling team sponsored by An Post	2·00	2·00
1948	55c. G.P.O., Dublin	2·00	2·00
1939/48	*Set of 10*	18·00	18·00

(b) *Booklet stamps. Size 20×24 mm. P 13½×14*

1949	55c. As Type **566**	1·75	2·00
	a. Booklet pane. Nos. 1949/58	16·00	
1950	55c. As No. 1940	1·75	2·00
1951	55c. As No. 1941	1·75	2·00
1952	55c. As No. 1942	1·75	2·00
1953	55c. As No. 1943	1·75	2·00
1954	55c. As No. 1944	1·75	2·00
1955	55c. As No. 1945	1·75	2·00
1956	55c. As No. 1946	1·75	2·00
1957	55c. As No. 1947	1·75	2·00
1958	55c. As No. 1948	1·75	2·00
1949/58 *Set of* 10		16·00	18·00

Nos. 1939/43 and 1944/8 were each issued in rolls of 100 containing the five designs in sequence.

Nos. 1949/58 were only issued in €5.50 stamp booklets, No. SB149.

(Des Q. Design. Litho Irish Security Stamp Ptg Ltd)

2009 (24 Apr). Birth Centenary of Francis Bacon (artist). T **567** and similar vert design. Multicoloured. Phosphor frame. Chalk-surfaced paper. P 13½.

1959	55c. Type **567**	1·60	1·60
MS1960 150×90 mm. 82c. Francis Bacon's studio		2·40	2·75

568 James Larkin (union organiser) addressing crowd, c. 1908

(Des John Conway. Litho Irish Security Stamp Ptg Ltd)

2009 (30 Apr). Centenary of IT&GWU (Irish Transport and General Workers Union). Phosphor frame. Chalk-surfaced paper. P 13.

1961	**568**	55c. multicoloured	1·25	1·25

569 *Green Dragon* (Irish entry)

(Des Vincent Killowry and Steve Simpson. Litho Irish Security Stamp Ptg Ltd)

2009 (8 May). Volvo Ocean Race. T **569** and similar multicoloured design. Phosphor frame. Chalk-surfaced paper. P 14½×14.

1962	55c. Type **569**	1·60	1·60
MS1963 150×90 mm. €3 *Green Dragon* and other yachts (27×47 mm)		8·75	9·50

570 Crab Nebula

571 CEPT Logo, '50', Telephone Dial and Pillar Box

(Des Richard Chaney. Litho Irish Security Stamp Ptg Ltd)

2009 (15 May). Europa. Astronomy. T **570** and similar square design. Multicoloured. Phosphor frame. Chalk-surfaced paper. P 13.

1964	55c. Type **570**	1·25	1·25
1965	82c. Brown Dwarf	1·75	2·25

(Des Steve Simpson. Litho Irish Security Stamp Ptg Ltd)

2009 (15 May). 50th Anniv of CEPT (European Conference of Postal and Telecommunications Administration). Phosphor frame. Chalk-surfaced paper. P 13.

1966	**571**	82c. multicoloured	1·75	2·25

572 "Aberann Conan" (Glen of Imaal terrier)

573 Castle and St. John's Bridge, Kilkenny City

(Des Steve Simpson. Litho Irish Security Stamp Ptg Ltd)

2009 (21 May). European Dog Show, Dublin. Phosphor frame. Chalk-surfaced paper. P 13.

1967	**572**	55c. multicoloured	1·50	1·50
	a. Booklet pane. No. 1967×10	13·50	

No. 1967 was only issued in €5.50 booklets, No. SB150.

(Des Roger O'Reilly and Steve Simpson. Litho Irish Security Stamp Ptg Ltd)

2009 (16 June). 400th Anniv of City Status for Kilkenny. Phosphor frame. Chalk-surfaced paper. P 13½.

1968	**573**	55c. multicoloured	1·75	1·50

574 Anthony Trollope (from albumen print by Julia Margaret Cameron, 1864)

575 Augustine Birrell (Sir Leslie Ward)

(Des Q. Design. Litho Irish Security Stamp Ptg Ltd)

2009 (26 June). Anthony Trollope (novelist) Commemoration. Phosphor frame. Chalk-surfaced paper. P 14×14½.

1969	**574**	82c. multicoloured	2·00	2·25

(Des Ger Garland. Litho Irish Security Stamp Ptg Ltd)

2009 (15 July). Centenary of the Birrell Land Act (Irish Land Act). Phosphor frame. Chalk-surfaced paper. P 13.

1970	**575**	82c. multicoloured	2·00	2·25

576 Wolfgang Amadeus Mozart (Josef Grassi) and Overture of Opera *Don Giovanni*

(Des Ger Garland. Litho Irish Security Stamp Ptg Ltd)

2009 (14 Aug). Classical Composers. T **576** and similar horiz designs, each showing composer and score. Multicoloured. Phosphor frame* (around pair). Chalk-surfaced paper. P 13.

1971	55c. Type **576**	1·60	1·60
	a. Pair. Nos. 1971/2	3·25	3·25
1972	55c. George Frideric Handel (Thomas Hudson, 1736) and last folio from opera *Susanna*, 1748	1·60	1·60
1973	82c. Joseph Haydn (John Carl Rossler, 1799) and Symphony No. 95	2·25	2·25
	a. Pair. Nos. 1973/4	4·50	4·50
1974	82c. Frédéric Chopin (Ary Scheffer) and Ballade Number 2 in F	2·25	2·25
1971/4 *Set of* 4		7·75	7·75
MS1975 150×90 mm. Nos. 1971/4		7·50	8·00

Nos. 1971/2 and 1973/4 were each printed together, *se-tenant*, as horizontal and vertical pairs in sheetlets of 16.

*Nos. 1971/4 and the stamps within **MS**1975 have a phosphor frame around the horizontal pairs, giving Nos. 1971 and 1973 a phosphor frame at top, left and bottom, and Nos. 1972 and 1974 a phosphor frame at top, right and bottom.

Stamps as Nos. 1970/4 were issued in a €12 premium booklet, No. SP11. They differ from the sheet stamps by having the phosphor frame around each individual stamp.

577 Arthur Guinness
(founder)

(Des Zinc Design. Litho Irish Security Stamp Ptg Ltd)

2009 (28 Aug). 250th Anniv of the Guinness Brewery. Phosphor frame. Chalk-surfaced paper. P 14×14½.

1976	**577**	82c. multicoloured	2·00	2·40

578 'Plantation of Ulster 1609' in Irish

579 Brian Friel

(Des Timothy O'Neill and Ger Garland. Litho Irish Security Stamp Printing Ltd)

2009 (4 Sept). 400th Anniv of the Plantation of Ulster. T **578** and similar horiz design. Multicoloured. Phosphor frame. Chalk-surfaced paper. P 14½×14.

1977		55c. Type **578**	1·40	1·60
		a. Pair. Nos. 1977/8	2·75	3·00
1978		55c. 'PLANTATION of ULSTER 1609' in English .	1·40	1·60

Nos. 1977/8 were printed together, *se-tenant*, as horizontal and vertical pairs in sheetlets of 16 stamps.

(Des James Hanley. Litho Irish Security Stamp Ptg Ltd)

2009 (18 Sept). Modern Irish Playwrights. T **579** and similar horiz designs. Multicoloured. Phosphor frame. Chalk-surfaced paper. P 14½×14.

1979		55c. Type **579**	1·40	1·60
1980		55c. Frank McGuinness	1·40	1·60
1981		55c. Tom Murphy	1·40	1·60
1979/81		Set of 3	3·75	4·25

580 Irish Bluet
(*Coenagrion lunulatum*)

(Des Ian Loe and Wendy Williams. Litho Irish Security Stamp Ptg Ltd)

2009 (16 Oct). Dragonflies. T **580** and similar multicoloured designs. Phosphor frame. Chalk-surfaced paper. P 14×14½ (vert), 14½×14 (horiz) or 13 (**MS**1985).

1982		55c. Type **580**	1·50	1·75
		a. Pair. Nos. 1982/3	3·00	3·50
1983		55c. Large Red Damselfly (*Pyrrhosoma nymphula*)	1·50	1·75
1984		82c. Four-spotted Chaser (*Libellula quadrimaculata*) (horiz)	2·25	2·75
1982/4		Set of 3	4·75	5·50
MS1985		150×65 mm. 95c. Banded Demoiselle (*Calopteryx splendens*) (60×26 mm)	2·75	3·00

Nos. 1982/3 were printed together, *se-tenant*, as horizontal and vertical pairs in sheetlets of 16.

581 Nativity

582 Dr. Douglas Hyde

(Des Steve Simpson)

2009 (6 Nov). Christmas. Illustrations from the Gospel Book, Gamaghiel Monastery, Khizan (1986/7) or the Rosarium of King Philip II of Spain (1988). T **581** and similar multicoloured designs. Phosphor frame. Chalk-surfaced paper.

(a) Litho Irish Security Stamp Printing Ltd. Ordinary gum. P 14½×14

1986		55c. Type **581**	1·60	70
1987		82c. Annunciation	2·40	3·00

(b) Litho Australia Post – Sprintpak. Self-adhesive. Size 25×30 mm. Die-cut perf 11

1988		55c. Virgin and Child (Simon Bening)	1·60	1·60
		a. Booklet pane. No. 1988×26	32·00	

The images from Nos. 1986/7 come from the Gospel Book from the Monastery of Gamaghiel, Khizan, and on No. 1988 from the Rosarium of Philip II, King of Spain.

No. 1988 was only issued in €13.75 stamp booklets, No. SB153.

(Des Q. Design. Litho Irish Security Stamp Ptg Ltd)

2010 (21 Jan). 150th Birth Anniv of Douglas Hyde (first President of Ireland 1938–45). Phosphor frame. Chalk-surfaced paper. P 14×14½.

1989	**582**	55c. multicoloured	1·25	1·25

583 Pair of Stylised 'Lovebirds'

584 Boy Astronaut and Heart

(Des Cathy Dineen and Steve Simpson. Litho Irish Security Stamp Ptg Ltd)

2010 (21 Jan). Weddings (5th issue). Phosphor frame. Chalk-surfaced paper. Self-adhesive. P 13.

1990	**583**	55c. multicoloured	1·40	1·75
		a. Booklet pane. No. 1990×10	12·50	

No. 1990 was only issued in €5.50 stamp booklets, No. SB154.

(Des Roger O'Reilly and Steve Simpson. Litho Irish Security Stamp Ptg Ltd)

2010 (28 Jan). Greetings Stamps. T **584** and similar horiz design. Multicoloured. Phosphor frame. Chalk-surfaced paper. P 13½×12½.

1991		55c. Type **584**	1·75	1·75
		a. Booklet pane. Nos. 1991/2, each ×5	16·00	
1992		55c. Girl astronaut riding rocket and birthday cake	1·75	1·75

Nos. 1991/2 were only issued in €5.50 booklets, No. SB155.

585 Tiger (18th century Tibetan painting)

586 St. Patrick (St. Patrick's Cathedral, Co. Armagh)

(Des Paul Raftery. Litho Irish Security Stamp Ptg Ltd)

2010 (11 Feb). Chinese New Year ("Year of the Tiger"). Phosphor frame. Chalk-surfaced paper. P 13½.

1993	**585**	82c. multicoloured	2·25	2·25
MS1994 150×90 mm. No. 1993×3			6·00	6·50

(Des Paul Raftery and Steve Simpson. Litho Irish Security Stamp Ptg Ltd)

2010 (18 Feb). St. Patrick's Day. Phosphor frame. Chalk-surfaced paper. P 14×14½.

1995	**586**	82c. multicoloured	2·00	2·25

587 Gaisce Symbol and Aras an Uachtarain (President's official residence)

588 Women playing Golf, Baking, Exercising and Painting

(Des John Conway. Litho Irish Security Stamp Ptg Ltd)

2010 (11 Mar). 25th Anniv of Gaisce the President's Award. Phosphor frame. Chalk-surfaced paper. P 13½.

1996	**587**	55c. multicoloured	1·25	1·25

(Des John Conway. Litho Irish Security Stamp Ptg Ltd)

2010 (25 Mar). Centenary of Irish Countrywoman's Association. Phosphor frame. Chalk-surfaced paper. P 13½.

1997	**588**	55c. multicoloured	1·25	1·25

589 Monasterboice Cross, Co. Louth

590 The Happy Prince (Oscar Wilde)

(Des Michael Craig and Steve Simpson. Litho Irish Security Stamp Ptg Ltd)

2010 (8 Apr). Ireland Series—High Crosses. T **589** and similar vert designs, each black. Phosphor frame. Chalk-surfaced paper. P 13.

1998		55c. Type **589**	1·40	1·50
		a. Horiz strip of 4. Nos. 1998/2001	5·00	5·50
1999		55c. Carndonagh Cross, Co. Donegal	1·40	1·50
2000		55c. Drumcliffe Cross, Co. Sligo	1·40	1·50
2001		55c. Ahenny Cross, Co. Tipperary	1·40	1·50
1998/2001 *Set of 4*			5·00	5·50

Nos. 1998/2001 were printed together, *se-tenant*, as horizontal strips of four in sheetlets of 12.

(Des P. J. Lynch. Litho Irish Security Stamp Ptg Ltd)

2010 (6 May). Europa. Children's Books. T **590** and similar vert design. Multicoloured. Phosphor frame. Chalk-surfaced paper. P 13½×13.

2002		55c. Type **590**	1·40	1·25
2003		82c. *Gulliver's Travels* (Jonathan Swift)	1·75	2·00

591 Mountain Avens *(Dryas octopetala)*

Two types of Nos. 2004/07:
I. No dot over "i" of "Eire"
II. With dot over "i" of "Eire"

(Des Susan Sex and Zinc Design. Digital print Label Art Ltd)

2010 (20 May). Irish Wild Flowers. Type **591** and similar horiz designs as Nos. 1665, 1671, 1674 and 1689. Multicoloured. Self-adhesive. Three phosphor bars. Die-cut perf 11.

2004		55c. Type **591**	6·00	6·00
		a. Vert strip of 4. Nos. 2004/07	22·00	22·00
		b. Type II	2·00	2·00
		ba. Vert strip of 4 Nos. 2004b/7b	7·25	7·25
2005		55c. Spring Gentian (*Gentiana verna*)	6·00	6·00
		b. Type II	2·00	2·00
2006		55c. Bloody Cranes-bill (*Geranium sanguineum*)	6·00	6·00
		b. Type II	2·00	2·00
2007		55c. Common Knapweed (*Centaurea nigra*)	6·00	6·00
		b. Type II	2·00	2·00
2004/07 *Set of 4* (Type I)			22·00	22·00
2004b/07b *Set of 4* (Type II)			7·25	7·25

Nos. 2004b/07b were distributed by the Philatelic Bureau on 22 July, the date on Bureau first day covers, and were all Type II, as illustrated. However, counter machines had been installed at four offices from 20 May (Blackrock, Co. Dublin) dispensing stamps as Type I.

592 Máirtín Ó Direáin and Aran Islands

593 The Breton Girl, 1906

(Des Thomas Ryan and Steve Simpson. Litho Irish Security Stamp Ptg Ltd)

2010 (27 May). Birth Centenary of Máirtín Ó Direáin (poet). Phosphor frame. Chalk-surfaced paper. P 14½×14.

2008	**592**	55c. multicoloured	1·25	1·25

(Des Ger Garland. Litho Irish Security Stamp Ptg Ltd)

2010 (27 May). 150th Birth Anniv of Roderic O'Conor (artist). T **593** and similar vert design. Multicoloured. Phosphor frame. Chalk-surfaced paper. P 13.

2009		55c. Type **593**	1·25	1·50
2010		55c. *Self-portrait, 1928*	1·25	1·50

594 Mother Teresa

(Des Ger Garland. Litho Irish Security Stamp Ptg Ltd)

2010 (17 June). International Humanitarians. T **594** and similar horiz designs. Multicoloured. Phosphor frame. Chalk-surfaced paper. P 13×13½.

2011		55c. Type **594**	1·50	1·50
		a. Horiz pair. Nos. 20011/12	3·00	3·00
2012		55c. Henry Dunant (founder of Red Cross) and Battle of Solferino	1·50	1·50

Nos. 2011/2 were printed together, *se-tenant*, as horizontal pairs in sheetlets of 12.

595 Top and Skirt (Paul Costelloe)

596 Buzzard (*Buteo buteo*)

(Des Ger Garland. Litho and embossed Irish Security Stamp Ptg Ltd)

2010 (15 July). Irish Fashion Designers. T **595** and similar vert designs. Multicoloured. Phosphorised paper. Chalk-surfaced paper. P 13½×13.

2013	55c. Type **595**	1·25	1·40
	a. Horiz strip of 3. Nos. 2013/5	3·25	3·75
2014	55c. Dark blue jacket (Louise Kennedy)	1·25	1·40
2015	55c. Olive-brown crocheted coat (Lainey Keogh)	1·25	1·40
2016	82c. Black dress with ruffled skirt (John Rocha)	1·75	2·00
	a. Horiz strip of 3. Nos. 2016/18	4·75	5·50
2017	82c. Black hat with white ribbons (Philip Treacy)	1·75	2·00
2018	82c. Handbag with leaf design (Orla Kiely)	1·75	2·00
2013/8	Set of 6	8·00	9·00

Nos. 2013/5 and 2016/18 were each printed together, *se-tenant*, as horizontal strips of three in sheetlets of 12 stamps.
Nos. 2013/18 were also issued in €13 booklets, No. SP12.

(Des Killian Mullarney and Steve Simpson. Litho Irish Security Stamp Ptg Ltd)

2010 (29 July). Birds of Prey. T **596** and similar square designs. Multlcoloured. Phosphor frame. Chalk-surfaced paper. P 13½.

2019	55c. Type **596**	1·50	1·50
	a. Horiz pair. Nos. 2015/16	3·00	3·00
2020	55c. Golden Eagle (*Aquila chrysaetos*)	1·50	1·50
2021	82c. Peregrine Falcon (*Falco peregrinus*)	2·25	2·25
2022	95c. Merlin (*Falco columbarius*)	2·75	2·75
2019/22	Set of 4	7·25	7·25
MS2023	150×90 mm. Nos. 2019/22	8·00	8·00

Nos. 2019/22 were printed together, *se-tenant*, as horizontal pairs in sheetlets of 16.

597 Anneli Alhanko and Per-Arthur Segerström in *Romeo and Juliet*

598 Oliver Murphy (founding member) and Shane Barker

(Des Gustav Martensson and Steve Simpson. Eng Czeslaw Slania. Recess and litho Swedish Post Printers)

2010 (26 Aug). Czeslaw Slania (engraver and stamp designer) Commemoration. Design as No. 850 of Sweden. Phosphor frame. Chalk-surfaced paper. P 12½×13.

2024	**597** 55c. black and light brown	2·00	1·60

Stamps in a similar design were issued by Sweden.

(Des Steve Simpson. Litho Irish Security Stamp Ptg Ltd)

2010 (8 Sept). 50th Anniv of the Irish Wheelchair Association. Phosphor frame. Chalk-surfaced paper. P 14½×14.

2025	**598** 55c. multicoloured	1·25	1·25

599 Green Tiger Beetle (*Cicindela campestris*)

(Des Zinc Design. Digital print Label Art Ltd)

2010 (8 Sept). Irish Animals and Marine Life (1st series). T **599** and similar horiz designs. Multicoloured. Self-adhesive. Three phosphor bars. Die-cut perf 11.

2026	55c. Type **599**	1·60	1·60
	a. Vert strip of 4. Nos. 2026/9	6·25	6·25
2027	55c. Golden Eagle (*Aquila chrysaetos*)	1·60	1·60
2028	55c. Tompot Blenny (*Parablennius gattorugine*)	1·60	1·60
2029	55c. Red Squirrel (*Sciurus vulgaris*)	1·60	1·60
2030	55c. Common Octopus (*Octopus vulgaris*)	1·60	1·60
	a. Vert strip of 4. Nos. 2030/3	6·25	6·25
2031	55c. Hermit Crab (*Pagurus bernhardus*)	1·60	1·60
2032	55c. Sea Slug (*Lomanotus genei*)	1·60	1·60
2033	55c. Bottlenose Dolphin (*Tursiops truncates*)	1·60	1·60
2026/33	Set of 8	12·00	12·00

Stamps in these and subsequent similar designs were also available from Postal Service Centre (PSC) machines in values from 1c. to €99.99 (see Machine Labels section).
See also Nos. 2073/80, 2132/9, 2172/9 and 2229/36.

600 The Miami Showband

(Des Steve Simpson. Litho Irish Security Stamp Ptg Ltd)

2010 (23 Sept). Legendary Showbands. T **600** and similar horiz designs. Multicoloured. Phosphor frame. Chalk-surfaced paper. P 13½.

2034	55c. Type **600**	1·25	1·25
2035	55c. The Drifters Showband	1·25	1·25
2036	82c. The Royal Showband	1·75	2·00
2037	82c. The Freshmen	1·75	2·00
2034/7	Set of 4	5·50	6·00
MS2038	150×90 mm. Nos. 2034/7	6·00	7·00

601 Early Patrolman

602 John MacKenna

(Des Q. Design. Litho Irish Security Stamp Ptg Ltd)

2010 (14 Oct). Centenary of Automobile Association Ireland. Phosphor frame. Chalk-surfaced paper. P 14½×14.

2039	**601** 55c. multicoloured	1·50	1·25

(Des Ger Garland. Litho Irish Security Stamp Ptg Ltd)

2010 (28 Oct). Bicentenary of Chilean Independence. T **602** and similar vert design. Multicoloured. Phosphor frame. Chalk-surfaced paper. P 13½×13.

2040	82c. Type **602**	1·75	2·00
	a. Horiz pair. Nos. 2040/1	3·50	4·00
2041	82c. Bernardo O'Higgins	1·75	2·00

Nos. 2040/1 were printed together, *se-tenant*, as horizontal pairs in sheetlets of 12.
Stamps in similar designs were issued by Chile.

603 The Nativity (St. Brigid's Church, Dangan, Co. Roscommon)

604 Robin

(Des Roger O'Reilly (2044) and Steve Simpson. Litho Irish Security Stamp Ptg Ltd (2042/3) or digital print by Label Art Ltd (2045/6))

2010 (4 Nov). Christmas. Multicoloured designs showing stained glass windows as T **603** (2042/3) or T **604** (2044). Chalk-surfaced paper (2042/4). Phosphor frame (2042/4) or three phophor bars (2045/6).

(a) Sheet stamps. Ordinary gum. P 13½

2042	55c. Type **603**	1·60	1·00
2043	82c. Annunciation (Church of Our Lady of Perpetual Help, Aughrim, Co. Roscommon)	2·00	2·00

(b) Booklet stamp. Self-adhesive. Size 30×25 mm. Die-cut perf 11

2044	**604** 55c. multicoloured	1·60	1·60
	a. Booklet pane. No. 2044×26	32·00	

No. 2044 was issued in €13.75 stamp booklets, No. SB156.

(c) 'Stamps on a roll'. Designs as Nos. 2042/3 but 55×24 mm. Three phosphor bars. Self-adhesive. Die-cut perf 11

2045	55c. As Type **603**	1·75	1·75
	a. Vert pair. Nos. 2045/6	3·75	3·75
2046	82c. As No. 2043	2·00	2·00

605 Bride and Groom sharing Umbrella

606 Tulips

(Des Laura Geraghty. Litho Irish Security Stamp Ptg Ltd)

2011 (20 Jan). Weddings (6th issue). Phosphor frame. Chalk-surfaced paper. Self-adhesive. Die-cut perf 13.

2047	**605**	55c. multicoloured	1·60	1·60
		a. Booklet pane. No. 2047×10	14·50	

No. 2047 was issued in €5.50 booklets, No. SB157. It was also available as a collector's pair from the Philatelic Bureau.

(Des Design Factory. Litho Irish Security Stamp Ptg Ltd)

2011 (27 Jan). Greetings Stamps. T **606** and similar horiz design. Multicoloured. Phosphor frame. Chalk-surfaced paper. Self-adhesive. Die-cut perf 13×12½.

2048		55c. Type **606**	1·60	1·60
		a. Booklet pane. Nos. 2048/9, each ×5 plus ten labels	14·50	
2049		55c. Balloons	1·60	1·60

Nos. 2048/9 were issued in €5.50 stamp booklets, No. SB158. They were also available as a collector's pair from the Philatelic Bureau.

607 USA and Ireland Flags and Entrance to American Chamber of Commerce, Dublin

(Des Vermillion Design. Litho Irish Security Stamp Ptg Ltd)

2011 (3 Feb). 50th Anniv of the American Chamber of Commerce, Ireland. Phosphor frame. Chalk-surfaced paper. P 14×14½.

2050	**607**	55c. multicoloured	1·40	1·40

608 Cearbhall Ó Dálaigh

(Des Steve Simpson. Litho Irish Security Stamp Printing Ltd)

2011 (10 Feb). Birth Centenary of Cearbhall Ó Dálaigh (President of Ireland 1974–6). Phosphor frame. Chalk-surfaced paper. P 13½.

2051	**608**	55c. multicoloured	1·40	1·40

609 St. Patrick (stone carving from St. Patrick's College Chapel, Maynooth)

610 'VOTES FOR WOMEN'

(Des Steve Simpson. Litho Irish Security Stamp Printing Ltd)

2011 (17 Feb). St. Patrick's Day. Phosphor frame. Chalk-surfaced paper. P 14×14½.

2052	**609**	82c. multicoloured	2·00	2·25

(Des Ger Garland. Litho Irish Security Stamp Printing Ltd)

2011 (3 Mar). Women's Rights. T **610** and similar square design. Multicoloured. Phosphor frame. Chalk-surfaced paper. P 13½.

2053		55c. Type **610**	1·25	1·25
2054		82c. 'EQUALITY'	1·60	1·75

611 Boxing Match

(Des Q. Design. Litho Irish Security Stamp Ptg Ltd)

2011 (14 Apr). Centenary of the Irish Amateur Boxing Association. Phosphor frame. Chalk-surfaced paper. P 14½×14.

2055	**611**	55c. multicoloured	1·10	1·10

612 Tulip Tree, Knockabbey Gardens

(Des Design Factory. Litho Irish Security Stamp Ptg Ltd)

2011 (5 May). Europa. Forests. T **612** and similar horiz design. Multicoloured. Chalk-surfaced paper. Phosphor frame. P 14½×14.

2056		55c. Type **612**	1·25	1·10
2057		82c. River Walk, Avondale Forest Park	2·00	2·25

613 Ceramic (Deirdre McLoughlin)

614 Ballycroy National Park

(Des Ger Garland. Litho Irish Security Stamp Ptg Ltd)

2011 (12 May). Year of Craft. T **613** and similar square designs. Multicoloured. Chalk-surfaced paper. Phosphor frame. P 13½.

2058		55c. Type **613**	1·25	1·50
		a. Booklet pane. Nos. 2058/62	5·50	
2059		55c. Glass artwork (Róisín de Buitléar)	1·25	1·50
2060		55c. Jewellery (Inga Reed)	1·25	1·50
2061		55c. Slippers (Helen McAllister)	1·25	1·50
2062		55c. Wooden pot (Liam Flynn)	1·25	1·50
2058/62		*Set of 5*	5·50	6·75

Nos. 2058/62 were issued in €2.75 stamp booklets, No. SB159. They were also issued in a €9 premium booklet, No. SP14.

(Des Steve Simpson. Litho Irish Security Stamp Ptg Ltd)

2011 (7 June). Ireland's National Parks. T **614** and similar horiz designs. Multicoloured. Chalk-surfaced paper. Phosphor frame. P 14½×14.

2063		55c. Type **614**	1·60	1·60
		a. Horiz strip of 3. Nos. 2063/5	4·25	4·25
2064		55c. The Burren National Park	1·60	1·60
2065		55c. Connemara National Park	1·60	1·60
2066		82c. Glenveagh National Park	2·50	2·50
		a. Horiz strip of 3. Nos. 2066/8	6·75	6·75
2067		82c. Killarney National Park	2·50	2·50
2068		82c. Wicklow Mountains National Park	2·50	2·50
2063/8		*Set of 6*	12·00	12·00
MS2069		150×90 mm. Nos. 2063/5	4·50	4·50
MS2070		150×90 mm. Nos. 2066/8	7·00	7·00

Nos. 2063/5 and 2066/8 were each printed together, *se-tenant*, as horizontal strips of three in sheetlets of 12.

Nos. 2063/8 were also issued in €13 booklets, No. SP15.

615 Hermit Crab (*Pagurus bernhardus*)

616 Candle wrapped with Barbed Wire

618 Coloured Horse

(Des Zinc Design Consultants. Litho Ashton-Potter (2071/a), Irish Security Stamp Ptg Ltd (others))

2011 (22 June)–**12**. Irish Animals and Marine Life. T **615** and similar vert design. Multicoloured. Chalk-surfaced paper. Self-adhesive. Phosphor frame. Die-cut perf 13½×14 (2071) or 14 (2071c).

2071	55c. Type **615**	1·50	1·60
	a. Booklet pane. No. 2071×10	13·50	
	b. Perf 14 (1.5.12)	1·25	1·25
	ba. Booklet pane. No. 2071b×10	12·00	
2071c	82c. Common Frog (*Rana temporaria*) (1.5.12)	1·75	1·75
	ca. Booklet pane. No. 2071c×10	16·00	

The official issue date of No. 2071 was 22 June 2011, but it is known commercially used before that.

Booklet pane No. 2071a has the phosphor around and between the stamps. Booklet pane No. 2071ba has a separate phosphor frame around each stamp.

Nos. 2071/b were issued in separate €5.50 booklets, Nos. SB160 and SB166.

No. 2071c was issued in €8.20 booklets, No. SB167.

See also Nos. 2092/3, 2155/8 and 2224/5.

(Des Zinc Design. Litho Irish Security Stamp Ptg Ltd)

2011 (30 June). 50th Anniv of Amnesty International. Chalk-surfaced paper. Phosphor frame. P 13.

2072	**616**	55c. greenish yellow, black and yellow-green	1·25	1·25

(Des Zinc Design. Digital print Label Art Ltd)

2011 (21 July). Irish Animals and Marine Life (2nd series). Horiz designs as T **599**. Multicoloured. Self-adhesive. Three phosphor bars. Die-cut perf 11.

2073	55c. Beadlet Anemone (*Actinia equina*)	1·60	1·60
	a. Vert strip of 4. Nos. 2073/6	6·25	6·25
2074	55c. Squat Lobster (*Munida rugosa*)	1·60	1·60
2075	55c. Cuckoo Wrasse (*Labrus mixtus*)	1·60	1·60
2076	55c. Common Frog (*Rana temporaria*)	1·60	1·60
2077	55c. Green Huntsman Spider (*Micrommata virescens*)	1·60	1·60
	a. Vert strip of 4. Nos. 2077/80	6·25	6·25
2078	55c. Elephant Hawk-moth (*Deilephila elpenor*)	1·60	1·60
2079	55c. Goldfinch (*Carduelis carduelis*)	1·60	1·60
2080	55c. Red Deer Stag (*Cervus elaphus*)	1·60	1·60
2073/80 Set of 8		12·00	12·00

619 Golfers

620 Brian O'Nolan (painting by Micheál Ó Nualláin)

(Des Q. Design. Litho Irish Security Stamp Ptg Ltd)

2011 (1 Sept). The Irish Horse. T **618** and similar horiz designs. Multicoloured. Phosphor frame. Chalk-surfaced paper. P 13½.

2086	55c. Type **618**	1·60	1·60
	a. Block of 4. Nos. 2086/9	6·25	6·25
2087	55c. Irish draught horse	1·60	1·60
2088	55c. Thoroughbred	1·60	1·60
2089	55c. Connemara pony	1·60	1·60
2086/9 Set of 4		6·25	6·25
MS2090 150×90 mm. Nos. 2086/9		6·25	6·25

Nos. 2086/9 were printed together, *se-tenant*, as blocks of four stamps in sheetlets of 16.

(Des Q. Design. Litho Irish Security Stamp Ptg Ltd)

2011 (15 Sept). Solheim Cup Women's Golf Tournament, Killeen Castle, Co. Meath. Chalk-surfaced paper. Phosphor frame. P 14½×14.

2091	**619** 55c. multicoloured	1·50	1·25

(Des Zinc Design Consultants. Litho Ashton Potter)

2011 (29 Sept). Irish Animals and Marine Life. As T **615** but 25×30 mm. Chalk-surfaced paper. Self-adhesive. Phosphor frame. Die-cut perf 11.

2092	55c. Red Squirrel (*Sciurus vulgaris*)	1·00	1·00
2093	55c. Bottlenose Dolphin (*Tursiops truncatus*)	1·00	1·00

Nos. 2092/3 were issued together in coils of 100.

(Des Steve Simpson. Litho Irish Security Stamp Ptg Ltd)

2011 (6 Oct). Birth Centenary of Brian O'Nolan (Flann O'Brien) (novelist). Chalk-surfaced paper. Phosphor frame. P 13½.

2094	**620** 55c. multicoloured	1·00	1·00

617 House with Solar Panels

(Des Rose Design. Litho Irish Security Stamp Ptg Ltd)

2011 (5 Aug). Renewable Energy. T **617** and similar horiz designs. Multicoloured. Chalk-surfaced paper. Self-adhesive. Phosphor frame. Die-cut perf 13.

2081	55c. Type **617**	1·60	1·60
	a. Horiz strip of 5. Nos. 2081/5	8·00	
	b. Booklet pane. Nos. 2081/5, each×2	14·50	
2082	55c. Ardnacrusha hydro electric power station	1·60	1·60
2083	55c. Wind turbines	1·60	1·60
2084	55c. Wave energy	1·60	1·60
2085	55c. Field of rape (Biofuel)	1·60	1·60
2081/5 Set of 5		8·00	8·00

Nos. 2081/5 were issued in €5.50 booklets of ten, No. SB161.

The strip of five No. 2070a could be purchased from the Philatelic Bureau.

Nos. 2081/5 were also issued in €9 premium booklets, No. SP16.

621 Flight into Egypt

622 Baubles

(Des Steve Simpson (2095) or Design Factory (2096/7). Litho Enschedé (2095) or digital print Label Art Ltd (2096/7))

2011 (10 Nov). Christmas. Multicoloured designs as T **621** (2095) or T **622** (2096/7). Chalk-surfaced paper. Self-adhesive. Die-cut perf 11.

(a) Booklet stamp. Phosphor frame

2095	55c. Type **621**	1·00	75
	a. Booklet pane. No. 2095×26	23·00	

(b) 'Stamps on a roll'. Two phosphor bars

2096	55c. Type **622**	1·40	1·00
2097	82c. Star tree decorations	1·75	2·00

No. 2095 was issued in €13.75 stamp booklets, No. SB162.

623 The Late Late Show Presenter
Gay Byrne

(Des Ger Garland. Litho Irish Security Stamp Ptg Ltd)

2011 (24 Nov). 50th Anniv of the First RTÉ (Radio Telefís Éireann) Broadcast. T **623** and similar horiz designs showing television screens. Multicoloured. Chalk-surfaced paper. Phosphor frame. P 14½×14.

2098		55c. Type **623**	90	90
	a.	Horiz strip of 3. Nos. 2098/100	2·40	2·40
2099		55c. Children's TV presenter Emma O'Driscoll on set of Hubble	90	90
2100		55c. Newsreader Anne Doyle	90	90
2098/2100 *Set of 3*			2·40	2·40

Nos. 2098/100 were printed together, *se-tenant*, as horizontal strips of three in sheets of 12 stamps

624 Bride and Groom   625 Wrapped Present

(Des Steve Simpson. Litho Irish Security Stamp Ptg Ltd)

2012 (19 Jan). Weddings (7th issue). Chalk-surfaced paper. Self-adhesive. Phosphor frame. Die-cut perf 13.

2101	**624**	55c. multicoloured	1·00	1·00
	a.	Booklet pane. No. 2101×10	9·00	

No. 2101 was issued in €5.50 stamp booklets, No. SB163.

(Des Kasia Ozmin. Litho Irish Security Stamp Ptg Ltd)

2012 (26 Jan). Greetings Stamps. T **625** and similar vert designs. Multicoloured. Chalk-surfaced paper. Self-adhesive. Phosphor frame. Die-cut perf 12½×13.

2102		55c. Type **625**	1·00	1·00
	a.	Booklet pane. Nos. 2102/3, each ×5	9·00	
2103		55c. Candles	1·00	1·00

Nos. 2102/3 were issued in €5.50 booklets, No. SB164.

626 Logo   627 St. Patrick (from icon painting by Ekaterina Platoshechkina)

(Des Red Dog Design. Litho Irish Security Stamp Ptg Ltd)

2012 (2 Feb). Ireland's Chairmanship of the OSCE (Organisation for Security and Co-operation in Europe). Chalk-surfaced paper. Phosphor frame. P 13½.

2104	**626**	55c. multicoloured	90	90

(Des Steve Simpson. Litho Irish Security Stamp Ptg Ltd)

2012 (9 Feb). St. Patrick's Day. Chalk-surfaced paper. Phosphor frame. P 14×14½.

2105	**627**	82c. multicoloured	1·60	1·75

NEW INFORMATION

The editor is always interested to correspond with people who have new information that will improve or correct this catalogue

---

628 Dancer from Fabulous Beast Dance Theatre

(Des Ger Garland. Litho Irish Security Stamp Ptg Ltd)

2012 (22 Mar). Contemporary Arts - Dance. T **628** and similar diamond-shaped designs. Multicoloured. Chalk-surfaced paper. Self-adhesive. Phosphor frame. P 13.

2106		55c. Type **628**	90	1·00
	a.	Booklet pane. Nos. 2106/9, each ×2	6·50	
2107		55c. Two dancers from Dance Theatre of Ireland	90	1·00
2108		55c. Male dancer (wearing white) from Irish Modern Dance Theatre	90	1·00
2109		55c. Underwater dancer from CoisCéim Dance Theatre	90	1·00
2106/9 *Set of 4*			3·25	3·50

Nos. 2106/9 were printed in €4.40 booklets, No. SB165.

629 Thomas Andrews (shipbuilder) and *Titanic* under Construction

(Des Ger Garland. Litho Irish Security Stamp Ptg Ltd)

2012 (12 Apr). Centenary of the Sinking of RMS *Titanic*. T **629** and similar horiz designs. Multicoloured. Chalk-surfaced paper. Phosphor frame. P 13×13½.

2110		55c. Type **629**	1·25	1·25
	a.	Horiz pair. Nos. 2110/11	2·50	2·50
2111		55c. Father Browne (photographer) and *Titanic*	1·25	1·25
2112		82c. Captain Edward Smith and *Titanic*	2·25	2·25
	a.	Horiz pair. Nos. 2112/13	4·50	4·50
2113		82c. Molly Brown and *Titanic*	2·25	2·25
2110/13 *Set of 4*			6·50	6·50

Nos. 2110/11 and 2112/13 were each printed together, *se-tenant*, in sheetlets of 16.
Nos. 2110/13 were also issued in €12 premium booklets, No. SP17.

630 Bram Stoker   631 Little Skellig, Co. Kerry

(Des David Rooney. Litho Irish Security Stamp Ptg Ltd)

2012 (19 Apr). Death Centenary of Bram Stoker (author of *Dracula*). T **630** and similar vert design. Multicoloured. Chalk-surfaced paper. Phosphor frame. P 14×14½.

2114		55c. Type **630**	90	1·00
	a.	Horiz pair. Nos. 2114/15	1·75	2·00
2115		55c. Count Dracula and victim	90	1·00
MS2116 150×90 mm. Nos. 2114/15			1·75	2·00

Nos. 2114/15 were printed together, *se-tenant*, as horizontal pairs in sheetlets of 16.

(Des Steve Simpson. Litho Irish Security Stamp Ptg Ltd)

2012 (3 May). Europa. Visit Ireland. T **631** and similar square design. Multicoloured. Chalk-surfaced paper. Phosphor frame. P 13.

2117		55c. Type **631**	1·00	80
2118		82c. Ha'penny Bridge, Dublin	1·75	2·00

632 The Chalice and Host

633 Yachts in Volvo Ocean Race

(Des Martin Barlow. Litho Irish Security Stamp Ptg Ltd)

2012 (7 June). 50th International Eucharistic Congress, Dublin. T **632** and similar vert design. Multicoloured. Chalk-surfaced paper. Phosphor frame. P 14×14½.

2119	55c. Type **632**	1·00	80
2120	82c. The Monstrance and the Blessed Sacrament	1·75	2·00

(Des Vincent Killowry and Steve Simpson. Litho Irish Security Stamp Ptg Ltd)

2012 (14 June). Volvo Ocean Race. T **633** and similar multicoloured design. Chalk-surfaced paper. Phosphor frame. P 14½×14.

2121	55c. Type **633**	1·00	1·00
MS2122	151×90 mm. €3 Two yachts (27×48 *mm*)	6·00	6·50

634 Rescuing Baby from Fire

(Des Zinc Design Consultants. Litho Irish Security Stamp Ptg Ltd)

2012 (28 June). 150th Anniv of Dublin Fire Brigade. T **634** and similar vert designs. Multicoloured. Phosphor frame. P 13.

2123	55c. Type **634**	1·60	1·60
	a. Horiz strip of 4. Nos. 2123/6	5·75	5·75
2124	55c. Fighting chemical fire	1·60	1·60
2125	55c. Rescuing trapped person from crashed car	1·60	1·60
2126	55c. Water rescue	1·60	1·60
2123/6	*Set of 4*	5·75	5·75

Nos. 2123/6 were printed together, *se-tenant*, as horizontal strips of four stamps in sheetlets of 16.

Nos. 2123/6 were also issued in €10 premium booklets, No. SP18.

635 The Conference Centre, Dublin and Molecular Structure of DNA

(Des Zinc Design Consultants. Litho Irish Security Stamp Ptg Ltd)

2012 (5 July). Significant Science Milestones. T **635** and similar horiz design. Multicoloured. Phosphor frame. P 13×13½.

2127	55c. Type **635** (Euroscience Open Forum and Dublin City of Science 2012)	1·00	1·10
	a. Horiz pair. Nos. 2127/8	2·00	2·10
2128	55c. Robert Boyle (chemist) and his formula (350th anniv of the formulation of Boyle's Law)	1·00	1·10
MS2129	150×90 mm. Nos. 2127/8	3·00	3·50

Nos. 2127/8 were printed together, *se-tenant*, as horizontal pairs in sheetlets of 16.

636 Medal Ceremony

(Des Red Dog Design. Litho Irish Security Stamp Ptg Ltd)

2012 (19 July). Olympic Games, London. T **636** and similar vert design. Multicoloured. Phosphor frame. P 14×14½.

2130	55c. Type **636**	90	90
2131	82c. 'EIRE IRELAND LONDON 2012' in vertical columns	1·60	1·75

(Des Zinc Design. Digital print Label Art Ltd)

2012 (9 Aug). Irish Animals and Marine Life. Horiz designs as T **599**. Multicoloured. Self-adhesive. Three phosphor bars. Die-cut perf 11.

2132	55c. Pike (*Esox lucius*)	1·50	1·50
	a. Vert strip of 4. Nos. 2132/5	5·50	5·50
2133	55c. Green Crab (*Carcinus maenas*)	1·50	1·50
2134	55c. Spiny Seahorse (*Hippocampus guttulatus*)	1·50	1·50
2135	55c. Fireworks Anemone (*Pachycerianthus multiplicatus*)	1·50	1·50
2136	55c. Kestrel (*Falco tinnunculus*)	1·50	1·50
	a. Vert strip of 4. Nos. 2136/9	5·50	5·50
2137	55c. Raft Spider (*Dolomedes fimbriatus*)	1·50	1·50
2138	55c. Irish Hare (*Lepus timidus hibernicus*)	1·50	1·50
2139	55c. Smooth Newt (*Lissotriton vulgaris*)	1·50	1·50
2132/9	*Set of 8*	11·00	11·00

637 *The Children of Lir*

638 Girl

(Des Fergus Lyons and Steve Simpson. Litho Irish Security Stamp Ptg Ltd)

2012 (13 Sept). Myths and Legends. T **637** and similar horiz designs. Multicoloured. Chalk-surfaced paper. Fluorescent frame. P 14½×14.

2140	55c. Type **637**	90	1·00
	a. Horiz pair. Nos. 2140/1	1·75	2·00
2141	55c. Deirdre of the Sorrows	90	1·00
2142	82c. Fionn Mac Cunhaill and the Salmon of Knowledge	1·60	1·75
	a. Horiz pair. Nos. 2142/3	3·00	3·50
2143	82c. Cú Chulainn	1·60	1·75
2140/3	*Set of 4*	4·50	5·00

(Des Zinc Design Consultants. Litho Irish Security Stamp Ptg Ltd)

2012 (11 Oct). 50th Anniv of Barnardos in Ireland. Chalk-surfaced paper. Phosphor frame. P 13½.

2144	**638**	55c. multicoloured	1·00	1·00

639 Candle

640 The Adoration of the Shepherds (Girolamo Troppa)

(Des Zinc Design Consultants. Litho Enschedé (2145) or digital print by Label Art Ltd (2146/7))

2012 (8 Nov). Christmas. Multicoloured designs as T **639** (2145) or T **640** (2146/7). Chalk-surfaced paper. Self-adhesive. Die-cut perf 11.

(a) Booklet stamp. Phosphor frame

2145	55c. Type **639**	1·00	75
	a. Booklet pane. No. 2145×26	23·00	

(b) "Stamps on a roll". Three phosphor bars

2146	55c.	Type **640**	1·25	1·25
	a.	Vert pair. Nos. 2146/7	3·00	3·25
2147	82c.	The Adoration of the Magi (Jan Brueghel the Elder)	1·75	2·00
2145/7	*Set of 3*		3·50	3·50

No. 2145 was issued in €13.75 stamp booklets, No. SB168.

641 Irish EU Presidency Logo

(Des Steve Simpson. Litho Irish Security Stamp Ptg Ltd)

2013 (17 Jan). Ireland's Presidency of the European Union, January to June 2013. Chalk-surfaced paper. Phosphor frame. P 14×14½.

2148	**641**	55c. greenish blue and bright yellow-green	1·00	1·00

642 Elements of The Gathering's Logo forming Map of Ireland

(Des Design Factory. Litho Irish Security Stamp Ptg Ltd)

2013 (24 Jan). The Gathering Ireland 2013. Chalk-surfaced paper. Phosphor frame. P 13½.

2149	**642**	82c. multicoloured	1·75	1·75

643 St. Patrick's Day Parade

(Des Steve Simpson. Litho Irish Security Stamp Ptg Ltd)

2013 (7 Feb). St. Patrick's Day. Chalk-surfaced paper. Phosphor frame. P 14½×14.

2150	**643**	82c. multicoloured	1·75	1·75

644 Bride and Groom lighting Candle

645 Girl carrying Giant Birthday Card

(Des Steve Simpson. Litho Irish Security Stamp Ptg Ltd)

2013 (14 Feb). Weddings (8th issue). Chalk-surfaced paper. Self-adhesive. Phosphor frame. Die-cut perf 13.

2151	**644**	(55c.) multicoloured	75	75
	a.	Booklet pane. No. 2151×10	6·50	

No. 2151 was inscr 'N' and was originally valid for 55c. It was issued in booklets of ten, No. SB169, originally sold for €5.50.

(Des Steve Simpson. Litho Irish Security Stamp Ptg Ltd)

2013 (7 Mar). Greetings Stamps. Paintings by Cathy Dineen. T **645** and similar horiz design. Chalk-surfaced paper. Phosphor frame. Die-cut perf 12½×13.

2152		(55c.) Type **645**	75	75
	a.	Booklet pane. Nos. 2152/3, each ×5	6·50	
2153		(55c.) Boy holding birthday card and balloon	75	75

Nos. 2152/3 were both inscr 'N' and originally valid for 55c. They were issued in booklets of ten stamps, No. SB170, originally sold for €5.50.

646 Daffodil

(Des Red Dog Design. Litho Irish Security Stamp Ptg Ltd)

2013 (21 Mar). 50th Anniv of the Irish Cancer Society. Chalk-surfaced paper. Phosphor frame. P 14½×14.

2154	**646**	(55c.) multicoloured	75	75

No. 2154 was inscr 'N' and was originally sold for 55c.

(Litho Ashton-Potter)

2013 (2 Apr). Irish Animals and Marine Life. Multicoloured designs as T **615**. Multicoloured. Chalk-surfaced paper (except 2157). Self-adhesive. Phosphor frame. Die-cut perf 11 (2155/6) or 14 (2157/8).

2155		60c. Golden Eagle (*Aquila chrysaetos*) (25×30 mm)	1·00	1·00
	a.	Vert pair. Nos. 2155/6	2·00	2·00
2156		60c. Red Deer (*Cervus elaphus*) (25×30 mm)	1·00	1·00
2157		60c. Goldfinch (*Carduelis carduelis*)	1·00	1·00
	a.	Booklet pane. No. 2157×10	9·00	
2158		90c. Beadlet Anemone (*Actinia equina*) (*horiz*)	1·40	1·40
	a.	Booklet pane. No. 2158×10	12·00	
2155/8	*Set of 4*		4·00	4·00

Nos. 2155/6 were issued in coils of 100 containing the two designs. No. 2157 was issued in €6 stamp booklets, No. SB171. No. 2158 was issued in €9 stamp booklets, No. SB172.

647 Doors and Sunlight (Stephen McKenna)

(Des Ger Garland. Litho Irish Security Stamp Ptg Ltd)

2013 (25 Apr). Contemporary Arts - Visual Arts (1st issue). T **647** and similar horiz designs. Multicoloured. Chalk-surfaced paper. Phosphor frame. P 14.

2159		60c. Type **647**	90	1·00
	a.	Booklet pane. Nos. 2159/62	3·25	
2160		60c. Ghost Ship (Dorothy Cross)	90	1·00
2161		60c. The Fall (Amanda Coogan) (performance art)	90	1·00
2162		60c. Smoke Tree (John Gerrard) (virtual sculpture)	90	1·00
2159/62	*Set of 4*		3·25	3·50

Nos. 2159/62 were printed in €2.40 stamp booklets, No. SB173. See also Nos. 2205/8.

648 Postmen pushing Trolley and on Bicycle

649 Story about Dublin by Eoin Moore

(Des Steve Simpson. Litho Irish Security Stamp Ptg Ltd)

2013 (2 May). Europa. Postal Vehicles. T **648** and similar horiz design. Multicoloured. Chalk-surfaced paper. Phosphor frame. P 14½×14.

2163		60c. Type **648**	1·40	1·25
2164		90c. Postman with Anpost van	2·10	2·00

(Des The Stone Twins. Litho Irish Security Stamp Ptg Ltd)

2013 (16 May). Dublin, UNESCO City of World Literature. Chalk-surfaced paper. Phosphor frame. P 14½×14.

2165	**649**	60c. black and lemon	1·00	1·00

(Des Zinc Design. Digital print Label Art Ltd)

2013 (6 June–12 July). Irish Animals and Marine Life. Horiz designs as T **599**. Multicoloured. Self-adhesive. Three phosphor bars. Die-cut perf 11.

2165a	5c. Irish Hare (*Lepus timidus hibernicus*)........	10	15
2165b	10c. Spiny Seahorse (*Hippocampus guttulatus*) (12.7.13)	15	20
2165c	€1 Kestrel (*Falco tinnunculus*) (12.7.13)........	1·40	1·50
2165a/c Set of 3..		1·50	1·70

Nos. 2165a/c were issued in sheets of 25 (5×5).

650 Pres. John F. Kennedy with Second Cousin Mary Ann Ryan at his Great Grandfather's Birthplace, Dunganstown, New Ross

(Des Steve Simpson. Litho Irish Security Stamp Ptg Ltd)

2013 (6 June). 50th Death Anniv of Pres. John F. Kennedy (1917–63, US President 1960–3). Pres. Kennedy's Visit to Ireland, June 1963. T **650** and similar square design. Multicoloured. Chalk-surfaced paper. Phosphor frame. P 13½.

2166	60c. Type **650**	1·00	1·00
2167	90c. Pres. Kennedy and Taoiseach Sean Lemass laying wreath for leaders of Easter Rising, Arbour Hill..................	1·50	1·75

651 Container Ship

(Des Steve Simpson. Litho Irish Security Stamp Ptg Ltd)

2013 (17 July). Port of Cork. T **651** and similar horiz designs. Multicoloured. Phosphor frame. P 14½×14.

2168	60c. Type **651**	1·40	1·40
	a. Horiz pair. Nos. 2168/9	2·75	2·75
2169	60c. Yachts in "Clipper Round the World Race", 2010.............................	1·40	1·40
2170	90c. Cunard liner *Queen Elizabeth*	2·10	2·10
2168/70 Set of 3..		4·50	4·50
MS2171 150×90 mm. Nos. 2168/70		5·50	6·00

Nos. 2168/9 were printed together, *se-tenant*, as horizontal pairs in sheetlets of 16.

(Des Zinc Design Consultants. Digital Print Label Art Ltd)

2013 (1 Aug). Irish Animals and Marine Life. Horiz designs as T **599**. Self-adhesive. Three phosphor bars. Die-cut perf 11.

2172	60c. Cushion Star..	1·60	1·60
	a. Vert strip of 4. Nos. 2172/5	6·25	6·25
2173	60c. Red Tube Worm......................................	1·60	1·60
2174	60c. European Eel...	1·60	1·60
2175	60c. Common Seal..	1·60	1·60
2176	60c. Natterjack Toad......................................	1·60	1·60
	a. Vert strip of 4. Nos. 2176/9	6·25	6·25
2177	60c. Red Fox..	1·60	1·60
2178	60c. Great Spotted Woodpecker.................	1·60	1·60
2179	60c. Black-legged Kittiwake	1·60	1·60
2172/9 Set of 8..		12·00	12·00

652 Jim Larkin (founder of ITGWU) and Bloody Sunday Riot, 31 August 1913

(Des Ger Garland. Litho Irish Security Stamp Ptg Ltd)

2013 (22 Aug). Centenary of the General Lockout. T **652** and similar horiz designs. Multicoloured. Phosphor frame (broken at bottom right). P 13.

2180	60c. Type **652**	90	1·00
	a. Horiz strip of 3. Nos. 2180/2..............	2·40	2·75
2181	60c. James Connolly and original Irish Transport and General Workers Union ..	90	1·00
2182	60c. Countess Markievicz (distributed food for workers) and children outside tenement buildings	90	1·00
2180/2 Set of 3..		2·40	2·75

Nos. 2180/2 were printed together, *se-tenant*, as horizontal strips of three stamps in sheetlets of 15 (3×5).

Nos. 2180/2 were also issued in premium booklets, No. SP19 sold for €10.

653 Helicopter

(Des Zinc Design Consultants. Litho Irish Security Stamp Ptg Ltd)

2013 (12 Sept). Irish Defence Forces. T **653** and similar horiz designs. Multicoloured. Chalk-surfaced paper. Phosphor frame. P 13.

2183	60c. Type **653**	1·40	1·40
	a. Block of 4. Nos. 2183/6	5·00	5·00
2184	60c. Troops performing medivac drill	1·40	1·40
2185	60c. Ships of Irish Naval Service	1·40	1·40
2186	60c. UN tank and soldier	1·40	1·40
2183/6 Set of 4..		5·00	5·00

Nos. 2183/6 were printed together, *se-tenant*, as blocks of four stamps in sheetlets of 16.

Nos. 2183/6 were also issued in €10 premium booklets, No. SP20.

654 Dongdong Zheng in Garda Uniform

(Des Atelier David Smith. Litho Irish Security Stamp Ptg Ltd)

2013 (26 Sept). Ireland - An Integrated Society. T **654** and similar horiz designs. Multicoloured. Chalk-surfaced paper. Phosphor background. P 14½×14.

2187	60c. Type **654**	1·40	1·40
	a. Horiz pair. Nos. 2187/8........................	2·75	2·75
2188	60c. Luas Revenue Protection Officer Sammy Akorede....................................	1·40	1·40
2189	90c. Christian Tshibangu in hurling match....	1·75	2·00
	a. Horiz pair. Nos. 2189/90....................	3·50	4·00
2190	90c. Anna Gąciarz in marketing..................	1·75	2·00
2187/90 Set of 4...		6·00	6·25

Nos. 2187/8 and 2189/90 were printed together, *se-tenant*, as horizontal pairs in sheetlets of 16.

655 Volunteers, Waterford, c. 1915

(Des Zinc Design Consultants. Litho Irish Security Stamp Ptg Ltd)

2013 (3 Oct). Irish Volunteer Force. Chalk-surfaced paper. Phosphor frame. P 13.

2191	**655**	60c. multicoloured...............................	1·00	1·00

656 Glucksman Gallery, University College, Cork

(Des Zinc Design Consultants. Litho Irish Security Stamp Ptg Ltd)

2013 (17 Oct). Contemporary Public Buildings. T **656** and similar horiz designs. Multicoloured. Chalk-surfaced paper. Phosphor frame. P 13.

2192	60c. Type **656**	90	1·00
	a. Horiz pair. Nos. 2192/3	1·75	2·00
2193	60c. Cork Institute of Technology	90	1·00
2194	90c. Fingall County Hall, Swords	1·40	1·75
	a. Horiz pair. Nos. 2194/5	2·75	3·50
2195	90c. Croke Park Stadium	1·40	1·75
2192/5 Set of 4		4·25	5·00
MS2196 150×90 mm. Nos. 2192/5		4·25	5·00

Nos. 2192/3 and 2194/5 were each printed together, *se-tenant*, as horizontal pairs in sheetlets of 16.

657 Nativity (stained glass window), Black Abbey Church, Kilkenny

658 Robin

(Des Red & Grey Design. Litho Enschedé (2197) or digital print Label Art Ltd (2198/9))

2013 (7 Nov). Christmas. Multicoloured designs as T **657** (2197) or T **658** (2198/9). Chalk-surfaced paper (2197). Self-adhesive. Die-cut perf 11.

(a) Booklet stamp. Phosphor frame

2197	60c. Type **657**	1·00	75
	a. Booklet pane. No. 2197×26	23·00	

(b) 'Stamps on a roll'. Three phosphor bars.

2198	60c. Type **658**	1·25	1·00
	a. Vert pair. Nos. 2198/9	3·00	3·00
2199	90c. Sprig of holly	1·75	2·00
2197/9 Set of 3		3·50	3·25

No. 2197 was issued in €15 stamp booklets, No. SB174.

659 Robot and Alien   **660** Red Rose

(Des Phil Elliott. Litho Irish Security Stamp Ptg Ltd)

2014 (30 Jan). Greetings Stamps. T **659** and similar horiz design. Multicoloured. Chalk-surfaced paper. Self-adhesive. Phosphor frame. Die-cut perf 13×12½.

2200	60c. Type **659**	1·00	1·00
	a. Booklet pane. Nos. 2200/1, each ×5	9·00	
2201	60c. Adult and child robots with birthday cake	1·00	1·00

Nos. 2200/1 were issued in €6 booklets, No. SB175.

(Des Kelvin Gillmor. Litho Irish Security Stamp Ptg Ltd)

2014 (13 Feb). Love and Marriage. Chalk-surfaced paper. Self-adhesive. Phosphor frame. Die-cut perf 13.

2202	**660** 60c. multicoloured	1·00	75
	a. Booklet pane. No. 2202×10	9·00	

No. 2202 was issued in €6 booklets, No. SB176.

661 St. Patrick (detail from stained glass window, St. Canice's Church, Kilkenny)

662 Brendan Behan

(Des Oonagh Young. Litho Irish Security Stamp Ptg Ltd)

2014 (20 Feb). St. Patrick's Day. Chalk-surfaced paper. Phosphor frame. P 14×14½.

2203	**661** 90c. multicoloured	1·50	1·50

(Des Conor & David. Litho Irish Security Stamp Ptg Ltd)

2014 (20 Mar). 50th Death Anniv of Brendan Behan (writer). Chalk-surfaced paper. Phosphor frame. P 14×14½.

2204	**662** 60c. grey, black and olive-grey	1·00	1·00

(Des Ger Garland. Litho Irish Security Stamp Ptg Ltd)

2014 (27 Mar). Contemporary Arts - Visual Arts (2nd issue). Horiz designs as T **647**. Multicoloured. Chalk-surfaced paper. Phosphor frame. P 14.

2205	60c. Maesta (Sean Scully)	90	1·00
	a. Booklet pane. Nos. 2205/8	3·25	
2206	60c. Light Receiver (sculpture) (Eilis O'Connell)	90	1·00
2207	60c. Patterned Behaviour (Diana Copperwhite)	90	1·00
2208	60c. Chaplet (Alice Maher)	90	1·00
2205/8 Set of 4		3·25	3·50

Nos. 2205/8 were printed in €2.40 stamp booklets, No. SB177.

663 Cumann na mBan Members in Nationalist Funeral Procession, 1914

(Des Ger Garland. Litho Irish Security Stamp Ptg Ltd)

2014 (3 Apr). Centenary of Cumann na mBan (nationalist women's association). Chalk-surfaced paper. Phosphor frame. P 14.

2209	**663** 60c. multicoloured	1·00	1·00

664 Irish Citizen Army at Croydon House, Dublin

(Des Ger Garland. Litho Irish Security Stamp Ptg Ltd)

2014 (17 Apr). Centenary of the Irish Citizen Army. Chalk-surfaced paper. Phosphor frame (broken at lower right). P 13.

2210	**664** 60c. multicoloured	1·00	1·00

A version of No. 2210 showing Captain Jack White at right was recalled by An Post before issue, when it was realised that the uncorrect portrait had been used.

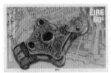

665 Waterford Kite Brooch (c. 1090) and Map of Waterford City

(Des Ger Garland. Litho Irish Security Stamp Ptg Ltd)

2014 (24 Apr). Viking Heritage. T **665** and similar horiz design. Multicoloured. Chalk-surfaced paper. Phosphor frame. P 13.

2211	60c. Type **665**	1·00	1·10
	a. Horiz pair. Nos. 2211/12	2·00	2·10
2212	60c. 10th-century Viking sword and portion of the *Annals of the Four Masters*	1·00	1·10

Nos. 2211/12 were printed together, *se-tenant*, as horizontal pairs in sheetlets of 16.

666 The Irish Bodhrán (drum)   **667** John Redmond and Edward Carson

(Des Design Factory. Litho Irish Security Stamp Ptg Ltd)

2014 (8 May). Europa. National Musical Instruments. T **666** and similar square design. Multicoloured. Chalk-surfaced paper. Phosphor frame. P 13.

2213	60c. Type **666**	1·00	80
2214	90c. The Irish Harp	1·50	1·75

(Des Ger Garland. Litho Irish Security Stamp Ptg Ltd)

2014 (22 May). Centenary of the Home Rule Act. Chalk-surfaced paper. Phosphor frame. P 13.

2215	**667** 60c. multicoloured	1·00	1·00

668 Silver Medal Winning Garden

(Des Atelier David Smith. Litho Irish Security Stamp Ptg Ltd)

2014 (22 May). Bloom (garden festival), Dublin. T **668** and similar horiz design. Multicoloured. Chalk-surfaced paper. Phosphor frame (broken at top right (2216) or top left (2217)). P 13.

2216	60c. Type **668**	1·00	1·10
	a. Horiz pair. Nos. 2216/17	2·00	2·10
2217	60c. Exhibitor holding box of produce	1·00	1·10
MS2218	150×90 mm. Nos. 2216/17	2·50	2·75

Nos. 2216/17 were printed together, *se-tenant*, as horizontal pairs in sheetlets of 16 stamps.

669 *Phalaenopsis* Orchids   **670** 'JOIN AN IRISH REGIMENT TO-DAY'

(Des Atelier David Smith. Litho Irish Security Stamp Printing Ltd)

2014 (12 June). World Flower Show, Dublin. T **669** and similar square design. Multicoloured. Chalk-surfaced paper. Phosphor frame (around horiz pair) . P 13.

2219	60c. Type **669**	1·25	1·25
	a. Horiz pair. Nos. 2219/20	2·50	2·50
2220	60c. *Phalaenopsis* Orchids (petals pink and pale yellow-olive)	1·25	1·25
MS2221	150×90 mm. Nos. 2219/20	3·50	3·50

Nos. 2219/20 were printed together, *se-tenant*, as horizontal pairs in sheetlets of 16 stamps, each pair forming a composite design of orchid flowers along a branch.

Nos. 2219/20 and the stamps within **MS**2221 have a phosphor frame around the horizontal pairs, giving No. 2219 a phosphor frame at top, left and foot and No. 2220 a phosphor frame at top, right and foot.

(Litho)

2014 (21 July). Irish Animals and Marine Life. Vert designs as T **615**. Multicoloured. Chalk-surfaced paper. Self-adhesive. Phosphor frame. Die-cut perf 14.

2224	68c. Cushion Star (*Asterina gibbosa*)	1·10	1·10
	a. Booklet pane. No. 2224×10	10·00	
2225	€1 Fireworks Anemone (*Pachycerianthus multiplicatus*)	1·60	1·75
	a. Booklet pane. No. 2225×10	14·50	

Nos. 2222/3 are left for self-adhesive coil stamps not yet received.
No. 2224 was issued in €6.80 stamp booklets, No. SB178.
No. 2225 was issued in €10 stamp booklets, No. SB179.

(Des Kelvin Gillmor. Litho Irish Security Stamp Ptg Ltd)

2014 (21 July). Love and Marriage. As No. 2202 but new face value. Chalk-surfaced paper. Self-adhesive. Phosphor frame. Die-cut perf 13.

2226	68c. As Type **660**	1·10	1·10
	a. Booklet pane. No. 2226×10	10·00	

No. 2226 was issued in €6.80 booklets, No. SB180.

(Des Ger Garland. Litho Irish Security Stamp Ptg Ltd)

2014 (24 July). Centenary of World War I. Propaganda Posters. T **670** and similar vert design. Multicoloured. Chalk-surfaced paper. Phosphor frame. P 13.

2227	68c. Type **670**	1·10	80
2228	€1 "I'll go too" 'THE REAL IRISH SPIRIT'	1·75	2·00

(Des Zinc Design Consultants. Digital print Label Art Ltd)

2014 (31 July). Irish Animals and Marine Life. Horiz designs as T **599**. Multicoloured. Self-adhesive. Three phosphor bars. Die-cut perf 11.

2229	68c. Scallop (*Pecten maximus*)	1·40	1·40
	a. Vert strip of 4. Nos. 2229/32	5·00	5·00
2230	68c. Violet Snail (*Janthina janthina*)	1·40	1·40
2231	68c. Basking Shark (*Cetorhinus maximus*)	1·40	1·40
2232	68c. Mute Swan (*Cygnus olor*)	1·40	1·40
2233	68c. Otter (*Lutra lutra*)	1·40	1·40
	a. Vert strip of 4. Nos. 2233/6	5·00	5·00
2234	68c. Viviparous Lizard (*Zootoca vivipara*)	1·40	1·40
2235	68c. Badger (*Meles meles*)	1·40	1·40
2236	68c. Wren (*Troglodytes troglodytes*)	1·40	1·40
2229/36	Set of 8	10·00	10·00

671 Prison Officer (Care and Custody)

(Des Zinc Design Consultants. Litho Irish Security Stamp Ptg Ltd)

2014 (7 Aug). Irish Prison Service. T **671** and similar horiz designs. Multicoloured. Chalk-surfaced paper. Phosphor frame. P 13×13½.

2237	68c. Type **671**	1·25	1·25
	a. Block of 4. Nos. 2237/40	4·50	4·50
2238	68c. Prisoner in workshop (Rehabilitation)	1·25	1·25
2239	68c. Cleaning wall (Restorative Justice)	1·25	1·25
2240	68c. Prisoners in classroom (Education)	1·25	1·25
2237/40	Set of 4	4·50	4·50

Nos. 2237/40 were printed together, *se-tenant*, as blocks of four stamps in sheetlets of 16.

672 Seamus Heaney   **673** Maine Coon (Fred)

(Des Vermilion Design. Litho Irish Security Stamp Ptg Ltd)

2014 (28 Aug). Seamus Heaney (1939–2013, poet) Commemoration. Chalk-surfaced paper. Phosphor frame. P 13½.

2241	**672** 68c. multicoloured	1·10	1·10

(Des Red & Grey Design. Litho Irish Security Stamp Ptg Ltd)

2014 (4 Sept). Cats. T **673** and similar square designs. Multicoloured. Chalk-surfaced paper. Phosphor frame. P 13.

2242	68c. Type **673**		1·25	1·25
	a. Block of 4. Nos. 2242/5		4·50	4·50
2243	68c. Burmese (Púca)		1·25	1·25
2244	68c. British Shorthair (Queenie)		1·25	1·25
2245	68c. Persian (Candy)		1·25	1·25
2242/5	Set of 4		4·50	4·50

Nos. 2242/5 were printed together, se-tenant, as blocks of four stamps in sheetlets of 16.

Nos. 2242/5 were also issued in €12 booklets, No. SP21.

MACHINE LABELS

Frama label   Klussendorf label

Amiel Pitney/Bowes label

For a trial period of three months from 8 October 1990 labels in the above designs, ranging in value from 1p. to £99.99, were available from the head post offices at Dublin (Frama), Limerick (Klussendorf) and Cork (Amiel Pitney/Bowes). The Amiel Pitney/Bowes machine (Cork) was taken out of service on 31 January 1991. The other two machines were withdrawn on 31 May 1991.

Frama labels in the above design, providing values from 1p. to £99.99, were introduced at head post offices in Dublin (001), Cork (003), Limerick (004) and Galway (005) on 6 April 1992. The system was extended to Bray (008), Killarney (009) and Sligo (007) on 20 July 1992, and to Kilkenny (010) and Waterford (006) on 7 September when a second machine (002) was also provided at Dublin. Both the Dublin machines were relocated to Dublin Airport in August 1994. The Killarney machine was out of use by the end of 1998 and the two at Dublin Airport were withdrawn on 28 July 1999.

From 2010 machine labels in designs as Nos. 2015/18, 2026/33 and 2073/80 were available in post offices in all values 1c. to €99.99. They differ from the listed stamps in not having a vertically preprinted number at bottom right. Many commercial firms have 'desktop' machines, dispensing similar labels; these have the preprinted number, but the denomination appears within a rectangular black box.

STAMP BOOKLETS

Nos. SB1 to SB24 are stitched. Subsequent booklets have their panes attached by the selvedge, unless otherwise stated.

Booklets are illustrated at half actual size except where otherwise stated.

B **1** Harp and Monogram

1931 (21 Aug)–**40**. Black on red cover as Type B **1**.
SB1   2s. booklet containing six ½d., six 2d. (Nos. 71, 74), each in block of 6, and nine 1d. (No. 72) in block of 6 and pane of 3 stamps and 3 labels (No. 72d or 72dw) .... From £3750
Edition Nos.:—31–1, 31–2, 32–3, 33–4, 33–5, 34–6, 34–7, 35–8, 35–9, 36–10, 36–11, 37–12, 37–13, 37–14, 15–38, 16–38, 17–38
    a. Cover as Type B **2** .... From £4250
Edition Nos.:–18–39, 19–39, 20–39, 21–40, 22–40

B **2** Harp and "EIRE"

1940. Black on red cover as Type B **2**.
SB2   2s. booklet containing six ½d., six 2d. (Nos. 71, 74), each in block of 6, and nine 1d. (No. 72) in block of 6 and pane of 3 stamps and 3 labels (No. 112d or 112dw) £11000
Edition No.:—22–40

1940. Black on red cover as Type B **2**.
SB3   2s. booklet containing six ½d., six 2d. (Nos. 111, 114), each in block of 6, and nine 1d. (No. 112) in block of 6 and pane of 3 stamps and 3 labels (No. 112d or 112dw) £11000
Edition No.:—23–40

1941–44. Black on red cover as Type B **2**.
SB4   2s. booklet containing twelve ½d., six 1d. and six 2d. (Nos. 111/12, 114) in blocks of 6 .... From £2000
Edition Nos.:—24–41, 25–42, 26–44

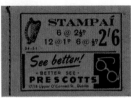

B **3**

1945. Black on red cover as Type B **3**.
SB5   2s. booklet containing twelve ½d., six 1d. and six 2d. (Nos. 111/12, 114) in blocks of 6 .... £2000
Edition No.:—27–45

1946. Black on buff cover as Type B **2**.
SB6   2s. booklet containing twelve ½d., six 1d. and six 2d. (Nos. 111/12, 114) in blocks of 6 .... £1300
Edition No.:—28–46

1946–47. Black on buff cover as Type B **2**.
SB7   2s. booklet containing twelve ½d., six 1d. and six 2d. (Nos. 133, 112, 114) in blocks of 6 .... From £650
Edition Nos.:—29–46, 30–47

B **4** Harp only

1948–50. Black on orange-buff cover as Type B **4**.
SB8   2s.6d. booklet containing six ½d., twelve 1d. and six 2½d. (Nos. 133, 112, 115) in blocks of 6 .... From £300
Edition Nos.:—31–48, 32–49, 33–50

1951–53. Black on buff cover as Type B **4**.
SB9   2s.6d. booklet containing six ½d., twelve 1d. and six 2½d. (Nos. 133, 112, 115) in blocks of 6 .... From 70·00
Edition Nos.:—34–51, 35–52, 36–53

1954 (24 Nov). Black on buff cover as Type B **4**.
SB10   4s. booklet containing six ½d., six 1½d. and twelve
       3d. (Nos. 133, 113, 116) in blocks of 6 .... £120
    Edition No.:—37–54.

1956 (17 Dec). Black on buff cover as Type B **4**.
SB11   4s. booklet containing twelve 1d. and twelve 3d.
       (Nos. 112, 116) in blocks of 6 .... £110
    Edition No.:—38–56.

B **5**

1958–61. Black on buff cover as Type B **5**.
SB12   4s. booklet containing twelve 1d. and twelve 3d.
       (Nos. 112, 116) in blocks of 6 .... £110
    Edition Nos.:—39–58, 40–59, 41–60, 42–61.

1962 (23 Oct)–**63**. Black on buff cover as Type B **5**.
SB13   3s. booklet containing six 2d. and six 4d.
       (Nos. 114, 117) in blocks of 6
       .... *From* £100
    Edition Nos.:—43–62, 44–63 (June).

B **6**

1964 (Sept). Red on yellow cover as Type B **6**.
SB14   3s. booklet containing twelve 1d. and six 4d.
       (Nos. 112, 117) in blocks of 6 .... 60·00

B **7**

1966 (1–9 Dec). Covers as Type B **7** in red (No. SB15), blue (No. SB16)
    or green (No. SB17).
SB15   2s.6d. booklet containing six 2d. and six 3d.
       (Nos. 114, 116) in blocks of 6 (9 Dec) .... 19·00
SB16   2s.6d. booklet containing six 5d. (No. 228) in
       block of 6 (9 Dec) .... 15·00
SB17   5s. booklet containing twelve 5d. (No. 228) in
       blocks of 6 .... 35·00

B **8**

1969 (12 Sept). Plain blue-green cover as Type B **8**.
SB18   6s. booklet containing twelve 6d. (No. 253) in
       blocks of six .... 50·00

1971 (15 Feb). Plain slate-green cover as Type B **8**.
SB19   30p. booklet containing six ½p., twelve 1p. and six
       2½p. in panes of 6 (Nos. 287ab or 287awb,
       288ca or 288cwa, 291ba or 291bwa) .... 38·00

1974 (11 Mar). Green cover as Type B **8**.
SB20   50p. booklet containing ten 5p. in panes of 5
       stamps and 1 label (No. 295ad or 295adw) .... 22·00

1974 (11 Mar). Blue cover as Type B **8**.
SB21   50p. booklet containing five 1p. in pane of 5
       stamps and 1 label (No. 288cb or 288cwb), six
       2½p. and six 5p. in panes of 6 (Nos. 291ba or
       291bwa, 295ae or 295awe) .... 10·00

1975 (27 Jan). Covers as Type B **8**, in rose (No. SB22) or light grey
    (No. SB23).
SB22   40p. booklet containing five 1p, 2p. and 5p. each in
       panes of 5 stamps and 1 label (Nos. 288cb or
       288cwb, 290ba or 290bwa, 295ad or 295awd)... 3·00
SB23   70p. booklet containing ten 2p. and 5p. each in
       panes of 5 stamps and 1 label (Nos. 290ba or
       290bwa, 295ad or 295awd) .... 3·75

1977 (21 Mar). Yellow-olive cover similar to Type B **8**.
SB24   50p. booklet containing five 1p, 2p. and 7p. each in
       panes of 5 stamps and 1 label (Nos. 288cb or
       288cwb. 290ba or 290bwa, 348a) .... 8·00

B **9** Four Courts

1983 (15 Aug). Yellow-green cover as Type B **9**.
SB25   £1 booklet containing *se-tenant* pane of 7 stamps
       and 1 label (No. 535a) .... 2·00
    No. SB25 was an experimental issue available from two machines,
accepting two 50p. coins, at the G.P.O. Dublin, and from the Philatelic
Bureau.

B **10**

1984 (9 July). Dull green, greenish yellow and black cover as
    Type B **10**.
SB26   £2 booklet containing *se-tenant* pane of 12
       (No. 535ba) .... 4·00
    No. SB26 actually contains £2.26 worth of stamps, but was sold at
a discount of 26p. by the Irish Post Office from 9 July until 10 August.

B **11** Custom House, Dublin,
in 19th Century

1985 (27 June). Yellowish green cover as Type B **11**.
SB27   £1 booklet containing *se-tenant* pane of 6 (No. 533ab). 4·00

B **12**

1985 (27 June). Bright green cover as Type B **12**.
SB28   £2 booklet containing *se-tenant* pane of 12
         (No. 533ac).. 5·50

B **13**

1986 (8 Sept). Black, light green and pale yellow cover as Type B **13**.
SB29   £2 booklet containing *se-tenant* pane of 12
         (No. 533ad).. 5·50

B **14** Custom House, Dublin (*Illustration further reduced. Actual size 137×70 mm*)

1988 (1 Mar). Dublin Millennium. Multicoloured cover as Type B **14**.
SB30   £2.24 booklet containing eight 24p. in panes of 4
         (No. 688a) (one inscr in Irish, one in English)...... 4·00
   No. SB30 also exists with the booklet cover overprinted for
"SPRING STAMPEX 1988", "7 Internationale Briefmarken-Messe" (Essen),
"FINLANDIA 88" and "SYDPEX 88" exhibitions.

1988 (24 Nov). Maroon and black cover as Type B **11**, but showing
Courthouse, Cork.
SB31   £2 booklet containing *se-tenant* pane of 12
         (No. 533ae).. 5·00

B **15** Gordon Bennett Race, 1903 (*Illustration further reduced. Actual size 132×60 mm*)

1989 (11 Apr). Irish Motoring Classics. Multicoloured cover as Type B **15**.
SB32   £2.41 booklet containing two different *se-tenant*
         panes of 4 (Nos. 718a/b)...................................... 5·25

B **16** 8th-century Gilt-silver Brooch (*Illustration further reduced. Actual size 160×100 mm*)

1989 (15 June). 1300th Death Anniv of Saints Kilian, Totnan and
Colman. Multicoloured cover as Type B **16**. Stitched.
SB33   £4.48 booklet containing sixteen 28p. in panes of 4
         (No. 726a)... 7·00
   No. SB33 exists overprinted for "PHILEXFRANCE 89" or "WORLD
STAMP EXPO '89".

B **17** (*Illustration further reduced. Actual size 136×74 mm*)

1990 (22 Mar). Greetings Booklet. Multicoloured cover as Type B **17**.
Stitched.
SB34   £1.98 booklet containing two *se-tenant* panes of 4
         (No. 766a) and eight greetings labels.................... 11·00
   No. SB34 was sold at £1.98, providing a discount of 26p. off the
face value of the stamps.

B **18** (*Illustration further reduced. Actual size 161×99 mm*)

1990 (3 May). 150th Anniv of the Penny Black. Multicoloured cover as
Type B **18**. Stitched.
SB35   £6 booklet containing *se-tenant* panes of 8, 4
         and 5 (Nos. 535ca, 547ba/bb) and pane of 4
         (No. 774a)... 20·00
   No. SB25 exists overprinted for "Stamp World London 90"
exhibition.

B **19** Garden at Powerscourt, Co. Wicklow (*Illustration further reduced. Actual size 150×75 mm*)

1990 (30 Aug). Garden Flowers. Multicoloured cover as Type B **19**.
Stitched.
SB36   £2.59 booklet containing two different *se-tenant*
         panes of 4 (Nos. 781a/b)...................................... 7·00

B **20** 7th-century Tara Brooch

1990 (15 Nov). Irish Heritage. Black and bright blue cover as
Type B **20**.
SB37   £1 booklet containing *se-tenant* pane of 7 stamps
         and 1 label (No. 747ab).. 5·00

B **21** View of Dublin (*Illustration further reduced. Actual size 140×85 mm*)

1991 (11 Apr). "Dublin 1991 European City of Culture". Multicoloured cover as Type B **21**.
SB38   £2.60 booklet containing two different *se-tenant* panes of 3 (Nos. 800a/b) .... 7·50

B **22** Ardagh Chalice

1991 (14 May)–**92**. Covers as Type B **22**.
SB39   £1 booklet containing *se-tenant* pane of 5 stamps and 1 label (No. 808a) (black and green cover as Type B **22**)... 4·25
SB40   £1 booklet containing *se-tenant* pane of 5 stamps and 1 label (No. 808a) (black and orange-yellow cover showing St. Patrick's Bell Shrine) (25.2.92) .... 10·00

B **23** (*Illustration further reduced. Actual size 161×99 mm*)

1991 (17 Oct). Fishing Fleet. Multicoloured cover as Type B **23**. Stitched.
SB41   £5 booklet containing *se-tenant* panes of 5 and 7 and 1 label (Nos. 747ac, 748ba) and two different *se-tenant* panes of 4 (Nos. 819a/b) .... 17·00

B **24** (*Illustration further reduced. Actual size 138×75 mm*)

1992 (2 Apr). Greetings Booklet. Multicoloured cover as Type B **24**. Stitched.
SB42   £2.40 booklet containing two *se-tenant* panes of 4 (No. 840a) and eight greetings labels..................... 8·00

B **25** (*Illustration further reduced. Actual size 161×100 mm*)

1992 (15 Nov). Single European Market. Deep bluish violet and greenish yellow cover as Type B **25**. Stitched.
SB43   £4.80 booklet containing fifteen 32p. in three panes of 4 (No. 856a) and one pane of 3 (No. 856b).... 8·00

B **26** "Banks of the Seine, near Paris" (N. Hone) (*Illustration further reduced. Actual size 161×100 mm*)

1993 (4 Mar). Irish Impressionist Painters. Multicoloured cover as Type B **26**. Stitched.
SB44   £4.68 booklet containing four *se-tenant* panes (Nos. 867a×2, 867b and 869a) .... 10·00

B **27** Lismore Crozier

1993 (24 Sept)–**95**. Covers as Type B **27**.
SB45   £1 booklet containing *se-tenant* pane of 4 (No. 748ca) (bright greenish blue cover as Type B **27**)... 6·00
SB46   £1 booklet containing *se-tenant* pane of 4 (No. 748cb) (black and bright vermilion cover showing enamelled latchet brooch) (2.3.94)........ 6·50
SB46*a*   £1 booklet containing *se-tenant* pane of 4 (No. 748cb) (black and bright orange-red cover showing Gleninsheen Collar) (28.2.95) .... 6·50
SB46*b*   £1 booklet containing *se-tenant* pane of 4 (No. 748a) (black and bright reddish violet cover showing Broighter Collar) (16.11.95).......... 8·00

B **28** Front and Side View of Dublin Bus Leyland Olympian (*Illustration further reduced. Actual size 131×61 mm*)

1993 (12 Oct). Irish Buses. Multicoloured cover as Type B **28**. Stitched.
SB47   £2.84 booklet containing two different *se-tenant* panes (Nos. 886a/b)... 6·00

B **29** (*Illustration further reduced. Actual size* 138×75 *mm*)

1994 (27 Jan). Greetings Booklet. Multicoloured cover as Type B **29**. Stitched.
SB48 £2.56 booklet containing two *se-tenant* panes of four
32p. (No. 896a)... 7·00

B **30** (*Illustration further reduced. Actual size* 137×60 *mm*)

1994 (27 Apr). Parliamentary Anniversaries. Multicoloured cover as Type B **30**. Stitched.
SB49 £1.92 booklet containing two different *se-tenant*
panes (Nos. 908a/b)... 4·00

B **31** (*Illustration further reduced. Actual size* 161×101 *mm*)

1994 (18 Oct). Irish Nobel Prizewinners. Multicoloured cover as Type B **31**. Stitched.
SB50 £4.84 booklet containing four different *se-tenant*
panes (Nos. 928b/d and 930a).................................. 8·00

B **32** (*Illustration further reduced. Actual size* 138×75 *mm*)

1995 (24 Jan). Greetings Booklet. Multicoloured cover as Type B **32**. Stitched.
SB51 £2.56 booklet containing two *se-tenant* panes of four
32p. (No. 936a)... 9·00

B **33** Blessing before Battle (*Illustration further reduced. Actual size* 161×100 *mm*)

1995 (15 May). Military Uniforms. Multicoloured cover as Type B **33**. Stitched.
SB52 £4.80 booklet containing four different *se-tenant*
panes (Nos. 954a/d).. 9·00

B **34** (*Illustration further reduced. Actual size* 140×82 *mm*)

1995 (9 Oct). Bicentenary of National Botanic Gardens, Glasnevin. Multicoloured cover as Type B **34**. Stitched.
SB53 £2.60 booklet containing two different *se-tenant*
panes (Nos. 973a/b).. 6·00

B **35** (*Illustration further reduced. Actual size* 137×74 *mm*)

1996 (23 Jan). Greetings Booklet. Multicoloured cover as Type B **35**. Stitched.
SB54 £2.56 booklet containing two *se-tenant* panes of four
32p. (No. 982a)... 15·00

B **36** Steeplechasing (*Illustration further reduced. Actual size* 161×100 *mm*)

1996 (12 Mar). Irish Horse Racing. Multicoloured cover as Type B **36**. Stitched.
SB55 £4.92 booklet containing four different *se-tenant*
panes (Nos. 991a, 992b/c and 993a)...................... 13·00

B **37** Coastal Patrol Vessel and Sailor (*Illustration further reduced. Actual size 150×90 mm*)

(Des Design Image)

1996 (18 July). 50th Anniv of Irish Naval Service. Multicoloured cover as Type B **37**. Stitched.
SB56   £2.24 booklet containing pane of three 32p. and
pane of three values *se-tenant* (Nos. 1013a/b) ...   5·50

B **38** Farmyard Animals (*Illustration further reduced. Actual size 137×73 mm*)

1997 (28 Jan). Greetings Booklet. Multicoloured cover as Type B **38**. Stitched.
SB57   £2.56 booklet containing two *se-tenant* panes of four
32p. (No. 1100a) ....   7·50

B **39** Robin

1997 (6 Mar). Birds. Multicoloured cover as Type B **39**. Stamps attached by selvedge.
SB58   £1 booklet containing pane of 4 (2×2)
(No. 748bb) ....   6·00

B **40** The Baily Lighthouse (*Illustration further reduced. Actual size 160×100 mm*)

1997 (1 July). Lighthouses. Multicoloured cover as Type B **40**. Stitched.
SB59   £4.64 booklet containing four different *se-tenant*
panes (Nos. 1136b/c, 1136da and 1138da) ....   14·00

B **41** Christmas Tree

1997 (18 Nov). Christmas. Multicoloured cover as Type B **41**. Self-adhesive.
SB60   £5.32 booklet containing pane of twenty 28p. (2×10)
(No. 1149a) ....   14·50
No. SB60 was sold at £5.32 providing a discount of 28p. off the face value of the stamps.

1997 (6 Dec). Multicoloured cover as Type B **39** showing Peregrine Falcon. Stamps attached by selvedge.
SB61   £1 booklet containing pane of 4 (2×2)
(No. 1080a) ....   6·25

B **42** On Swing (*Illustration further reduced. Actual size 138×74 mm*)

1998 (26 Jan). Greetings Booklet. Multicoloured cover as Type B **42**. Stitched.
SB62   £2.56 booklet containing two different *se-tenant*
panes of four 32p. (No. 1150a) ....   7·50

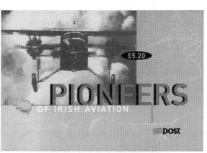

B **43** Early Aeroplane and Map (*Illustration further reduced. Actual size 160×100 mm*)

1998 (24 Feb). Pioneers of Irish Aviation. Multicoloured cover as Type B **43**. Stitched.
SB63 $5.20 booklet containing four different *se-tenant*
panes (Nos. 1155a/b and1156a/b) ....   11·00

IRELAND

B **44** Blackbird

1998 (2 Apr). Multicoloured cover as Type B **44**. Stamps attached by selvedge.
SB64 £1 booklet containing pane of 5 stamps and 1
label (No. 1081a)... 6·75
a. Containing pane No. 1081ba..................................... 35·00

1998 (6 May). Greetings Booklet. Multicoloured cover as Type B **42**, but inscribed "*LETTER POST*" in green border at foot. Stitched.
SB65 £2.40 booklet containing two different *se-tenant*
panes of four 30p. (No. 1173a)................................. 7·00

B **45** *Asgard II* (cadet brigantine) (*Illustration further reduced. Actual size 138×89 mm*)

1998 (20 July). *Cutty Sark* International Tall Ships Race, Dublin. Multicoloured cover as Type B **45**. Stitched.
SB66 £2.65 booklet containing two different *se-tenant*
panes of 3 (Nos. 1185ba and 1186ba)................... 7·00

B **46** Blackbird

1998 (4 Sept)–**99**. Multicoloured cover as Type B **46**. Stamps attached by selvedge.
SB67 £3 booklet containing pane of 10 (5×2) 30p.
stamps (No. 1038ab)... 17·00
a. Containing pane No. 1038ar (stamps with
phosphor frames) (25.1.99)............................ 18·00
b. Containing pane No. 1038at (stamps
perforated 11×13) (4.01).................................. 19·00
No. SB67 exists overprinted for "Stampa' 99" National Stamp Exhibition, Dublin, in red.

B **47** Choir Boys

1998 (17 Nov). Christmas. Multicoloured cover as Type B **47**. Self-adhesive.
SB68 £5.40 booklet containing pane of twenty 30p. (5×4)
(No. 1209a)... 12·00
No. SB68 was sold at £5.40 providing a discount of 60p. off the face value of the stamps.

B **48** Domestic Pets (*Illustration further reduced. Actual size 139×73 mm*)

1999 (26 Jan). Greetings Booklet. Pets. Multicoloured cover as Type B **48**. Stitched.
SB69 £2.40 booklet containing two different *se-tenant*
panes of four 30p. (No. 1210a)............................. 7·00

B **49** Goldcrest

1999 (16 Feb). Multicoloured cover as Type B **49**. Stamps attached by selvedge.
SB70 £1 booklet containing pane of 5 stamps and 1
label (No. 1081bb)... 7·50

B **50** Dublin

1999 (30 June). Multicoloured covers as Type B **50**. Stamps attached by selvedge.
SB71 £1.60 booklet containing pane of five 32p. plus 5
airmail labels (No. 1053pa)................................ 9·00
SB72 £1.80 booklet containing pane of four 45p. and 4
airmail labels (No. 1057pa) (cover showing
ornamental garden)... 9·00
a. Containing stamps on chalk-surfaced paper
(No. 1057apa).. 9·00

B **51** "the Kingdom"

1999 (17 Aug). Gaelic Athletics Association "Millennium Football Team". Multicoloured covers as Type B **51**. Self-adhesive.

SB73	£2.40 booklet containing pane of 8 stamps (No. 1251a) (cover as Type B **51**)	11·00
SB74	£2.40 booklet containing pane of 8 stamps (No. 1252a) (cover inscr "the West awake")	4·50
SB75	£2.40 booklet containing pane of 8 stamps (No. 1256a) (cover inscr "ulster abu")	3·25
SB76	£2.40 booklet containing pane of 8 stamps (No. 1257a) (cover inscr "Kings of Leinster")	3·50

B **52** Boeing 707 (*Illustration further reduced. Actual size 160×100 mm*)

1999 (9 Sept). Commercial Aviation. Multicoloured cover as Type B **52**. Stitched.

SB77	£4.91 booklet containing four different *se-tenant* panes of 3 (No. 1266d) or 4 (Nos. 1266a/c)	10·00

B **53** Angel

1999 (4 Nov). Christmas. Multicoloured cover as Type B **53**. Self-adhesive.

SB78	£5.40 booklet containing pane of twenty 30p. (2×10) (No. 1282a)	12·50

No. SB78 was sold at £5.40 providing a discount of 60p. off the face value of the stamps.

B **54** (*Illustration further reduced. Actual size 138×75 mm*)

2000 (26 Jan). Greetings Stamps. Mythical Creatures. Multicoloured cover as Type B **54**. Stitched.

SB79	£3 booklet containing three *se-tenant* panes of 30p. (Nos. 1295a×2 and 1295b)	9·50

B **55**

2000 (2 Aug). "Hurling Team of the Millennium". Multicoloured covers as Type B **55** showing photograph of players in action and County name. Self-adhesive.

SB80	£3 booklet containing pane of ten 30p. (No. 1344a)	5·50
SB81	£3 booklet containing pane of ten 30p. (No. 1347a) ("Kilkenny Cats")	8·00
SB82	£3 booklet containing pane of ten 30p. (No. 1351a) ("Offaly Waterford Limerick")	5·50
SB83	£3 booklet containing pane of ten 30p. (No. 1354a) ("The Boys of Wexford")	5·50
SB84	£3 booklet containing pane of ten 30p. (No. 1356a) ("The Rebel County")	5·50

2000 (9 Oct). Military Aviation. Multicoloured cover as Type B **52** showing Marchetti SF.260 in flight. Booklet contains text and illustrations on interleaving pages. Stitched.

SB85	£5.55 booklet containing four different *se-tenant* panes of 4 (Nos. 1364b/c and 1366b) or 3 (No. 1364d)	15·00

2000 (14 Nov). Christmas. Multicoloured cover as Type B **53** showing design of No. 1376. Self-adhesive.

SB86	£6.60 booklet containing pane of twenty-four 30p. (2×12) (No. 1376a)	20·00

No. SB86 was sold at £6.60 providing a discount of 60p. off the face value of the stamps.

B **56**

2001 (24 Jan). Greetings Stamps. Pets. Multicoloured cover as Type B **56**. Self-adhesive.

SB87	£3 booklet containing pane of ten 30p. (2×5) (No. 1390a) and ten greetings labels	9·00

B **57**

2001 (26 Apr). Irish Motorsport. Multicoloured cover as Type B **57**. Self-adhesive.

SB88   £3 booklet containing pane of ten 30p. (5×2)
            (No. 1411a) .... 11·00

B **58**

2001 (5 Sept). Gaelic Athletic Association Hall of Fame 2001. Multicoloured cover as Type B **58**. Self-adhesive.

SB89   £3 booklet containing pane of ten 30p.
            (No. 1448a) .... 7·00

B **59** Blackbird

2001 (9 Oct). Birds. Multicoloured covers as Type B **59**. Self-adhesive.

SB90   (£3) booklet containing se-tenant pane of ten "N"
            stamps (No. 1453a) .... 14·00
SB91   (£3.20) booklet containing pane of ten "E" stamps
            (No. 1455a) with 10 airmail labels on the inner
            cover (Robin) .... 16·00
SB92   (£4.50) booklet containing pane of ten "W" stamps
            (No. 1456a) with 10 airmail labels on the inner
            cover (Song Thrush)... 18·00

B **60** "F-I-S-H" in the Shape of a Fish (*Illustration further reduced. Actual size* 160×100 *mm*)

2001 (9 Oct). Freshwater Fish. Multicoloured cover as Type B **60**. Stitched.

SB93   £5.82 booklet containing four se-tenant panes of 4
            (Nos. 1457b×2, 1457c and 1458b)............................. 14·00

B **61** "Madonna and Child"

2001 (5 Nov). Christmas. Paintings by Richard King. Multicoloured cover as Type B **61**. Self-adhesive.

SB94   £6.60 booklet containing pane of twenty-four 30p.
            (2×12) (No. 1465a)... 25·00
    No. SB94 was sold at £6.60 providing a discount of 60p. off the face value of the stamps.

B **62**

2002 (1 Jan). New Currency. Birds. Multicoloured cover as Type B **62**.

SB95   €2 booklet containing se-tenant pane of 6 (2×3)
            (No. 1487a) .... 6·75

B **63** Teddy Bear

2002 (22 Jan). Greetings Stamps. Toys. Multicoloured cover as Type B **63**. Self-adhesive.

SB96   €3.80 booklet containing pane of ten 38c. (2×5)
            (No. 1510a) and ten greetings labels...................... 7·00

B **64**

2002 (2 Apr). New Currency. Birds. Multicoloured covers as Type B **64**. Self-adhesive.
SB97 €4.10 booklet containing *se-tenant* pane of ten 41c.
(2×5) (No. 1493b).. 8·50
SB98 €4.40 booklet containing pane of ten 44c. (2×5)
(No. 1495a) (Robin)...................................... 11·00
SB99 €5.70 booklet containing pane of ten 57c. (2×5)
(No. 1497a) (Song Thrush) .... 13·00

B **65** Footballers

2002 (14 May). World Cup Football Championship, Japan and Korea (2002). Irish Footballers. Multicoloured cover as Type B **65**. Self-adhesive.
SB100 €4.10 booklet containing *se-tenant* pane of ten 41c.
(2×5) (No. 1533a) .... 9·00

B **66** Chaffinch

2002 (6 Aug). New Currency. Birds. Multicoloured cover as Type B **66**.
SB101 €4.10 booklet containing *se-tenant* pane of ten 41c.
(2×5) (No. 1474a) .... 13·00

2002 (6 Aug). New Currency. Birds. Multicoloured cover as Type B **62**.
SB102 €2 booklet containing *se-tenant* pane of 5
(No. 1488a).. 6·00

B **67** Paintings (*Illustration further reduced. Actual size* 160×100 *mm*)

2002 (29 Aug). 140th Anniv of National Gallery of Ireland (2004) (1st series). Multicoloured cover as Type B **67**. Stitched.
SB103 €6.56 booklet containing four *se-tenant* panes of 4
(Nos. 1546b/9b).................................... 10·00

B **68** "The Nativity"

2002 (7 Nov). Christmas. Illustrations from *Les Très Riches Heures du Duc de Berry*. Multicoloured cover as Type B **68**. Self-adhesive.
SB104 €9.43 booklet containing pane of twenty-four 41c.
(2×12) (No. 1563a)............................... 22·00
No. SB104 was sold at €9.43 providing a discount of 41c. off the face value of the stamps.

2003 (6 Jan). New Currency. Birds. Multicoloured cover as Type B **64** but showing Puffin. Self-adhesive.
SB105 €5 booklet containing *se-tenant* pane of ten 50c. (2×5) (No. 1496a) with ten self-adhesive "PRIORITY AERPHOST" labels on the inner panel .... 16·00

2003 (28 Jan). Greetings Stamps. Baby Animals. Multicoloured cover as Type B **63**, but showing Labrador puppies. Self-adhesive.
SB106 €4.10 booklet containing pane of ten 41c. (2×5) and ten greetings labels (No. 1565a) .... 7·00

B **69** St. Patrick

2003 (28 Feb). St. Patrick's Day. Multicoloured covers as Type B **69**, each showing the design of the stamp included. Self-adhesive.
SB107 €4.10 booklet containing pane of 10 (2×5)
(No. 1574a) .... 8·50
SB108 €5 booklet containing pane of 10 (2×5)
(No. 1575a) .... 8·50
SB109 €5.70 booklet containing pane of 10 (2×5)
(No. 1576a) .... 9·50

2003 (25 Aug). New Currency. Birds. Multicoloured cover as Type B **64** but showing Peregrine Falcon. Self-adhesive.
SB110 €4.80 booklet containing *se-tenant* pane of 10
(No. 1495bb) .... 18·00

2003 (9 Sept). 140th Anniv of National Gallery of Ireland (2004) (2nd issue). Multicoloured cover as Type B **67**. Stitched.
SB111 €7.68 booklet containing four *se-tenant* panes of 4
(Nos. 1606b, 1607b×2 and 1609b) .... 13·00

2003 (30 Sept). New Currency. Birds. Multicoloured cover as Type B **62**.
SB112 €2 booklet containing *se-tenant* pane of 5
(No. 1486ab)... 5·50

2003 (30 Sept). New Currency. Birds. Multicoloured cover as Type B **66** but showing Peregrine Falcon and inscr "10 gummed 48c stamps".
SB113 €4.80 booklet containing *se-tenant* pane of ten 48c.
(5×2) (No. 1477ab) .... 18·00

2003 (30 Sept). New Currency. Birds. Multicoloured cover as Type B **64** but showing Peregrine Falcon. Self-adhesive.
SB114 €4.80 booklet containing *se-tenant* pane of ten 48c.
(No. 1495db) .... 11·00

B **70** Letters flying through Letterbox

2003 (10 Nov). Christmas. Multicoloured cover as Type B **70**. Self-adhesive.
SB115 €11.04 booklet containing pane of twenty-four 48c.
(12×2) (No. 1627a).. 23·00
No. SB115 was sold at €11.04 providing a discount of 48c. off the face value of the stamps.

2004 (5 Jan). New Currency. Birds. Multicoloured covers as Type B **64**. Self-adhesive.
SB116 €6 booklet containing *se-tenant* pane of ten 60c.
(No. 1497ba) (Puffin).. 15·00
SB117 €6.50 booklet containing *se-tenant* pane of ten 65c.
(No. 1497ca) (Song Thrush) .... 16·00

B **71** "Jolly Panda"

2004 (30 Jan). Greetings Stamps. Animals. Multicoloured cover as Type B **71**. Self-adhesive.
SB118 €4.80 booklet containing *se-tenant* pane of ten
48c. and ten half stamp-size greetings labels
(No. 1631a) .... 9·00

B **72**

2004 (9 Sept). Wild Flowers. Multicoloured covers as Type B **72**. Stamps attached by selvedge (SB119) or self-adhesive (SB120).
SB119 €4.80 booklet containing pane of 10 stamps
(No. 1675a) .... 15·00
SB120 €4.80 booklet containing pane of 10 stamps
(No. 1693b).. 15·00
€4.80 booklets with green cover as Type B **82** and containing pane Nos. 1675a and 1693ca were probably issued in early 2007. Further details are sought.

2004 (16 Sept). 140th Anniv of National Gallery of Ireland (3rd issue). Multicoloured cover as Type B **67**. Stitched.
SB121 €8 booklet containing four *se-tenant* panes of 4
(Nos. 1700b/3b).. 11·00

B **73** Library

2004 (1 Oct). Irish Winners of Nobel Prize for Literature. Multicoloured cover as Type B **73**. Stamps attached by selvedge.
SB122 €1.92 booklet containing pane of 4 stamps
(No. 1704b).. 3·50

B **74** Row of Houses and Envelopes

(Des Javelin Direct. Litho SNP Sprint)

2004 (10 Nov). Christmas. Multicoloured cover as Type B **74**. Self-adhesive.
SB123 €11.04 booklet containing pane of twenty-four 48c.
(12×2) (No. 1713a).. 22·00
No. SB123 was sold at €11.04 providing a discount of 48c. off the face value of the stamps.

GREETINGS STAMP BOOKLET €4.80

B **75** Rooster

2005 (28 Jan). Love, Greetings and Chinese New Year of the Rooster. Multicoloured cover as Type B **75**. Self-adhesive.
SB124 €4.80 booklet containing pane of ten 48c. and ten
half stamp-size greetings labels (No. 1716a) .... 7·50

2005 (21 Nov). Christmas. Multicoloured cover as Type B **74**. Self-adhesive.
SB125 €12 booklet containing pane of twenty-six 48c.
(2×13) (No. 1766a).. 21·00
No. SB125 was sold at €12 providing a discount of 48c. off the face value of the stamps.

B **76** Two Chinese Crested Dogs

2006 (25 Jan). Love, Greetings and Chinese New Year of the Dog. Multicoloured cover as Type B **76**. Self-adhesive.
SB126   €4.80 booklet containing *se-tenant* pane of ten 48c. and ten greetings labels (No. 1770a) ....   16·00

B **77**

2006 (27 Mar). Wild Flowers. Multicoloured cover as Type B **77**. Self-adhesive.
SB127   €7.50 booklet containing pane of 10 stamps (No. 1698a) with ten self-adhesive "PRIORITY AERPHOST" labels on the inner panel ....   17·00

B **78** River Shannon (*Illustration further reduced. Actual size 161×100 mm*)

(Des P. Raftery)

2006 (20 Oct). Inland Waterways. Multicoloured cover as Type B **78**. Booklet contains text and illustrations on panes and interleaving pages. Stitched.
SB128   €12 booklet containing four panes of 4 (Nos. 1809a/12a) ....   21·00

B **79** Robin

2006 (9 Nov). Christmas. Multicoloured cover as Type B **79**. Self-adhesive.
SB129   €12 booklet containing pane of twenty-six 48c. (2×13) (No. 1820a)..   26·00
No. SB129 was sold at €12 providing a discount of 48c. off the face value of the stamps.

B **80** Back of Wedding Dress

2007 (26 Jan). Weddings (1st issue). Multicoloured cover as Type B **80**. Self-adhesive.
SB130   (€4.80) booklet containing pane of 10 (No. 1825a) ....   9·00
No. SB130 was sold at €4.80.

B **81** Birthday Cake

2007 (26 Jan). Greetings Stamps. Multicoloured cover as Type B **81**. Self-adhesive.
SB131   (€4.80) booklet containing *se-tenant* pane of 10 stamps and 10 greetings labels (No. 1826a)......   10·00
No. SB131 was sold at €4.80.

B **82**

2007 (1 Mar). Wild Flowers. Multicoloured cover as Type B **82**. Self-adhesive.
SB132   €5.50 booklet containing pane of ten (No. 1695b) ....   15·00
See also note below No. SB120.

B **83**

2007 (20 Apr). Wild Flowers. Multicoloured cover as Type B **83**. Pane attached by selvedge.
SB133   €2 booklet containing pane of six stamps (No. 1690a) ....   6·25
            a. Containing No. 1690b (2009)............................   35·00

2007 (20 Apr). Wild Flowers. Multicoloured covers. Pane attached by selvedge (SB134) or self-adhesive (SB135/6).

SB134 €5.50 booklet pane of ten 55c. (No. 1678a) (cover as Type B **82** but 82×54 mm)...................... 12·50
SB135 €5.50 booklet pane of ten 55c. (No. 1697a) (cover as Type B **82** but inscr "€5.50" at top right)............... 12·50
SB136 €7.80 booklet pane of ten 78c. (No. 1699a) with ten self-adhesive "PRIORITY AERPHOST" labels on the inner panel (cover as Type B **77**)...................... 20·00

B **84**

2007 (19 June). RTÉ Performing Groups. Multicoloured cover as Type B **84**. Self-adhesive.
SB137 €5.50 booklet pane of ten 55c. (No. 1854a)...................... 10·00

B **85** Linked Hands

2007 (25 July). Weddings (2nd issue). Multicoloured cover as Type B **85**. Self-adhesive.
SB138 €5.50 booklet containing pane of ten 55c. (2×5) (No. 1862a). 11·00

B **86** Snowman

2007 (8 Nov). Christmas. Multicoloured cover as Type B **79**. Self-adhesive.
SB139 €13.75 booklet containing pane of twenty-six 55c. (2×13) (No. 1878a)........................ 26·00
No. SB139 was sold at €13.75 providing a discount of 55c. off the face value of the stamps.

B **87** Bride and Groom Embracing

2008 (16 Jan). Weddings (3rd issue). Multicoloured cover as Type B **87**. Self-adhesive.
SB140 €5.50 booklet containing pane of ten 55c. (5×2) (No. 1880a) .... 11·00

B **88** Juggler

2008 (11 Feb). Greetings stamps. Multicoloured cover as Type B **88**. Self-adhesive.
SB141 €5.50 booklet containing se-tenant pane of ten 55c. stamps and ten greetings labels (No. 1884a)...... 12·50

2008 (3–18 Mar). Multicoloured covers as Type B **77** but map in turquoise and light blue. Pane attached by selvedge (SB142) or self-adhesive (SB143).
SB142 €8.20 booklet containing ten 82c. (No. 1683a)   17·00
SB143 €8.20 booklet containing ten 82c. (No. 1699ba) with ten self-adhesive 'PRIORITY AERPHOST' labels on the inner panel (18 Mar)........................ 20·00

B **89** Children making Plasticine Planet Earth Models

2008 (28 Apr). International Year of Planet Earth. Multicoloured cover, 95×95 mm, as Type B **89**. Self-adhesive.
SB144 €5.50 booklet containing pane of ten 55c. (2×5) (No. 1894a) .... 13·50

Christmas Stamp Booklet
2008
INCLUDES one free stamp
€13.75

B **90** Infant Jesus in Manger

2008 (7 Nov). Christmas. Multicoloured cover, 59×76 mm, as Type B **90**. Self-adhesive.
SB145 €13.75 booklet containing pane of twenty-six 55c. (2×13) (No. 1928a)........................ 30·00
No. SB145 was sold at €13.75 providing a discount of 55c. off the face value of the stamps.

2008 (5 Dec). Wild Flowers. Multicoloured cover, 77×58 mm, as Type B **82** but without illustration of stamp and inscr '10 self-adhesive stamps NATIONAL'. Self-adhesive.
SB146 €5.50 booklet containing pane of ten (No. 1699da)..... 17·00

B **91** Pair of Wedding Rings

2009 (23 Jan). Weddings (4th issue). Multicoloured cover, 88×61 mm, as Type B **91**. Self-adhesive.
SB147 €5.50 booklet containing pane of ten 55c. (5×2)
(No. 1929a) .... 14·50

B **92** Woman reading Birthday Cards

2009 (6 Mar). Greetings Stamps. Multicoloured cover, 60×87 mm, as Type B **92**. Self-adhesive.
SB148 €5.50 booklet containing se-tenant pane of ten 55c. stamps and ten half stamp-size greetings labels (No. 1934a) .... 14·50

B **93** Woman with Young Child at Post Office Counter

2009 (3 Apr). 25th Anniv of An Post. Multicoloured cover, 78×59 mm, as Type B **93**. Self-adhesive.
SB149 €5.50 booklet containing pane of ten 55c. (5×2) and two stamp-size labels (No. 1949a)........................... 16·00

B **94** 'Aberann Conan' (Glen of Imaal terrier)

2009 (21 May). European Dog Show, Dublin. Multicoloured cover, 60×88 mm, as Type B **94**. Self-adhesive.
SB150 €5.50 booklet containing pane of ten 55c. (2×5)
(No. 1967a) .... 13·50

2009 (7 Aug). Wild Flowers. Multicoloured cover as Type B **77**, 77×59 mm. Self-adhesive.
SB151 €8.20 booklet containing ten 82c. (No. 1699fa) with ten self-adhesive 'PRIORITY AERPHOST' labels on the inner panel .... 24·00

2009 (16 Oct). Wild Flowers. Multicoloured cover, 78×59 mm, as Type B **82**. Self-adhesive.
SB152 €5.50 booklet containing pane of ten 55c.
(No. 1699ea) .... 17·00

B **95** Virgin and Child (Simon Bening)

2009 (6 Nov). Christmas. Multicoloured cover, 58×76 mm, as Type B **95**. Self-adhesive.
SB153 €13.75 booklet containing pane of twenty-six 55c.
(2×13) (No. 1988a)............................. 32·00
No. SB153 was sold at €13.75 providing a discount of 55c. off the face value of the stamps.

B **96** Pair of Stylised 'Lovebirds'

2010 (21 Jan). Weddings (5th issue). Multicoloured cover, 88×61 mm, as Type B **96**. Self-adhesive.
SB154 €5.50 booklet containing pane of ten 55c. (5×2)
(No. 1990a) .... 12·50

B **97** Girl opening Birthday Cards

2010 (28 Jan). Greetings Stamps. Multicoloured cover, 60×87 mm, as Type B **97**. Self-adhesive.
SB155 €5.50 booklet containing pane of ten 55c. (5×2) and ten half stamp-size greetings labels
(No. 1991a)...................................... 16·00

B **98** Robin, Holly Sprig and Snowman

2010 (4 Nov). Christmas. Multicoloured cover, 58×76 mm, as Type B **98**. Self-adhesive.
SB156 €13.75 booklet containing pane of twenty-six 55c.
(2×13) (No. 2044a)............................ 32·00
No. SB156 was sold at €13.75 providing a discount of 55c. off the face value of the stamps.

B **99** Bride and Groom under Umbrella

2011 (20 Jan). Weddings (6th issue). Multicoloured cover, 60×87 mm, as Type B **99**. Self-adhesive.
SB157 €5.50 booklet containing pane of ten 55c. (2×5)
(No. 2047a) .... 14·50

B **100** '2011'

2011 (27 Jan). Greetings Stamps. Multicoloured cover, 60×87 mm, as Type B **100**. Self-adhesive.
SB158 €5.50 booklet containing pane of ten 55c. (5×2) and ten greetings labels (No. 2048a) .... 14·50

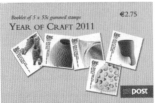

B **101** Year of Craft Stamps

2011 (12 May). Year of Craft. Multicoloured cover, 84×54 mm, as Type B **101**. Pane attached by selvedge.
SB159 €2.75 booklet containing pane of five 55c. (5×1)
(No. 2058a) .... 5·50

B **102** Hermit Crab (*Pagurus bernhardus*)

2011 (22 June). Irish Animals and Marine Life. Multicoloured cover, 78×59 mm, as Type B **102**. Self-adhesive.
SB160 €5.50 booklet containing pane of ten 55c. (5×2)
(No. 2071a) .... 13·50
A sticker was applied to remaining stocks of SB160 when the maximum weight carried by the 55c. stamp was reduced from 100g. to 50g. in 2012.

B **103** Field of Rape (Biofuel)

2011 (5 Aug). Renewable Energy. Multicoloured cover, 88×61 mm, as Type B **103**. Self-adhesive.
SB161 €5.50 booklet containing pane of ten 55c. (5×2)
(No. 2081b).. 16·00

B **104**

2011 (10 Nov). Christmas. Multicoloured cover, 58×76 mm, as Type B **104**. Self-adhesive.
SB162 €13.75 booklet containing pane of twenty-six 55c.
(2×13) (No. 2095a)....................................... 23·00
No. SB162 was sold at €13.75 providing a discount of 55c. off the face value of the stamps.

B **105** Bride and Groom

2012 (19 Jan). Weddings (7th issue). Multicoloured cover as Type B **105**, 87×61 mm. Self-adhesive.
SB163 €5.50 booklet containing pane of ten 55c. (5×2)
(No. 2101a) .... 9·00

B **106** Wrapped Presents

2012 (26 Jan). Greetings Stamps. Multicoloured cover as Type B **106**, 60×87 mm. Self-adhesive.
SB164 €5.50 booklet containing pane of ten 55c. (2×5)
and ten half stamp-size greetings labels
(No. 2102a) .... 9·00

B **107** Dancer

2012 (22 Mar). Contemporary Arts - Dance. Multicoloured cover, 85×86 mm, as Type B **107**. Self-adhesive.
SB165 €4.40 booklet containing pane of eight 55c. (in 2 blocks 2×2) (No. 2106a) .... 6·50

2012 (1 May). Irish Animals and Marine Life. Multicoloured covers, 77×58 mm, as Type B **102**. Self-adhesive.
SB166 €5.50 booklet containing pane of ten 55c. (5×2)
(No. 2071ba) .... 12·00
SB167 €8.20 booklet containing pane of ten 82c.
(No. 2071ca) with ten self-adhesive 'PRIORITY AERPHOST' labels on the inner panel .... 16·00

B **108** Candle Stamp and Christmas Tree

2012 (8 Nov). Christmas. Multicoloured cover, 58×75 mm, as Type B **108**. Self-adhesive.
SB168 €13.75 booklet containing pane of twenty-six 55c.
(2×13) (No. 2145a) .... 23·00
No. SB168 was sold at €13.75 providing a discount of 55c. off the face value of the stamps.

B **109** Bride and Groom lighting Candle

2013 (14 Feb). Weddings (8th issue). Multicoloured cover, 87×60 mm, as Type B **109**. Self-adhesive.
SB169 (€5.50) booklet containing pane of ten (55c.) stamps
(5×2) (No. 2151a) .... 6·50

B **110** Table with Cards and Birthday Cake

2013 (7 Mar). Greetings Stamps. Paintings by Cathy Dineen. Multicoloured cover, 61×87 mm, as Type B **110**. Self-adhesive.
SB170 (€5.50) booklet containing pane of ten (55c.) stamps
(2×5) and ten half stamp-size greetings labels
(No. 2152a) .... 6·50

2013 (2 Apr). Irish Animals and Marine Life. Multicoloured covers, 77×59 mm, as Type B **102**. Self-adhesive.
SB171 €6 booklet containing pane of ten 60c. (5×2)
(No. 2157a) .... 9·00
SB172 €9 booklet containing pane of ten 90c. (2×5)
(No. 2158a) with ten self-adhesive 'PRIORITY AERPHOST' labels on the inner panel .... 12·00

B **111**

2013 (25 Apr). Contemporary Arts - Visual Arts (1st issue). Multicoloured cover, 100×50 mm, as Type B **111**. Stamps attached by selvedge.
SB173 €2.40 booklet containing pane of four 60c.
(No. 2159a) .... 3·25

B **112** Nativity in Stained Glass Stamp and Sprig of Holly

2013 (7 Nov). Christmas. Multicoloured cover, 58×75 mm, as Type B **112**. Self-adhesive.

SB174   €15 booklet containing pane of twenty-six 60c.
(2×13) (No. 2197a)................................ 23·00

B **113** Aliens

2014 (30 Jan). Greetings Stamps. Multicoloured cover, 60×87 mm, as Type B **113**. Self-adhesive.

SB175   €6 booklet containing pane of ten 60c. (5×2) and
ten half stamp-size greetings labels (No. 2200a)   9·00

B **114** Red Rose

2014 (13 Feb). Love and Marriage. Multicoloured cover, 87×60 mm, as Type B **114**. Self-adhesive.

SB176   €6 booklet containing pane of ten 60c. (5×2)
(No. 2202a) .... 9·00

2014 (27 Mar). Contemporary Arts - Visual Arts (2nd issue). Multicoloured cover, 100×50 mm, as Type B **111**. Stamps attached by selvedge.

SB177   €2.40 booklet containing pane of four 60c.
(No. 2205a) .... 3·25

2014 (21 July). Irish Animals and Marine Life. Multicoloured covers, 77×58 mm, as Type B **102**. Self-adhesive.

SB178   €6.80 booklet containing pane of ten 68c. (5×2)
(No. 2224a) (Cushion Star) .... 10·00

SB179   €10 booklet containing pane of ten €1 (No. 2225a)
with ten self-adhesive 'PRIORITY AERPHOST'
labels on the inner panel............................ 14·50

2014 (21 July). Love and Marriage. As No. SB176 but new face value. Multicoloured cover, 87×60 mm, as Type B **114**. Self-adhesive.

SB180   €6.80 booklet containing pane of ten 68c. (5×2)
(No. 2226a) .... 10·00

PREMIUM BOOKLETS

The following booklets were sold at a premium over the face value of the stamps. They measure 160×100 mm and are illustrated at one-third actual size *Except where otherwise stated* (SP5).

P **1** Shamrock

2003 (28 Feb). St. Patrick's Day. Green and yellow cover as Type P **1**. Booklet contains text and illustrations on panes and interleaving pages. Stitched.

SP1   €8 booklet containing four panes comprising
Nos. 1571/3 as separate panes of four and
se-tenant pane of three................................ 12·00

The contents of No. SP1 have a face value of €7.40. This booklet was only available from the Irish Philatelic Bureau.

P **2** Pack Ice and Trapped *Endurance*

2004 (19 Mar). 90th Anniv of Shackleton's Antarctic Expedition. Multicoloured cover as Type P **2**. Booklet contains text and illustrations on panes and interleaving pages. Stitched.

SP2   €9.50 booklet containing four panes: Nos. 1637/8,
each ×2; Nos. 1639/40, each ×2; and two
panes of Nos. 1637/40................................. 22·00

The contents of No. SP2 have a face value of €9.04.

P **3** S Class Steam Locomotive No. 170, *Errigal*, on Viaduct, Malahide, Co. Dublin

(Des G. Garland)

2005 (5 Apr). 150th Anniv of Dublin—Belfast Railway. Multicoloured cover as Type P **3**. Booklet contains text and illustrations on panes and interleaving pages. Stitched.

SP3   €9 booklet containing Nos. 1730/3 as four
separate panes of four .... 16·00

The contents of No. SP3 have a face value of €8.84.

P **4** K Club Golf Course and Emblem in Flowers

(Des G. Garland)

2005 (27 Sept). Ireland and the Ryder Cup. Multicoloured cover as Type P **4**. Booklet contains text and illustrations on panes and interleaving pages. P 15×14½.

SP4   €9.50 booklet containing Nos. 1753/6 as four
separate panes of four .... 13·00

The contents of No. SP4 have a face value of €8.84.

P **5** Ryder Cup Trophy and EU and US Flags (*Illustration reduced. Actual size 210×148 mm*)

(Des Javelin and Young & Rubicam)

2006 (19 Sept). Ryder Cup Matches. Multicoloured cover as Type P **5**. Booklet contains text and illustrations on panes and interleaving pages. Stitched.

SP5   €12 booklet containing: Nos. 1795/8×2; As No. **MS**1799 but without emblem on margin; Nos. 1753/5 in pairs of each design; No. 1756×2; No. **MS**1808.. 21·00

No. **MS**1808 is supplied in a clear plastic mount attached to the back cover. The contents of No. SP5 have a face value of €11.68.

P **6** Fiddle Player

(Des Detail Design Studio)

2006 (7 Nov). Irish Music. Multicoloured cover as Type P **6**. Booklet contains text and illustrations on panes and interleaving pages. Stitched.

SP6   €10 booklet containing Nos. 1813/16 as four separate panes of four .... 16·00

The contents of No. SP6 have a face value of €9.84.

P **7** Sun and Planets

2007 (25 May). The Planets. Multicoloured cover as Type P **7**. Booklet contains text and illustrations on panes and interleaving pages. Stitched.

SP7   €12 booklet containing four panes of Nos. 1842/5 ... 22·00

The contents of No. SP7 have a face value of €10.64.

P **8** Applause

2007 (19 June). RTÉ Performing Groups. Multicoloured cover as Type P **8**. Booklet contains text and illustrations on panes and interleaving pages. Stitched.

SP8   €11.50 booklet containing two panes of Nos. 1849/51×2 and two panes of Nos. 1852/3×2 .... 16·00

The contents of No. SP8 have a face value of €11.

P **9** A Grey Day on the Bog (detail)

2008 (17 Apr). Paul Henry Landscape Paintings. Multicoloured cover, 161×100 mm, as Type P **9**. Booklet contains text and illustrations on panes and interleaving pages. Stitched.

SP9   €9 booklet containing four panes of Nos. 1889/92 ... 15·00

The contents of No. SP9 have a face value of €8.80.

No. SP9 commemorates the 50th death anniversary of Paul Henry.

P **10** Cinema Entrance

2008 (8 July). 'Filmed in Ireland'. Multicoloured cover, 160×100 mm, as Type P **10**. Booklet contains text and illustrations on interleaving pages. Stitched.

SP10   €12 booklet containing four panes of Nos. 1902/5 ... 20·00

The contents of No. SP10 have a face value of €10.96.

P **11** Playing Cello

2009 (14 Aug). Classical Composers. Multicoloured cover, 161×100 mm, as Type P **11**. Booklet contains text and illustrations on interleaving pages. Stitched.
SP11   €12 booklet containing four panes of stamps as
       Nos. 1971/4 .... 22·00
    Stamps from SP11 have a phosphor frame around each individual stamp.
    The contents of No. SP11 have a face value of €12.

P **12** Designer Labels

2010 (15 July). Irish Fashion Designers. Multicoloured cover, 161×100 mm, as Type P **12**. Booklet contains text and illustrations on panes and interleaving pages. Stitched.
SP12   €13 booklet containing Nos. 2009/14 as six
       separate panes of three................................. 20·00
    The contents of No. SP12 have a face value of €12.33.

P **13** Brendan Bowyer, Derek Dean, Joe Dolan and Dickie Rock

2010 (23 Sept). Legendary Showbands. Multicoloured cover, 161×100 mm, as Type P **13**. Booklet contains text and illustrations on panes and interleaving pages. Stitched.
SP13   €12 booklet containing four panes of Nos. 2034/7 ... 20·00
    The contents of No. SP13 have a face value of €10.96

P **14** Eye Candy (Catherine Keenan) and Mother You (Berina Kelly)

2011 (12 May). Year of Craft. Multicoloured cover, 160×100 mm, as Type P **14**. Booklet contains text and illustrations on panes and interleaving pages. Stitched.
SP14   €9 booklet containing Nos. 2058/62 as five
       separate panes of three................................. 18·00
    The contents of No. SP14 have a face value of €8.25.

P **15** Killarney National Park

2011 (6 June). Ireland's National Parks. Multicoloured cover, 160×100 mm, as Type P **15**. Booklet contains text and illustrations on panes and interleaving pages. Stitched.
SP15   €13 booklet containing Nos. 2063/8 as six separate
       panes of three... 22·00
    The contents of No. SP15 have a face value of €12.33.

P **16** Wave Energy

2011 (5 Aug). Renewable Energy. Multicoloured cover, 160×100 mm, as Type P **16**. Stitched.
SP16   €9 booklet containing Nos. 2081/5 as five separate
       panes of three... 19·00
    The contents of SP16 have a face value of €8.25.

P **17** Titanic

2012 (12 Apr). Centenary of the Sinking of RMS Titanic. Multicoloured cover, 162×100 mm, as Type P **17**. Booklet contains text and illustrations on panes and interleaving pages. Stitched.
SP17   €12 booklet containing four panes of
       Nos. 2110/13.. 24·00
    The contents of No. SP17 have a face value of €10.96.

P **18** Firefighter

2012 (28 Jun). 150th Anniv of Dublin Fire Brigade. Multicoloured cover, 161×100 mm, as Type P **18**. Stitched.

SP18 €10 booklet containing Nos. 2123/6 as four separate panes of four .... 25·00

The contents of No. SP18 have a face value of €8.80.

P **19** Arrest of Jim Larkin, 31 August 1913

2013 (22 Aug). Centenary of the General Lockout. Multicoloured cover, 161×100 mm, as Type P **19**. Booklet contains text and illustrations on panes and interleaving pages. Stitched.

SP19 €10 booklet containing five panes: Nos. 2180/2 in separate panes of three and two panes containing Nos. 2180/2 .... 16·00

The contents of No. SP19 have a face value of €9.

P **20** Reserve Defence Forces on Training Exercise

2013 (12 Sept). Irish Defence Forces. Multicoloured cover, 160×101 mm, as Type P **20**. Booklet contains text and illustrations on panes and interleaving pages. Stitched.

SP20 €10 booklet containing Nos. 2183/6 as four separate panes of four .... 22·00

The contents of No. SP20 have a face value of €9.60.

P **21** Burmese Cat

2014 (4 Sept). Cats. Multicoloured cover, 162×101 mm, as Type P **21**. Stitched.

SP21 €20 booklet containing Nos. 2242/5 as four separate panes of four .... 20·00

The contents of No. SP21 have a face value of €10.88.

POSTAGE DUE STAMPS

From 1922 to 1925 Great Britain postage due stamps in both script and block watermarks were used without overprint.

D **1**

D **2**

D **3**

(Des Ruby McConnell. Typo Govt Printing Works, Dublin)

1925 (20 Feb). W **10**. P 14×15.

D1	D **1**	½d. emerald-green..................	12·00	16·00
D2		1d. carmine...........................	15·00	3·50
		a. Wmk sideways..................	£1200	£600
		w. Wmk inverted..................	£350	75·00
		y. Wmk inverted and reversed...........	£170	£170
D3		2d. deep green......................	50·00	5·50
		a. Wmk sideways..................	55·00	17·00
		aw. Wmk sideways inverted..................	85·00	45·00
		w. Wmk inverted..................	90·00	35·00
D4		6d. plum...............................	7·00	7·50
D1/4 Set of 4...			75·00	29·00

The normal sideways watermark shows the top of "e" to the left, *as seen from the back of the stamp.*

1940–70. W **22**. P 14×15.

D5	D **1**	½d. emerald-green (1942).........	35·00	24·00
		w. Wmk inverted..................	—	£500
D6		1d. carmine (1941)..................	1·50	70
		w. Wmk inverted..................	—	£475
D7		1½d. vermilion (1953).............	4·00	9·50
		w. Wmk inverted..................	17·00	38·00
D8		2d. deep green (1940)............	2·75	70
		w. Wmk inverted..................	£500	£100
D9		3d. blue (10.11.52).................	5·00	4·00
		w. Wmk inverted..................	11·00	5·50
D10		5d. blue-violet (3.3.43)...........	5·00	4·00
		w. Wmk inverted..................	11·00	5·00
D11		6d. plum (21.3.60).................	6·00	3·50
		a. Wmk sideways (1968)........	15·00	15·00
		aw. Wmk sideways inverted..................	1·00	2·00
D12		8d. orange (30.10.62)............	9·00	17·00
		w. Wmk inverted..................	17·00	32·00
D13		10d. bright purple (27.1.65)......	8·50	8·50
D14		1s. apple-green (10.2.69).........	8·50	11·00
		a. Wmk sideways (1970)........	75·00	11·00
D5/14 Set of 10...			70·00	25·00

The normal sideways watermark shows the top of "e" to the left, *as seen from the back of the stamp.*

Stamps in these designs but in different colours were issued between 1971 and 1978.

1971 (15 Feb). As Nos. D5/14, but with values in decimal currency and colours changed. W **22**. P 14×15.

D15	D **1**	1p. sepia...............................	30	60
		a. Wmk sideways..................	1·75	1·50
		w. Wmk inverted..................	1·50	2·00
D16		1½p. light emerald.................	40	1·50
D17		3p. stone...............................	60	2·00
		w. Wmk inverted..................	1·25	2·00
D18		4p. orange.............................	60	1·25
D19		5p. greenish blue..................	60	3·00
		w. Wmk inverted..................	2·25	3·50
D20		7p. bright yellow...................	40	3·50
		w. Wmk inverted..................	1·50	3·50
D21		8p. scarlet.............................	40	2·75
D15/21 Set of 7...			3·00	13·00

1978 (20 Mar). As Nos. D17/19, but no wmk. Chalk-surfaced paper. P 14×15.

D22	D **1**	3p. stone...............................	1·50	7·00
D23		4p. orange.............................	6·00	10·00
D24		5p. greenish blue..................	1·50	5·00
D22/4 Set of 3...			8·00	20·00

1980 (11 June)–**85**. Photo. Chalk-surfaced paper. P 15.

D25	D **2**	1p. apple green.....................	30	70
D26		2p. dull blue.........................	30	70
D27		4p. myrtle-green...................	40	70
D28		6p. flesh...............................	40	80
D29		8p. chalky blue.....................	40	85
D30		18p. green.............................	75	1·25
D31		20p. Indian red (22.8.85)........	2·00	6·50
D32		24p. bright yellowish green......	75	2·00
D33		30p. deep violet blue (22.8.85)..	2·25	7·50
D34		50p. cerise (22.8.85)..............	3·00	7·50
D25/34 Set of 10...			9·50	25·00

The 1p. to 18p. are on white paper and the 20p., 30p. and 50p. on cream. The 24p. value exists on both types of paper.

(Des Q. Design. Litho Irish Security Stamp Ptg Ltd)

1988 (6 Oct). Chalk-surfaced paper. P 14×15.

D35	D **3**	1p. black, orange-vermilion and lemon..............................	10	60
D36		2p. black, orange-vermilion and purple-brown..................	15	60
D37		3p. black, orange-vermilion and plum	20	60
D38		4p. black, orange-vermilion and bright violet	20	1·00
D39		5p. black, orange-vermilion and royal blue..........................	25	60

D40	17p. black, orange-vermilion and deep yellow-green	50	80
D41	20p. black, orange-vermilion and slate-blue	65	1·10
D42	24p. black, orange-vermilion and deep turquoise-green	75	1·00
D43	30p. black, orange-vermilion and deep grey	90	1·60
D44	50p. black, orange-vermilion and brownish grey	1·40	1·75
D45	£1 black, orange-vermilion and bistre-brown	2·00	2·50
D35/45 Set of 11		6·25	11·00

THOMOND AND LONG ISLAND

Labels inscribed "Principality of Thomond" appeared on the philatelic market in the early 1960s. Thomond is the name of a district in western Ireland. The area does not have its own administration or postal service and the labels were not recognised by the Department of Posts & Telegraphs, Dublin.

Local carriage labels were issued for Long Island, County Cork in April 1973; they were intended to cover the cost of taking mail from the island to the nearest mainland post office. A local service operated for a few weeks before it was suppressed by the Irish Post Office. As the stamps were not accepted for national or international mail they are not listed here.

From 20 September 1993 labels in the above style were used to indicate postage due charges in the Dublin 2 delivery area. They are dispensed by a Pitney/Bowes machine, in much the same way as a meter mark, and can show any face value between 1p. and £99.99. Such labels are not normally postmarked. Labels with face values of 32p. and 50p. were sold to collectors by the Philatelic Bureau.

Est 1856

STANLEY GIBBONS

Dear Catalogue User,

As a collector and Stanley Gibbons catalogue user for many years myself, I am only too aware of the need to provide you with the information you seek in an accurate, timely and easily accessible manner. Naturally, I have my own views on where changes could be made, but one thing I learned long ago is that we all have different opinions and requirements.

I would therefore be most grateful if you would complete the form overleaf and return it to me. Please contact Lorraine Holcombe (lholcombe@stanleygibbons.co.uk) if you would like to be emailed the questionnaire.

Very many thanks for your help.

Yours sincerely,

Hugh Jefferies,
Editor.

Hugh Jefferies (Catalogue Editor)
Catalogue Questionnaire Responses
Stanley Gibbons Limited
7 Parkside, Ringwood
Hampshire BH24 3SH
United Kingdom

Questionnaire

2015 Ireland

1. **Level of detail**

   Do you feel that the level of detail in this catalogue is:
   a. too specialised ○
   b. about right ○
   c. inadequate ○

2. **Frequency of issue**

   How often would you purchase a new edition of this catalogue?
   a. Annually ○
   b. Every two years ○
   c. Every three to five years ○
   d. Less frequently ○

3. **Design and Quality**

   How would you describe the layout and appearance of this catalogue?
   a. Excellent ○
   b. Good ○
   c. Adequate ○
   d. Poor ○

4. How important to you are the prices given in the catalogue:
   a. Important ○
   b. Quite important ○
   c. Of little interest ○
   d. Of no interest ○

5. Would you be interested in an online version of this catalogue?
   a. Yes ○
   b. No ○

6. Do you like the new format?
   a. Yes ○
   b. No ○

7. What changes would you suggest to improve the catalogue? E.g. Which other indices would you like to see included?

   ....
   ....
   ....
   ....

8. Which other Stanley Gibbons Catalogues do you buy?

   ....
   ....
   ....
   ....

9. Would you like us to let you know when the next edition of this catalogue is due to be published?
   a. Yes ○
   b. No ○

   If so please give your contact details below.

   Name: ....
   Address:...
   ....
   ....
   ....
   Email: ....
   Telephone:...

10. Which other Stanley Gibbons Catalogues are you interested in?
    a. ....
    b. ....
    c. ....

Many thanks for your comments.

Please complete and return it to: Hugh Jefferies (Catalogue Editor)
Stanley Gibbons Limited, 7 Parkside, Ringwood, Hampshire BH24 3SH, United Kingdom
or email: lholcombe@stanleygibbons.co.uk to request a soft copy

Ireland Order Form

YOUR ORDER

Stanley Gibbons account number ☐☐☐☐☐☐

Condition (mint/UM/ used)	Country	SG No.	Description	Price	Office use only
			POSTAGE & PACK-ING	£3.60	
			TOTAL		

The lowest price charged for individual stamps or sets purchased from Stanley Gibbons Ltd, is £1.

Payment & address details

Name ....

Address (We cannot deliver to PO Boxes) ....

....

Postcode ....

Tel No. ....

Email ....

PLEASE NOTE Overseas customers MUST quote a telephone number or the order cannot be dispatched. Please complete ALL sections of this form to allow us to process the order.

☐ Cheque (made payable to Stanley Gibbons)

☐ I authorise you to charge my

☐ Mastercard   ☐ Visa   ☐ Diners   ☐ Amex   ☐ Maestro

Card No. ☐☐☐☐☐☐☐☐☐☐☐☐☐☐☐☐☐☐☐ (Maestro only)

Valid from ☐☐   Expiry date ☐☐   Issue No. (Maestro only) ☐☐   CVC No. (4 if Amex) ☐☐☐☐

CVC No. is the last three digits on the back of your card (4 if Amex)

Signature ....   Date ....

4 EASY WAYS TO ORDER

Post to
Lesley Mourne, Stamp Mail Order Department, Stanley Gibbons Ltd, 399 Strand, London, WC2R 0LX, England

Call
020 7836 8444
+44 (0)20 7836 8444

Fax
020 7557 4499
+44 (0)20 7557 4499

Click
lmourne@ stanleygibbons.com/ co.uk?

If YOU Buy at Auction this is How You Can Save £250+ EACH Year

ANDREW PROMOTING PHILATELY ON THE ALAN TITCHMARSH SHOW ITV

... I'll Give You £55 OFF to get you started

(... some Collectors Save thousands of pounds)

By Andrew McGavin, Managing Director, Universal Philatelic Auctions (UPA)

In all my 40+ years in the trade I have never seen an introductory offer to new clients like this .. so you may be wondering the reason why my company UPA can afford to make this offer to you?

In *'plain talk'* most auctions charge 'Buyers Premiums' –YES! You have to pay up to 25% (some charge more) **on top of the *winning price you paid*.** That is Simply an Incredible surcharge. Apparently this significant premium is justified by charging the seller a lower fee in order to entice consignments for sale.

My company UPA does not charge any premiums which is one of the reasons why we hold the UK record of 1,975 different bidders in our last auction – an amazing 89% of whom were successful. Fortunately the average bidder spends an average of £250+ per auction...so that with 4 auctions a year offering 80,000+/- lots from £1 to £100,000 for you to choose from ....

with NO Buyer's Premium You Save up to £250+ <u>EACH YEAR PLUS</u> You take NO RISK with our 28 day unconditional Guarantee

So How can UPA offer You £55 OFF too?

1. **Our Business Model is Different.** Fundamentally I believe that if a stamp/philatelic item is not selling then it is too expensive. Compare that with the stamp business whose stock is the same each time you see or hear from them. At the risk of boring you ...

2. **Stamp Industry's BIGGEST problem.** ... twenty years ago I started to ponder upon what is the biggest problem faced by the average stamp dealer? The answer came back loud and clear. The biggest problem faced by a stamp dealer is not what sells ... **but what does not sell**. This is the reason why most stamp dealers have lots of unsold stock you have seen time and time again – worse still this is what prevents that dealer from buying new stock to offer you.

3. **Surface Sell.** There is an actual name for this – it is called 'surface sell' – good material 'floats' on the surface and sells. Less desirable stock sinks so that unless a dealer pays almost nothing to replace his stock then the profit in the business becomes stagnant and bound in less saleable stock. If only that dealer could move this stock he would have more money to invest in new stock to offer to you.

4. **Cover-up.** Twenty years ago almost the entire stamp industry spent its time disguising what did not sell – in those days so pernicious were 'unsolds' that it was common practice for one auction house to sell batches of 'unsolds' to another auction where the new auction could present them to (hopefully) different collectors as new lots. 'Passing the Philatelic Parcel' was common practice.

5. **E-Bay.** Today the philatelic world is almost unrecognisably different. In large part courtesy of the internet. How things have changed. Few 'pass the parcel'. Really active Dealers - these days they **also** sell on eBay - large lots, small lots, all manner of stamps, covers, down to fakes and forgeries – today's equivalent of the Wild West – there's philatelic 'gold' to be mined in those hills ... but Boy – you have to work to find it and sadly 'all that glistens is not gold' – you pays your money and you takes your chance often with little support or recourse. UPA too sells surpluses on eBay backed by support and our guarantee – access eBay links via *www.upastampauctions.co.uk*

Continued overleaf ☞